D1548625

Advances in Pulping and Papermaking
The 1994 Forest Products Symposium

Elmer L. Gaden Jr, Series Editor

Peter W. Hart, Volume Editor
Alan W. Rudie and James C. Joseph, Volume Co-Editors

Cyrus K. Aidun
Joseph K. Baker
Paul D. Beuther
Debra Breed
H.P. Call
Wei-Yin Chen
Barbara Cole
Lou Edwards
Tom H. Egenes
Theodore E. Farrington, Jr.
A.L. Fricke
Joseph Genco
James Griggs
Torbjørn Helle
Jeffrey S. Hseih

Prashant Juvekar
Peder J. Kleppe
Agnes Kovacs
Michael X. Meng
Ingo Mücke
Seiji Nakamoto
Philip E. Quinnett
John Ransdell
T.D. Rogers
Jeff Rounsaville
Gunilla Saltin
C.L. Sanford
J.A. Shands
Patrick E. Sharpe
Jeff A. Stevens

A.A. Zaman

AIChE Staff
Maura N. Mullen, Managing Editor; Julie A. McBride, Editorial Assistant
Cover Design: Joseph A. Roseti

Inquiries regarding the publication of Symposium Series Volumes should be directed to:
Mark Rosenzweig, Editor-in-Chief
American Institute of Chemical Engineers, 345 E 47 St., New York, N.Y. 10017
(212) 705-7576 • FAX: (212) 705-7812

AIChE Symposium Series

Number 307   1995   Volume 91

American Institute of Chemical Engineers

345 East 47 Street   New York, N.Y. 10017

AIChE shall not be responsible for statements or opinions
advanced in their papers or printed in their publications.

ISBN 0-8169-0687-4

ISSN 0065-8812

TS
1171
F67
1994

Foreword

This 1994 Forest Products Symposium Volume consists of papers obtained from the ten conference sessions sponsored by the Division during 1994. Six sessions were held at the AIChE Annual Meeting in San Francisco, California on November 14 through 18, 1994. The four remaining sessions were held in conjunction with the Tappi Pulping Conference held in San Diego, California on November 7 through 10, 1994. This publication represents the first time papers presented at the joint sessions with Tappi were considered for inclusion in a symposium volume.

A total of thirty-five papers were submitted for possible inclusion. Due to space limitations, only a select few of the top-quality papers could be published. Every effort was made to accept a representative spectrum of the Forest Products Division interests. The papers published have been grouped into four sections. The first part contains two papers dealing with developments in pulping. The second consists of a series of papers on bleaching. Papers on mechanical pulp brightening, kraft pulp bleaching with oxygen-based chemicals, and bleaching of recycled fiber topics are also included in this section. The third section details advances in the papermaking arena with the inclusion of both fundamental and commercial studies. The final section of this volume examines advances in fuel materials (black liquor and bark) as well as advances in sludge handling and disposal. In order to ensure the quality of the papers published, at least two reviewers were required to agree on the acceptability of each paper.

The range of studies contained in this volume vary from fundamental studies to materials of current industrial applicability. The papers should provide a valuable resource for both academic researchers as well as industrial engineers.

The assistance of the authors regarding manuscript preparation in a timely manner and of the volume co-editors is acknowledged and appreciated. The help of the session chairs for providing the manuscripts and obtaining the speakers is also appreciated. Without their assistance, this work could not have been prepared. Past editor, Christopher L. Verrill is acknowledged for his valuable advise and suggestions. AIChE Symposium Series Editor, Elmer Gaden, and AIChE Editor-in-Chief, Mark Rosenzweig are thanked for their continued support of our Division's activities, as evidenced by their commitment to produce this archival quality volume. The help of Maura Mullen and Julie McBride of the AIChE publication staff is gratefully acknowledged and they are thanked for producing this volume.

Peter W. Hart, *volume editor*
Westvaco Corporation
Pulping and Bleaching Group
Charleston Research Center
Charleston, SC 29423

CONTENTS

Part 1. Advances in Pulping

Part 2. Advances in Bleaching

Part 3. Advances in Papermaking

Part 4. Advances in Fuel Material and Sludge Handling

Kraft Pulping Kinetics of Eastern White Cedar

Prashant Juvekar, John Ransdell, Barbara Cole, and Joseph Genco
University of Maine, Department of Chemical Engineering, Orono, Maine 04469

Cedar species are unique softwoods that are characterized by low specific gravity, short, thin-walled, wide lumen tracheids. Because of restrictions on land use and restrictions for harvesting pulpwood, cedar species are now being more widely used in the production of chemical wood pulp.

Available literature on the kraft pulping characteristics of various cedar species are summarized. Experimental data are presented on the kinetics of kraft pulping of eastern (northern) white cedar (Thuja occidentalis). Data for the pulp yield, chemical composition, and alkali consumption are presented as a function of time. These data were correlated using kinetic models presented by Hatton [Tappi, 56, [7], 97, 1973)], and Kerr [(Tappi, 59, [5] 89, (1976)]. Stoichiometric coefficients for alkali reaction with lignin, carbohydrates and extractives are presented. One notable characteristic of kraft pulping of cedar is the marked effect of aging on the wood and the difficulty to pulp to low kappa numbers if the wood is allowed to age for any significant length of time.

The single most important long term issue facing the paper industry is potential shortage of wood because of environmental and land use issues. This is particularly true in the Northwest where timber harvesting on government land has decreased markedly. Land use regulations and habitat diversity issues are beginning to surface in the Northeast. This trend has created interest in the development of high yield pulps that have properties that are equivalent to kraft pulp and also in the pulping of species that were here-to-fore considered of little value for the production of pulp. This is particularly true for various species of cedar.

Wood Properties

McDermitt (1981) and later Genco (1989) in an unpublished work, reported data on physical properties (Table 1) of eastern white cedar (Thuja occidentalis). Eastern white cedar has one of the lowest specific gravities (0.29) of any softwood. It compares with 0.37 for red spruce (Picea rubens Sarg.); see Table 1. Ethanol-benzene extractives were estimated to be 7.1% (6.1% water extractives).

University of Maine, Orono, Maine,

Electron microscopy studies show that cedar is a wood composed of short (2.2 mm), thin-walled, wide lumen tracheids having a high percentage of early wood. Cedar is characterized as a low coarseness wood, that is, cells with low mass per unit length.

Chemistry

Gardner and Barton (1958) studied the water- and acetone-soluble extraneous (extractives) components of western red cedar (Thuja plicata Donn), which sometimes exceeds 20% of the wood weight. A complex mixture of substances was extracted when western red cedar heartwood was treated with acetone. The extraneous components of western red cedar consists of the volatile components: α, β, and γ-thujaplicin, 7-hydroxy-4 isopropyltropolone, thujic acid and methyl thujate: and the non-volatile components, arabinose, an unidentified sterol, and several uncharacterized phenols. The tropolone derivatives, the thujaplicins and the 7-hydroxy-4 isopropyltropolone, and also the phenols, are natural preservatives and their presence in the heartwood accounts for the high natural resistance of the species. When hot water was used as the extracting solvent, the extractives obtained were mainly phenolic in nature. The presence of these groups of compounds account for high levels of digester corrosion encountered in the kraft pulping of western red cedar. Methyl thujate is mainly responsible for the characteristic smell of cedar.

MacLean and Murakami (1966A, 1966B, and 1967) studied the lignin of western red cedar. Lignans present in the hot-water extractives of western red cedar heartwood were identified as thujaplicatin, thujaplicatin methyl ether, and hydroxythujaplicatin methyl ether and dihydroxythujaplicatin methyl ether.

Kraft Pulping Studies

Few published data are available on the kraft pulping kinetics and pulp properties of cedar species. Hatton (1975) summarizes data on the kraft pulping of western red cedar. Pulping studies on eastern white cedar were performed at the U. S. Forest Products Laboratory, Madison, Wisconsin by Hyttinet et al. (1958). Pulping studies were performed at constant H-factor and variable initial active alkali (13.7 to 23.4% Na2O based on wood) and constant sulfidity (25.5%). At a kappa number of 30 ml (permanganate number of 20 ml) total pulp yield for eastern white cedar was about 40%.

Studies were performed at the University of Maine Agricultural Station by Dyer (1967), Chase (1976) and Chase and Young (1976) on whole tree pulping of eastern white cedar. Pulp yields for the composite materials ranged between 42 and 44.4% depending on tree diameter and the part of the tree utilized. Higher yields were obtained with larger diameter trees provided that the wood was fresh.

Kraft pulping data were obtained by Genco (1989) for pulp yield, kappa and permanganate numbers. These data were obtained as a function of H-factor at constant active alkali (24%) and sulfidity (30%). Fresh cedar could be readily delignified to kappa number 30 but the yield was only about 41%. The data of Genco (1989) were similar to those of Hyattinen and co-workers (1958) reported earlier (Figure 1). These studies were also performed with fresh wood.

Using the principal of conservation of mass, Juvekar and Genco (1991) derived an expression for the residual alkali [OH-] of various softwoods in terms of the yield (Y) and lignin content (x1) of the pulp. The mathematical expression obtained was:

$$[OH^-]=(e+f\,x_1\,Y+gY)/(d-Y) \qquad (1)$$

where the coefficients e, f, and g are related to stoichiometric coefficients r_1, r_2, r_3 which represent the amount (moles) of OH^- ion that react per gram of lignin (r_1), carbohydrates (r_2), and extractives (r_3). The parameters in equation (1) also depend upon the initial mass fractions of the wood constituents (x_1^0, x_2^0, x_3^0) and the parameters associated with the digester. Equation (1) could be fit to data for alkali consumption for red spruce, scotch pine and eastern white cedar to a high level of statistical significance. The results of Juvekar and Genco (1991) for eastern white cedar and red spruce are summarized in Table 1.

EXPERIMENTAL RESULTS

Juvekar (1991) conducted kraft pulping experiments using eastern white cedar. Experimental methods are summarized in the Appendix A. The wood was aged at room temperature for about 6 months prior to use in pulping experiments for comparison to pulping of fresh cedar reported by Genco (1989). The wood samples were obtained from the Georgia Pacific Corporation in Woodland, Maine in one cord lots.

Two sets of experiments were conducted. Data set A involved pulping experiments conducted at 170o at constant effective alkali (20.4%) and variable time (H-factor) and were identical to conditions used by Genco (1989), including the same digester. Data set B involved kraft pulping experiments which were again conducted at 170o C but at constant time (210 minutes) and variable values of effective alkali (17, 18.7, 20.4 and 22.1% on wood). Experiments for data sets A and B were conducted at constant sulfidity of 30%. Data were obtained for pulp composition, yield, alcohol-benzene extractives, soluble and insoluble lignin, kappa number, residual alkali and density of black liquor.

Yield Versus Time

Figure 2 shows the variation of pulp yield versus cooking time during the kraft pulping experiments (Data Set A). The curve almost reaches a plateau after about 150 minutes. There is a very small loss in yield after this point which suggests that removal of residual lignin and carbohydrates is very slow. Also, there is a point of inflection in the curve at about 75 minutes. This point is thought to be related to the removal of wood extractives, low molecular weight carbohydrates and acetyl groups, during the early stage of the pulping process and the heat-up period. Approximately 25% of the wood is consumed at this point and about one third of the alkali is also depleted.

Alkali Consumption

Figure 3 shows the residual alkali measured versus time. The alkali consumption curve is very rapid in the initial delignification period. Almost 30 to 40% of the alkali is consumed in the first 60 minutes of the cook during the heat-up period. During this time, most of the alkali is consumed in hydrolysis of acetyl side groups associated with hemicellulose polymers (Genco, 1990), neutralizing the acid products in the wood and reactions with carbohydrates in peeling reactions. After this initial rapid consumption, alkali consumption per unit mass of wood dissolved decreases appreciably relative to the initial delignification period. During this period most of the alkali is consumed in neutralizing the products of peeling reactions, but also in hydrolysis of lignin and in formation of lignin phenolate groups that render the lignin more soluble. Alkali concentration at the maximum temperature is about half of the alkali concentration initially present in the digester.

Lignin Versus Time

Figure 4 shows the variation in total lignin content in the pulp (Klason and acid soluble lignin) as a function of time. The three delignification periods are well defined in the literature (Kleppe, 1970; Gustafson, 1983). The fraction of lignin in the pulp actually increases in the beginning of the cook. In the experiments with eastern white cedar, this occurred at pulping times less than about 60 minutes.

This increase in lignin content is thought to be due to the rapid dissolution of short chain carbohydrates during the digester heat up period and has been observed by other researchers, notably Aurell and Hartler (1964), Busayasakul (1986), and Iber (1986). After this initial delignification period, bulk delignification starts and continues until about 150 minutes. The major portion of the lignin is removed during this time period. The last part of the delignification curve (Figure 4) represents the residual delignification period where residual lignin is removed very slowly. Comparing Figures 3 and 4 suggests that the residual lignin is being removed by physical processes since the alkali concentration is essentially constant.

Ross Diagram and Selectivity

The Ross diagram (Figure 5) introduced by Stropp (1956) treats pulping as the dissolution of two homogeneously mixed components and is a plot of the lignin to carbohydrate ratio versus pulp yield. The calculation is based on the amount of lignin and carbohydrates present in the pulp (% on wood):

$$L_p \,/\, Ca = \frac{L_p}{Y - L_p} = f(Y) \qquad (2)$$

where L_p and Ca are the lignin and carbohydrate content of the pulp. The data of Busayasakul (1986) for red spruce are plotted on the Ross diagram for purpose of comparison. The marked difference between the two curves suggest that cedar has higher lignin content than red spruce at the same yield. These differences are thought to result from both the higher extractives and lignin contents in the cedar compared to red spruce (Table 1). Eastern white cedar, which had a 7.1% initial extractives and 30.7% initial lignin content appears to be more difficult to delignify than red spruce which had a 1.5% extractives and 26.5 % initial lignin content. The charge of active alkali and sulfidity were the same for both sets of pulping data (24% AA and 30% sulfidity); although the liquor to wood ratio was higher in the study of eastern white cedar (12) compared to red spruce (9).

Comparison to Literature Data

The experimental data reported here can be compared directly to other pulping data (Figure 1) available for eastern white cedar (Genco, 1989; and Hyttinen et al., 1958). The data reported by Hyttinen et al. (1958) were obtained at constant H-factor and variable alkali. The data of Genco (1989) were obtained at constant alkali and variable time. Both the data of Genco and Hyttinen et al. were obtained using fresh wood in their experiments.

Figure 6 shows the kappa number data plotted versus time (Genco 1989; Juvekar 1991). The two curves are similar in shape since pulping conditions were identical in the two studies including the digester and the source of the wood. The major difference between the two curves is thought to be related to the conditions and quality of the wood. Pulp yield versus time and yield versus kappa number (Juvekar, 1991) show that the lignin and yield curve obtained with fresh wood lie below those obtained with aged wood. At equivalent yield, the aged wood show higher lignin content. As the white cedar ages, it apparently become more resistant to hydrolysis reactions; or alternatively more susceptible to lignin condensation reaction.. In other data measured by Juvekar (unpublished) the effect of aging was quite noticeable and a kappa number 30 could not be reached without significantly raising the alkali (30+%) at equivalent H-factor.

Figure 7 shows the variation in kappa number with initial active alkali compared to Hyttinen et al. (1958). Since Hyttinen et al. reported results in terms of 40 ml permanganate number, the data were converted using standard coefficients published by Hatton (1975). The kappa number for the Juvekar data is higher than those obtained in the Hyttinen work at the same initial alkali concentration in spite of the longer cooking time and higher sulfidity used in the Juvekar work. The most likely explanation relates to differences in lignin reactivity and the significantly lower liquor to wood ratio (L/W = 4), hence higher concentration of alkali, used in the Hyttinen study compare to that used by Juvekar (L/W = 12). This same behavior is reflected in yield versus initial alkali data plotted by Juvekar (1991) but not shown here.

KINETIC MODELS

The pulping literature is replete with mathematical expressions that attempt to represent the kinetics of kraft pulping. An excellent summary of the kinetics and modeling of the kraft pulping process is given by Grace, Malcolm and Kocurek (1983). The development of rate expressions is complicated by the heterogeneous nature of the system. Kinetic expressions may be roughly classified as empirical models which are used primarily for digester control and those that attempt to represent the kinetic mechanism of delignification and carbohydrate loss. Wells (1990) summarizes various empirical models used for digester control. Delignification models may be further subdivided into simple-homogeneous and complex-kinetic models (Grace et al. 1983). Others attempt to consider kinetics and mass transport phenomena simultaneously, and models based upon principles of polymerization (Yan, 1981). Representative samples of available predictive models are shown in Table 2.

Empirical Models

Kleppe (1970) proposed that over a narrow kappa number range (K) there is an approximately linear relationship between the total pulp yield (Y) and the kappa number:

$$Y = \Omega + \theta K \tag{3}$$

where the empirical constants Ω and θ depend on the range of the kappa number. The form of Kleppe's equation (3) holds for many species and is seen to hold for eastern white cedar in Figure 1 for the data of Genco (1989), Hyattinen et al. (1958) and Juvekar (1991). The data can be correlated with a high degree of statistical significance ($R2 = 0.922$) as:

$$Y = 36.62 + 0.1658 K \tag{4}$$

The starting point for most empirical models is the method of Vroom (1957) who used the principle of the Arrhenius rate equation to show how the variables of time and temperature can be combined into one variable, the H-factor:

$$H = \int_0^t \exp\left(43{,}118 - \frac{16{,}113}{T}\right) \, dt \qquad (5)$$

where t is given in hours and T is the temperature in Ko. Hatton (1973, 1975, 1976) related the total pulp yield (Y) and kappa number of the pulp (K) to the physical and chemical energy input of the process by linear expression of the form:

$$Y = A - B[(\log_{10} H) * (EA^n)] \qquad (6)$$

$$K = a - b[(\log_{10} H) * (EA^n)] \qquad (7)$$

where A, B and n are empirical coefficients and EA is the effective alkali based upon wood. Hatton prepared listed values of A, B, and n for different woods. Hatton's equations have found widespread use in digester control algorithms. Note that Kleppe's equation (3) follows directly from the form of Hatton's equations (6 and 7).

The empirical coefficients A, B, n, a, b, and n` were determined from the available data for cedar. Coefficients n and n` were obtained from the data of Hyttinen (1958) which was performed at constant H-factor. Coefficients A, B, a, and b were obtained using the data obtained by Juvekar (1991). These values are listed in Table 3 together with those values given by Hatton (1973) for western red cedar. Figures 8 and 9 plot the correlating equations and show that a target kappa number or yield can be obtained by varying either the H-factor or the initial effective alkali. The usual procedure in industrial practice is to vary the alkali to achieve the target kappa number leaving the digester rather than by changing the temperature.

A variation of Hatton's equation is that of Chari (1973) where the Kappa number is correlated in terms of the H-factor, effective alkali concentration and the liquor to wood ratio in the digester.

$$K = \alpha(EA)^\beta * (H)^\gamma * (L / W)^\delta \qquad (8)$$

where α, β, γ, and δ are empirically determined constants. Chari's model and variants are perhaps the most widespread models used for predicting the kappa number in digester control.

Kerr`s Semi-Empirical Model

One of the earliest and still most successful semi-empirical kinetic models is that of Kerr (1970, 1976A, 1976B). In Kerr's model, the delignification kinetics are assumed to be first order in effective alkali (C) and un-dissolved lignin (L):

$$-\int_{L_i}^{L_f} \frac{dL}{C(L)\,L} = \int_0^t k \, dt \qquad (9)$$

where the un-dissolved lignin concentration (L) is given as a percentage based upon initial wood content and the reaction rate constant (k) is Vroom's constant. The initial and final lignin contents are given by Li and Lt, respectively. Kerr's basic equation (9) inherently involves the pulp yield (Y) since, by definition, the lignin concentration based upon its initial wood content (L) is related to the concentration in the pulp (Lp):

$$100 L = Y L_p \qquad (10)$$

The alkali concentration C(L) is expressed by two straight lines with a transition point (Lt). Kerr was required to make a series of assumptions, the most notable being that the Ross diagram is linear over a limited range of yield values. Kerr also assumed that there is a linear expression between the lignin content in the pulp and the kappa number. Under these assumptions the final mathematical model takes the general form:

$$\left[\frac{1}{b_1}\ln\left(\frac{L}{L + b_1 / a_1}\right)\right]_{L_t}^{L_i} +$$

$$\left[\frac{1}{b_2}\ln\left(\frac{L}{L + b_2 / a_2}\right)\right]_{L_{f_4}}^{L_t} = a_3 H + a_4 \qquad (11)$$

where

$$b_2 = b_1 + a_5 \qquad (12)$$

$$b_1 = a_6 \, C_i + a_7 \qquad (13)$$

$$L_f = \frac{K^2 + a_8 K + a_9}{a_{10}K + a_{11}} \qquad (14)$$

and a1, ...a11 are empirical constants. As a general rule the first term on the left hand side in equation (6) is small in comparison to the second term and (Kerr, 1976) simplified the model:

$$\left[\frac{1}{b_2} \ln\left(\frac{L}{L + b_2 / a_2}\right)\right]_{L_f}^{L_i} = a_3 H + a_4 \qquad (15)$$

Table 4 summarizes the constants applicable to Kerr's model for eastern white cedar. Figures 10 and 11 illustrate the kinetics of kraft pulping for yield and kappa number plotted as a function of initial effective alkali.

The major difference between Kerr's model and that of Hatton is that Kerr's model takes into account the liquor to wood ratio in the digester. The two models can be compared directly (Figure 15). As a general rule, Kerr's model more accurately represents the experimental data because of the larger number of constants; six (6) in Hatton's model and thirteen (13) in Kerr's model, although the simplified version can be reduced to seven (7).

Neither Kerr's nor Hatton's model is particularly gratifying because of the large number of empirical constants. Also, there is no basis for the form of equation (9) since the molecular nature of the delignification reaction is ignored.

CONCLUDING REMARKS

Eastern white cedar can be readily pulped by the kraft process although extensive aging (6 months or more) makes pulping difficult and results in higher lignin content at equivalent pulping time. At kappa number 30 the pulp yield will be about 42 to 43% using standard pulping conditions. The lignin removal process is characterized by the normal three delignification phases; initial, bulk, and residual. Compared to a widely used species like red spruce, the lignin to carbohydrate ratio versus yield curve

(Ross Diagram) is significantly higher for the eastern white cedar at equivalent yield values. The kinetic data can be represented by kinetic models proposed by Hatton and Kerr both of which involve numerous empirical constants.

APPENDIX A

EXPERIMENTAL METHODS

Wood Preparation

A one (1) cord samples of eastern white cedar was obtained from Georgia Pacific Corporation in Woodland, Maine. The wood was cut into logs 3-4 feet long from the merchantable bole of mature wood and aged (stored) in the U Maine Pilot Plant for approximately 6 months prior to its use. The wood was debarked, split and chipped to proper size in a laboratory chipper. The chips were then screened for thickness and length. The chips retained on a 7 mm thick tray were stored in one kilogram lots in polyethylene bags for use in the pulping experiments. Prior to refrigerated storage, the moisture content was determined using Tappi Standard T-18.

Pulping Procedures

Synthetic white liquor was prepared from reagent grade sodium hydroxide and sodium sulfide using distilled water. A stainless steel bomb digester of 15 liters capacity was used to carry out the pulping experiments (Juvekar, 1991) with indirect electrical heat by circulation the black liquor. The digester was equipped with a sampling system that would permit black liquor sampling at the end of each cook.

The chips were soaked overnight, placed in the digester and steamed for ten minutes using low pressure steam and then weighed to obtain the weight of water associated with the chips. Soaking and steaming facilitated the penetration of the cooking liquor inside the chips. The amount of NaOH and Na2S required for the desired active alkali and sulfidity was added to distilled water to make a liquor to wood ratio of 12 to 1 which was required to cover the chips. The cooking conditions for the two sets of cooking conditions are summarized in Table 5.

The temperature of the digester was raised from room temperature to 340 Fo (170 Co) in 81 minutes in a linear fashion. The ramp was broken into two parts to avoid temperature "over-shoot". In the first 75 minutes, the temperature was raised to 328 Fo and in the next 6 minutes it was taken further to 340 Fo. After this ramp, the temperature was held constant at 340 Fo. The cooking times were varied to produce pulp yields from 50 to 100 %. The cooking experiments were done in triplicate for the duration of 150 minutes to ensure reproducibility of the results.

Analysis of Pulp

The total pulp from each cook was air-dried, weighed and stored. The moisture content of this air dried pulp was determined and used to estimate the pulp yield. The kappa number was determined using TAPPI method T-236. Wood and pulp samples obtained from all of the cooks were analyzed for soluble and insoluble (Klason) lignin, and extractives were determined using standard methods. Representative samples of the fresh wood and pulp were milled according to TAPPI method T-11 using a Wiley mill until the sample passed a 40 mesh screen but were retained on a 60 mesh screen. Particles of 40-mesh (0.40 mm diameter) or smaller are readily attacked by the reagents used in present analytical methods, and finer grinding may degrade the wood. The TAPPI methods used for analysis of the samples were T-6 for extractives, T-13 for acid insoluble lignin and T-222 for acid insoluble lignin. Carbohydrates were estimated by difference. Black liquor was analyzed for residual effective alkali using TAPPI standard T-624 and density using a calibrated picnometer.

LITERATURE CITED

1. Akhtaruzzaman, A.F. M. and Virkola, N. E., Pap. Puu., 61:578 (1979).

2. Akhtaruzzaman, A.F. M. and Virkola, N. E., Pap. Puu., 62: 15 (1980).

3. Aurell, R. and Hartler, N., Svensk Papperstid., 67 (2), 43 (1964).

4. Busayasakul, N., "Total Organic Carbon As An Indicator For Wood Delignification", Ph. D. Thesis, University of Maine, 1986.

5. Chari, N. C. S., Tappi, 56 (7): 65 (1973)

6. Chase, A. J. and Young, H. E., "The Potential of Softwood Thinning and Standing Dead Softwoods as a Source of Wood Pulp", University of Maine Agricultural Experimental Station, Technical Bulletin 82, Orono, Maine (July, 1976).

7. Chase, A. J., Applied Polymer Symposium, No. 28: 503-515 (1976).

8. Christensen,, T., Smith, C.C., Albright, L. F., And Williams, T. J., Tappi, 66 (11):65 (1983).

9. Dyer, R. F., "Fresh and Dry Weight, Nutrient Elements and Pulping Characteristics of Northern White Cedar - Thuja Occidentalis", University of Maine Agricultural Experiment Station, Technical Bulletin 27, Orono, Maine (August, 1987); M. S. Thesis, University of Maine (1967).

10. Edwards, L., and Norberg, S., Tappi 56 (11): 108 (1973).

11. Gardner, J. and Baraton, B. M., Forest Products Journal, p. 3-6 (June, 1958).

12. Genco, J. M., "Pulping and Bleaching of Hemlock and Cedar", Unpublished Work (1989).

13. Genco, J. M., Busayasakul, N., Medhora, H. K., and Robbins, W., Tappi Journal 73 (4), 223-233 (1990).

14. Grace, T., Malcolm, E., W., and Kocurek, M. J., Pulp and Paper Manufacture, 3rd Ed., Chapter 4, Kinetics and Modeling of Kraft Pulping, pg. 45-73, Tappi Press, Atlanta, Georgia, (1983).

15. Gustafson, R. R., Slelcher, C. A., McKean, W. T., and Finlayson, B. A., Ind. Eng. Chem. Proc. Des. Dev., 22 (1), 87 (1983).

16. Juvekar, P., "Alkali Consumption During Kraft Pulping", M.S. Thesis, University of Maine (1991).

17. Juvekar P. and Genco, J., 1991 Tappi Pulping Conference, Tappi Press, page 93 (1991).

18. Iber, H., "Total Organic Carbon as an Indicator for Wood Delignification", M. S. Thesis, University of Maine (1986).

19. Hatton, J. V., Tappi, 59 (8): 48 (1976)

20. Hatton, J. V., Tappi, 58 (10): 150 (1975)

21. Hatton, J. V., Tappi, 56 (7): 97 (1973).

22. Hyttinen, A., Keller, E. L. Martin, J. S., Setterholm, V. C., and Kingsbury, R. M., "Pulping of Northern White Cedar and Tamarack", Forest Products Laboratory, U. S. Department of Agriculture, Report No. 2128 (1958).

23. Kerr, A. J., Appita, 24 (3): 180 (1970).

24. Kerr, A. J. and Upchurch, J. M., Appita, 30 (1): 48 (1976A).

25. Kerr, A. J., Tappi , 59 (5): 89 (1976B).

26. Kondo, R., and Sarkanen, K., V., Holzforschung 38(1): 31 (1984).

27. Kleppe, P. J., Tappi, 53 (1), 35 (1970).

28. LeMon, S.and Teder, A., Svensk Papperstid., 76 (11): 407 (1973).

29. Lin, C. P., Mao, M. Y. and Jane, C. Y., Tappi 61 (2): 72 (1978).

30. Lodzinski, F. P. and Karlsson, T., Tappi, 59 (9): 88 (1976).

31. Juvekar, P. and Genco, J. M., "Alkali Consumption in the Kraft Pulping of Softwoods", pages 93-106, 1991 Tappi Pulping Conference, Orlando, Florida (Nov. 3-7, 1991).

32. MacLean, H. and Murakami, K., Can. J. Chem., 44: 1541 (1966A).

33. MacLean, H. and Murakami, K., Can. J. Chem., 44: 1827 (1966B).

34. MacLean, H. and Murakami, K., Can. J. Chem., 45: 1541 (1967).

35. McDermitt, M. D., "An Evaluation of Selected Physical and Mechanical Properties of Northern White-Cedar in Maine", University of Maine, M.S., Thesis (1981).

36. Norden, S. and Teder, A., 1978 Tappi Pulping Conference, pg. 181, Tappi Press (1978).

37. Olm, L. and Tistad, G., Svensk Papperstid., 15: 458 (1979)

38. Pankonin, B. M., M. S. Thesis, Institute of Paper Chemistry (1979).

39. Panshin, A. J. and de Zeeuz, C., "Textbook of Wood Technology, Vol. 1, McGraw Hill, New York (1970).

40. Smith, C. and Williams, T. J., "Modeling and Control of Kraft Pulping Systems", Instrument Soc. of America, pg. 7-20 (1975).

41. Strapp, R. K., Tappi, 39 (4); 249-255 (1956).

42. Szabo, A., and Goring, D. A., Tappi 51 (10): 440 (1968).

43. Tasman, J. E., Tappi, 64 (3): 175-176 (1981).

44. Tyler, D. B., and Edwards, L. L., Svensk Papperstid, 85: R180-R184 (1982).

45. Vroom, K. E., Pulp and Paper Magazine. Can., 58: 228-231, (1957).

46. Wells, C. H., "Effective Alkali Sensors for Batch Digester Control", Tappi, 73(4): 181 (1990).

47. Wilder, H. D. and Daleski, E. J., Tappi, 48(5): 293 (1965).

48. Yan, J. F., Macromolecules, 14(5): 1438 (1981).

ACKNOWLEDGMENTS

The authors wish to acknowledge the kind assistance
of Ms. Proserfina Bennett and Dr. Albert Co for
assistance in preparation of this paper.

TABLE 1
PROPERTIES OF EASTERN WHITE CEDAR AND RED SPRUCE

Property	Eastern White Cedar (Thuja Occidentalis L.)	Red Spruce (*Picea Rubens Sarg.*)
Average Diameter [a] (μ)	20-30	25-30
Fiber Length [a] (mm)	2.17	3.01-3.17
Ray Volume [a] (%)	3.4	4.9
Specific Gravity [a]		
Green	0.29	0.37
Oven Dry	0.31	0.41
Chem. Comp. (%)(b,c)		
Extractives (%)		
EtOH Benzene	5.1 %[b]	1.5[c]
Lignin (%)	30.7	26.5
Cellulose (%)	(39.3)	40.8
Hemicelluloses (%)	25.0	30.6
Ash (%)	0.3	0.2
TOTAL (%)	(-)	99.6
Stoichiometric Coeff.[d]		
(Moles [OH⁻]/gram)	0.00206	0.00693
Lignin (r_1)	0.00492	0.00546
Carbohydrates (r_2)	0.01800	0.02470
Extractives (r_3)		

(a) Panshin and de Zeeuw (1970).
(b) Juvevar (1991).
(c) Busayasakul (1986).
(d) Juvekar and Genco (1991).

TABLE 2

REPRESENTATIVE SAMPLES OF AVAILABLE PREDICTIVE MODELS

Model Type	Authors
Empirical Models -	Wells (1990)
	Tasman (1983)
	Hatton (1973, 1975, 1976)
	Kleppe (1970)
	Lodzinski and Karlsson (1976)
	Chari (1973)
	Akhtaruzzaman and Virkola (1979,1980)
	Lin (1978)
Simple Homogeneous Models -	Vroom (1957)
	Kerr (1970, 1976)
	Edwards and Norberg (1973)
Complex Homogeneous -	LeMon and Teder (1973)
	Olm and Tistad (1979)
	Wilder and Daleski (1965)
	Kondo and Sarkanen (1984)
	Norden and Teder (1978)
	Smith and Williams (1975)
Kinetics and Mass Transport -	Gustafson (1982)
	Pankonin (1979)
	Chistensen (1983)
	Tyler (1982)
Polymer Degelation -	Szabo and Goring (1968)
	Yan (1981)

(a) Adopted from Grace, Malcolm and Kocurek (1983).

TABLE 3

SUMMARY OF COEFFICIENTS IN HATTON`S (1973) MODEL

Coefficients	White Cedar (This Study)	Western Red Cedar (Hatton, 1973)
A	107.36	84.1
B	7.69	4.68
n	0.293	0.35
a	566.32	304.9
b	97.78	33.56
n`	0.156	0.35

TABLE 4
SUMMARY OF COEFFICIENTS IN KERR'S (1976) MODEL

ITEM	VALUE
L_i = Initial Lignin Content	30.59%
L_t = Transition Lignin Content	27.40%
a_1	1.539842
a_2	0.114916
a_3	6.42×10^{-5}
a_4	0.024509
a_5	39.0456
a_6	0.885406
a_7	-45.4116
a_8	190.625
a_9	97.4897
a_{10}	-6.0316
a_{11}	$3.547858 \times 10^{+3}$
b_1	(-26.903)[a]
b_2	(12.14258)[a]

(a) b_1, b_2 are functions of C_i.

TABLE 5

SUMMARY OF COOKING CONDITIONS

Conditions	Value
Data Set A	
Wood Mass	1,000 Grams O. D. Basis
Temperature	170 C (340 F)
Time to Temperature	81 Minutes
Time at Temperature	Variable
Concentration	24 % Active alkali as Na_2O
	20.4% Effective Alkali as Na_2O
	30 % Sulfidity
Liquor to Wood Ratio	12 to 1
Data Set B	
Wood Mass	1,000 Grams O. D. Basis
Temperature	170 C (340 F)
Time to Temperature	81 Minutes
Time at Temperature	129 Minutes
Concentration	Variable
	30 % Sulfidity
Liquor to Wood Ratio	12 to 1

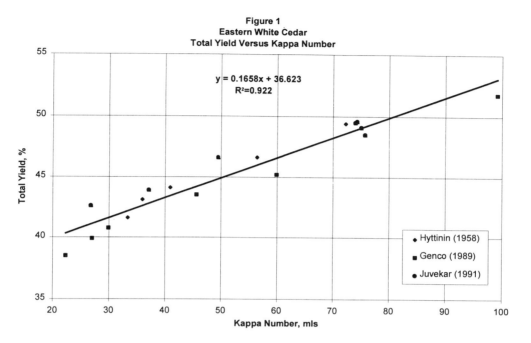

Figure 1
Eastern White Cedar
Total Yield Versus Kappa Number

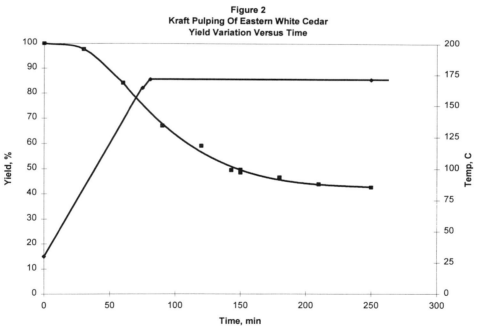

Figure 2
Kraft Pulping Of Eastern White Cedar
Yield Variation Versus Time

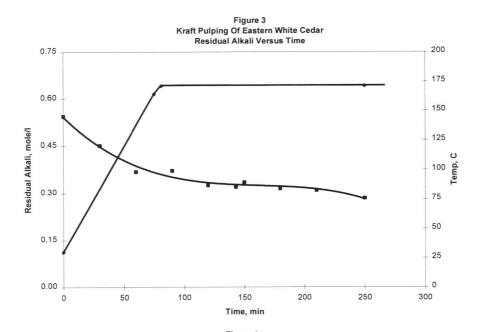

Figure 3
Kraft Pulping Of Eastern White Cedar
Residual Alkali Versus Time

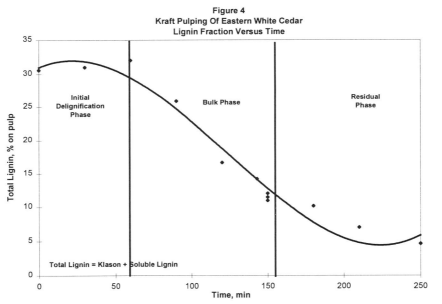

Figure 4
Kraft Pulping Of Eastern White Cedar
Lignin Fraction Versus Time

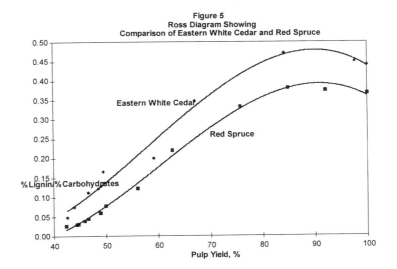

Figure 5
Ross Diagram Showing
Comparison of Eastern White Cedar and Red Spruce

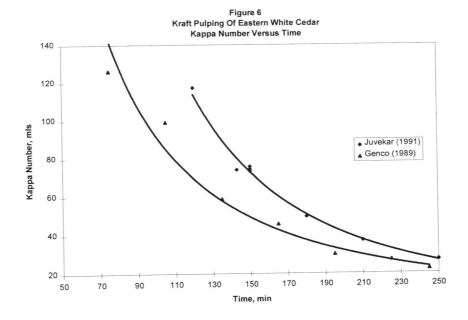

Figure 6
Kraft Pulping Of Eastern White Cedar
Kappa Number Versus Time

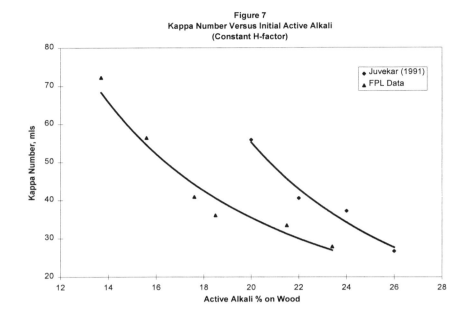

Figure 7
Kappa Number Versus Initial Active Alkali
(Constant H-factor)

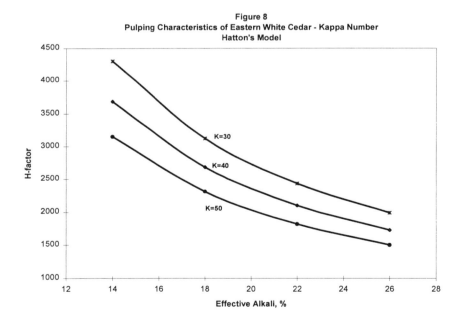

Figure 8
Pulping Characteristics of Eastern White Cedar - Kappa Number
Hatton's Model

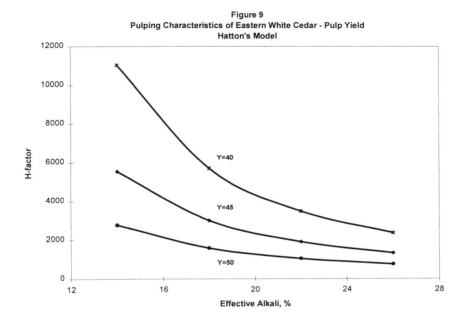

Figure 9
Pulping Characteristics of Eastern White Cedar - Pulp Yield
Hatton's Model

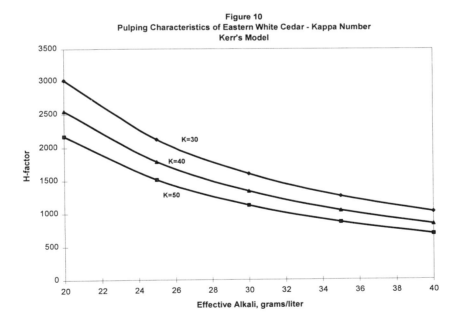

Figure 10
Pulping Characteristics of Eastern White Cedar - Kappa Number
Kerr's Model

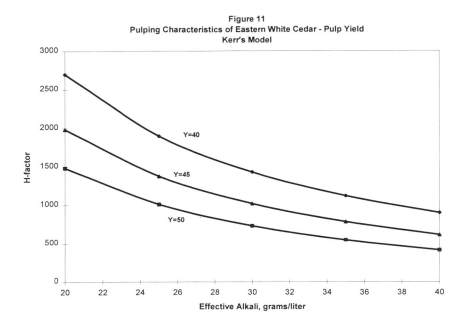

Figure 11
Pulping Characteristics of Eastern White Cedar - Pulp Yield
Kerr's Model

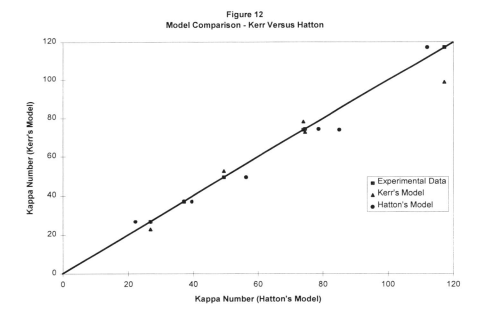

Figure 12
Model Comparison - Kerr Versus Hatton

The Challenges of Applying Polysulphide Pulping With AQ and Oxygen Delignification in Future Kraft Mills

Peder J. Kleppe
M. Peterson, and Søn AS, Moss, Norway

The results from mill scale application of polysulphide pulping in combination with AQ and oxygen delignification during two decades are given. A considerable reduction in wood consumption and improved pulping capacity is experienced. The pulp properties are comparable to the properties of conventional Kraft pulps. Since 1976 the polysulphide content in the cooking liquor has been produced by air oxydation of white liquor through the Moxy process. It has been demonstrated through Moxy pilot plast tests that, (1) the efficiency of converting sulphide for polysulphide is improved by increasing the white liquor sulphidity, and (2) air oxidation of green liquor has surprisingly given higher conversion of sulphide to polysulphide than white liquor. With the goal to obtain the highest possible pulp yield and desired pulp properties with a minimum environmental impact several new Kraft mill techniques for application of polysulphide-AQ pulping and multistage oxygen delignification are presented.

INTRODUCTION

Polysulphide pulping has been applied at the Peterson Kraftmill in Moss since 1973. The mill is an intergrated pulp and paper mill producing linerboard spesialities. The pulp mill has a production capacity of 550 ton/day and the pulping takes place in a Kamyr dual vessel digester. The kappa-no of the pulp from the digester is at a level of 60 - 65. The White Liquor sulphidity is in the range of 32 - 35%, and 0,35 kg AQ per ton of pulp is added to the cooking liquor.

The polysulphide cooking liquor is prepared by catalytic air-oxidation of the sulfide in the White Liquor by the Moxy- process (1). Approx. 50% of the sulphide is oxidized in the process giving a PS- consentration of 5 - 6.5 G. Sulphur/L.

The Moxy process shown in fig. 1 has been in operation since 1976. AQ-addition started in 1980.
The results of polysulphide - AQ - pulping at the Moss mill are:

1. Reduction in wood consumption (per ton of pulp)~ 4,3%
2. Increased pulp production capacity of the Kamyr-digester ~ 4,5%
3. Increased pulping capacity when chemical recovery is a «bottleneck» ~ 10%.
4. Corrosion protection of the Kamyr digester.

The properties of the PS-pulps are comparable to the properties of kraft pulp of equal lignin content.

A MC-oxygen delignification plant was started at the Peterson Moss mill in 1980. In 1989 the single stage oxygen delignification unit was converted into the two stage system, shown in fig. 2.

The two stage system consists of a coarse screen (flow-splitting device), a receiver standpipe, a MC-pump, a MC-screen, a pressure diffuser washer, a disc refiner (mixer), a 13m³ reactor, a MC-mixer, a 46 m³ reactor (old), a blow-tank and a wash press. The production capacity of the plant is approx. 150 ton/day. Fully oxidized White Liquor (Moxydizer) is used as a major part of the alkali charge (~ 50%).

The polysulphide - AQ - pulp of Kappa-no 60 - 65 from the Kamyr digester is by applying approx. 6 -7% NaOH and approx. 4% O_2 at 112 $^{\circ}$C - 122 $^{\circ}$C easily delignified to Kappa-no. 22. The pulp after further bleaching is well suited for the making of a top layer on liner-boards as well as for «greaseproof» paper.

THE YIELD INCREASE BY POLYSULPHIDE - (AQ) PULPING

The main reason for applying polysulphide pulping is to increase the pulp yield through stabilization of the carbohydrates in wood against alkaline degradation (peeling).

The yield increase is mainly dependent on the concentration of the polysulphide sulphur in the impregnation and cooking liquor, the impregnation and pulping conditions and wood specie (2). Reduction in chip size, improved impregnation by steaming of the chips and reduction in the maximum cooking temperature increases the yield effect. The yield gain decreases as the lignin content in the pulp diminishes.

The practical mill application of polysulphide pulping is at polysulphide charges of approx. 0,5% to 1,5% sulphur on wood. Obtainable yield increase by having this amount of PS-sulphur present in the cooking liquor charged to the digester is in the range of 1 to 2 times the amount of PS-sulphur added, dependent on the impregnation and cooking techniques, kappa-no. and wood specie (2).
By impregnation of the chips with a Na_2S_4 -liquor before alkaline pulping the yield gain, may be increased to 2.5 to 4 times of the charged polysulphide sulphur (2). This is demonstrated in fig. 3.

Fig. 4 shows the relationship between yield and kappa-no. for conventional kraft pulping, polysulphide pulping, polysulphide - AQ pulping and oxygen delignification at the Moss mill.

The data demonstrates especially the high selectivity of lignin removal by oxygen delignification in the kappa-no. range of 30 - 70 and the decreasing yield gain of 0,2% (on wood) for every 10 unit reduction in kappa-no by polysulphide pulping.

THE MOXY SYSTEM FOR MAKING OF POLYSULPHIDE

Convertion of sulphide in the white liquor to polysulphide sulphur has successfully been applied at the Moss mill since 1976. The mill is also producing the Moxy catalyst. The Moxy reactors contains 6.5 ton of catalyst handling a throughput of ~ 60 m^3 W.L./hr. By operating with a «clean» catalyst about 70% of the oxidized sulphide is convented to PS-sulphur at an oxygen/sulphide molar ratio of 0.35 - 0,4. The rest of the oxidized sulphide forms thio-sulphate, which is an inactive cooking chemical. The best pulping results are obtained, when 50 - 60% of the White Liquor sulphide is oxidized.
The efficiency of the Moxy system i very much dependent on the cleanliness of the White Liquor and good filtration of the White Liquor is very important. The suspended solids ($CaCO_3$) in the filtered White Liquor absorbed on the catalyst bed have to be removed by acid washing, normally required every 2 to 3 weeks. More frequent washing is needed at the end of the catalyst lifetime. The lifetime of the catalyst, one to three years, is very much dependent on the suspended solid content in the White Liquor feed to the Moxy reactors.

Increasing the White Liquor sulfidity to 70% will enhance the PS-convertion efficiency of oxidized sulphide to approx. 80%. This is demonstrated in fig. 5, which shows results from the Moxy pilot reactor in Moss.
Oxidation of green liquor (G.L.) in the pilot Moxy reactor has surprisingly given over 90% convertion of the sulphide to PS-sulphur (See fig. 5).

The PS-sulphur concentrations, which will be obtainable by oxidation of white and green liquors with a Na_2S-content varying from 30 to 50 G/L, are shown in fig. 6.

THE APPLICATION OF THE MOXY SYSTEM

As the sulphide present in green liquor is more efficiently oxidized to PS-sulphur by the Moxy system,(see fig. 5), the green liquor should preferably be chosen before white liquor. New filtration technology for green liquor (3) also gives an extremely cleanaffect, which should result in a long lifetime for the Moxy catalyst.

Fig. 7 shows a proposal for the application of the Moxy system in a kraft mill for polysulphide generation in the green liquor as well as for full oxidation of PS cooking -liquor. The PS- cooking liquor is prepared through causticizing of the PS-green liquor. The use of full oxidized PS-liquor as the main alkali source for oxygen delignification has successfully been applied in the Moss mill since 1980.

Demonstrated in fig. 8 is a more sophisticated proposal for application of the Moxy system in a kraft mill. By removing the main part of the Na_2CO_3 in the green liquor by crystallization, may a high sulphidity green liquor may be produced. This liquor may then be selectively oxidized through the Moxy-process to a Na_2S_{3-4} liquor, which without or with causticizing is well suited as the impregnation liquor for wood chips before cooking. Impregnation with a PS-Na_2S_{3-4} liquor gives especially high yield increases as demonstrated in fig. 3.

The Na_2CO_3 crystals from the green liquor will after dissolving in water and causticizing be used at the main alkali source for the pulping and the oxygen delignification process. This system will especially be of advantage in a «closed» cycled kraft mill producing bleached pulp grades.

POLYSULPHIDE AQ - PULPING AND OXYGEN DELIGNIFICATION IN FUTURE KRAFT MILLS

A combination of polysulphide - AQ - pulping and oxygen delignification may in many pulp mills give a good economical result due to increased pulp yield and improved production capacity. The challenges to obtain maximum profit by this approach are:

[1] Selection of the most efficient polysulphide generation method and the correct chip impregnation- and cooking technique for polysulphide pulping and
[2] the most appropriate reaction conditions for the oxygen delignification stage(s).

For production of linerboards, polysulphide - AQ- pulping may be interrupted in the Kappa-no range of 60 - 100 for making of the base liner pulp. Part of the base liner pulp may then be further delignified by oxygen and alkali to kappa-no 20 - 50, dependent on the required pulp cleanness and brightness for the top liner pulp. (fig. 9).
The combination of PS - AQ - pulping and oxygen delignification is in general an advantage in pulp mills needing different kappa-no. pulps from a single digester.

For production of bleached pulp grades, polysulphide - AQ pulping should preferentially be interrupted in the kappa-no range of 25 to 50 and followed by multistage oxygen delignification to kappa-no 8 - 12 before final TCF-bleaching. A Q-stage between the oxygen stages should be favourable for removing harmful metals and for «activation» of lignin (4). Based on present knowledge the TCF- final bleaching sequence ZEoP or PAAEoP is suggested. (fig. 10). The advantages of the given pulping and delignification technology compared to todays kraft pulping and bleaching practice are considerable such as woodsaving, higher production capacity and improved beatability of the pulps due to higher retention of hemi-celluloses. The combination of PS - AQ - pulping and multi stage oxygen delignification may also make it relatively easy to apply a «closed» mill concept and obtain a minimum environmental impact mill.

CONCLUSIONS

1. Based on long time experience from the Moss pulp mill, polysulphide - AQ pulping and oxygen delignification of PS - AQ - pulps results in a considerable reduction in wood consumption and improved pulping capacity compared to kraft pulping. The

pulp properties are comparable to kraft pulps.

2. The yield increase by polysulphide pulping is mainly dependent on the amount of polysulphide sulphur charged to the digester system and the impregnation and cooking conditions. Maximum yield gain for a given PS-sulphur charge is obtained by impregnation of the chips with a Na_2S_4 liquor before pulping.

3. The polysulphide generation at the Moss mill has been carried out since 1976 by catalytic air oxidation through the Moxy process of 50 - 60% of the sulphide present in the white liquor. A «new» catalyst converts approx. 70% of the oxidized sulphide to polysulphide sulphur. The life time of the catalyst is very much dependent on the suspended solid content of the white liquor. The time span between catalyst changes can vary from approx. one to three years.

4. Pilot plant Moxy trials have shown that by increasing the sulphidity of the white liquor from 25 - 40% to approx. 70%, the efficiency of converting sulphide to PS-sulfur has increased to approx. 80%.

5. Oxidation of <u>green liquor</u> in the pilot Moxy reactor has surprisingly given more than 90% convertion of sulphide to PS-sulphur.

6. Crystallization of Na_2CO_3 from green liquor may produce a high sulfiphity green liquor. Oxidation of this liquor through the Moxy system can result in a polysulphid (Na_2S_4) green liquor which with or without causticizing can be a very suitable impregnation liquor for wood-chips before alkaline cooking. The crystallized Na_2CO_3 from the green liquor can be dissolved in water and after causticizing be used as the major alkali source for pulping and oxygen delignification.

7. The application of polysulphide -AQ - pulping and multistage oxygen delignification in kraft-mills should result in considerable wood saving, increased production capacity and make it easier to apply a «closed» mill concept compared to todays conventional practice.

8. The challenges of applying polysulphide - AQ pulping and oxygen delignification in future kraft mills will be to find the optimum generation methods for polysulphide from the sulphide present in the pulping-chemical cycle and to combine it with the right impregnation and delignification techniques. The goal should be to obtain highest possible pulpyield and wanted pulp properties in a minimum environmental impact mill.

<u>REFERENCES</u>

1. Smith, G.C. and Sanders F.W
   US. Pat. 87.504 (1970),
   US. Pat. 2.151.465 (1972)

2. Kleppe, P.J. TAPPI 53(1) : 35 (1970)

3. Engdahl, H. and Törmikoski, P.,
   PAPERI JA PUU 76 (5) : 326 (1994)

4. Kleppe, P.J., Proceedings, Int. Non-chlorine Bleaching Conference, Amelia Island, Fl., March 6 - 10th, 1994.

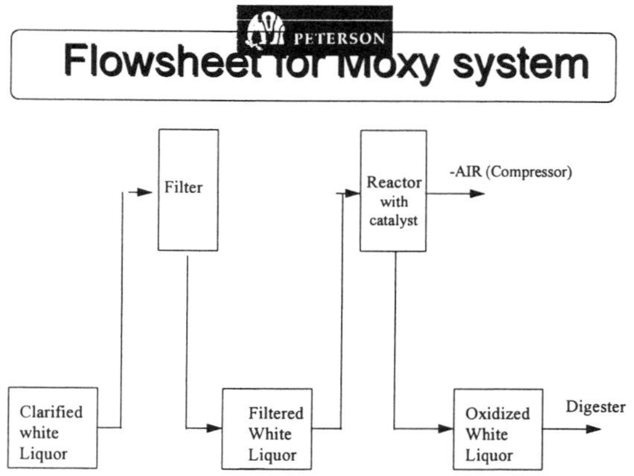

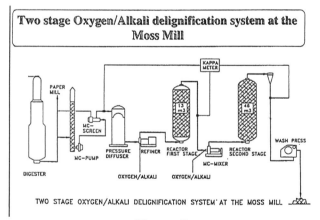

Figure 1

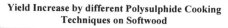

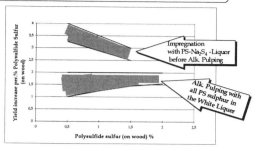

Figure 3

Two stage Oxygen/Alkali delignification system at the Moss Mill

Figure 2

Relationship between Yield and Kappa-no for Conv. Kraft Pulping, Polysulphide Pulping and Oxygen Delignification, (Data from the Moss Mill, Kappa-no. range 30-70)

- Conv. Kraft Pulping: Y = 0,14 Kappa-no + 44,7
- Polysulphide - Pulping: Y = 0,16 Kappa-no. + 45,4
- Polysulphide - AQ Pulping: Y = 0,16 Kappa-no + 45,9
- Oxygen Delignification: Y = 0,09 Kappa-no + A_o

-

- (Spruce wood, 35% W.L. sulphidity, 18% eff. alkali (NaOH), ~1% PS, 0,02% AQ (on wood))

Figure 4

Catalytic Polysulphide Production in White Liquor (W.L.) of moderate and high Sulphidity and in Green Liquor (G.L.) by the Moxy Process

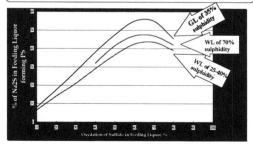

Figure 5

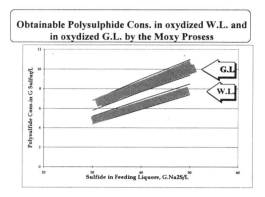

Figure 6

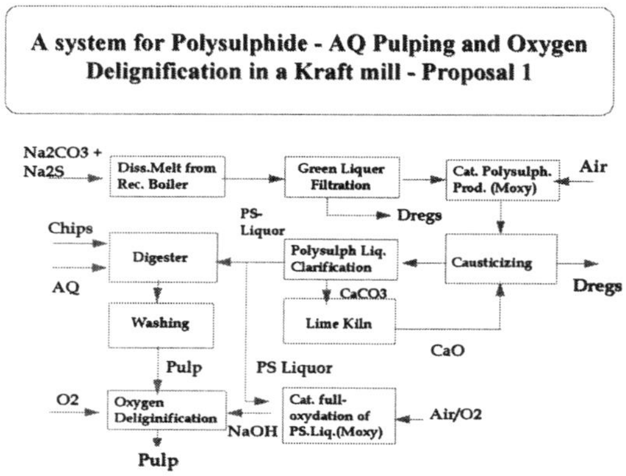

Application Polysulphide-AQ Pulping and Oxygen Delignification in Future Kraftmills

LINERBOARD PULPS:

◻ Poly-sulfiphe (AQ) - Pulping to Kappa-no 60 - 100 for making of Base Liner Pulp followed by Oxygen Delignification to Kappa-no. ~25 - 50 for making of TopLiner Pulp .

◻ RESULTS   Considerable increase in Pulp Yield and Production Capasity compared to conventional Kraftpulping

FIGURE 9

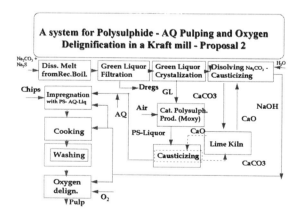

Figure 7

Application of Polysulphide - AQ - Pulping and Oxygen Delignification in Future Kraftmills

BLEACHED SOFTWOOD PULP:

◻ Poly-sulphide (AQ) - to Kappa-no ~ 25 - 50, followed by Multistage Oxygen Delignification to Kappa-no 8-12 and final TCF-bleaching: $(O)OQO_{(P)}ZE_oP$ or $(O)OQO_{(P)} PAAE_oP$

◻ RESULTS   1) Wood Saving due to higher Pulpyield

2) Increased Production Capasity

3) Easy beaten pulp

4) Easy to apply a "Closed" Mill Consept and obtain a Minimum Environmental Impact Mill

FIGURE 10

Figure 8

Kinetic Analysis of Hydrogen Peroxide Brightening of Thermomechanical Pulp

Jeff A. Stevens and Jeffery S. Hsieh

Pulp and Paper Engineering, School of Chemical Engineering
Georgia Institute of Technology, Atlanta, GA 30332

In order to better understand the mechanism of thermomechanical pulp (TMP) brightening using hydrogen peroxide, a series of kinetic data have been obtained and analyzed. The effects of chelation pretreatment for metal control, reaction temperature, percent pulp solids in the reaction mass, and peroxide concentration in the reaction mass have been determined on TMP pulp. This data is expressed as series of kinetic curves and equations relating both brightness and peroxide concentration to retention time in a batch reactor. It has been determined that most of the brightening effect and peroxide consumption takes place very early in the reaction. The reaction also takes place much quicker at higher temperatures, leading to an Arrhenius-type rate constant/temperature relationship. Also, at higher temperatures, competing darkening reactions take place, and these reactions are studied. Pulp brightening has also been related directly to elimination of color-producing bodies within the pulp, leading to the development of kinetic relationships between these pulp constituents, bleaching chemicals, time, and temperature. The reactions of hydrogen peroxide in alkaline media have also been examined, and a mechanism has been proposed. The result of this study is a comprehensive discussion of TMP pulp brightening reactions using hydrogen peroxide that may lead to better bleaching process design and optimization.

Introduction

The use of peroxide to bleach mechanical pulps has been an industrial reality since the 1940's ([1]). Peroxide is derived from both hydrogen and sodium peroxide, and when dissolved in water and adjusted to the same pH, the two chemicals are identical ([1]). The advantages of peroxide in mechanical pulp bleaching are that it is easy to handle, relatively non-explosive in moderate concentrations, and it is a lignin-preserving agent. The main advantage to mechanical pulp bleaching is that the yield from wood chips is greater than 85%, so a bleaching agent must also preserve the high yield of the pulping process, and hydrogen peroxide preserves yield to ~98% in the bleaching process ([1,2]).

Hydrogen peroxide bleaching of mechanical pulps can be carried out in one stage, two stages, or as the first stage in a peroxide-hydrosulfite bleaching sequence. Schematics of each of these sequences are shown in Figures 1 and 2. The purpose of a second peroxide or hydrosulfite stage is to increase brightness of the pulp by an additional 3 - 5 % ISO. Typical brightness gains in the first stage lie between 10 and 20% ISO.

With the recent focus on chlorine-free bleaching sequences in chemical pulp bleaching, hydrogen peroxide has begun to recieve considerable attention as a bleaching agent. Thus mass transfer and kinetic studies of mechanical pulp bleaching reactions will be helpful in designing and optimizing new processes for bleaching chemical pulps using hydrogen peroxide.

Mechanical Pulp Bleaching Chemistry

Hydrogen peroxide is a colorless weak acid with a pKa of 11.6 ([15]). Hydrogen peroxide is used to bleach pulp in alkaline media, and the chief bleaching agent is the perhydroxyl anion ([1,2,3,7,8,15]). The reactions of hydrogen peroxide in alkaline media are as follows:

$$H_2O_2 + OH^- \quad \Leftrightarrow \quad OOH^- + H_2O \tag{1}$$

$$H_2O_2 + OOH^- \quad \Leftrightarrow \quad OH^- + H_2O + O_2 \tag{2}$$

and decomposition of peroxide takes place as

$$H_2O_2 \quad \rightarrow \quad H_2O + \tfrac{1}{2}O_2 \tag{3}$$

It is speculated that free radicals formed by hydrogen peroxide reactions in alkaline media also have a role in pulp bleaching, chiefly the hydroxy radical, OH· ([1,5]).

The perhydroxyl anion reacts with the chromophores in the pulp lignin which give the pulp its dark color. The chromophores are converted to a colorless form by the action of the perhydroxyl anion. Reactions that occur include destruction of orthoquinones, demethylation, cleavage of side chains (Dakin reaction), and ring rupture (1).

Kinetics

Kinetic studies of bleaching reactions are helpful in designing and optimizing bleaching processes. Because cost of hydrogen peroxide is high, accurate modelling may result in processes which cost significantly less to operate than unoptimized processes. Kinetic models are also useful in the bleachplant as a process control aid.

The complex nature and uncertainty of the actual reaction mechanism in peroxide bleaching makes phenomenological kinetic studies very difficult. Lignin model compounds are used in literature to attempt to elucidate reaction mechanisms, but these may not be applied to actual bleaching kinetics due to the extremely complex nature of pulp itself. Pulp bleaching via hydrogen peroxide occurs in a heterogeneous system comprised of solid and liquid forms. Free radical formation and action on pulp is very difficult to measure in a pulp system. Also, mass transfer phenomena are difficult to model due to the highly complex nature of the flexible pulp support (14). Most literature studies involve the use of a semi-empirical fit of a rate equation to experimental rate data. These rate equations attempt to lump kinetics and mass transfer into one equation where the activation energy takes mass transfer into account (13,14). This accounting for mass transfer is never mentioned in the literature, however. Most bleaching reactions in literature are run at very low consistency where interfiber mass transfer effects can be neglected, or they are run in very poorly mixed systems. This presents a significant departure from industrial practice, where the bleach solution and the pulp are very well mixed in a mixer before going to a retention tower. Literature suggests the following form of rate equation:

$$dC_k/dt = A_0 exp(-E_a/RT)[H2O2]^a[OH-]^b C_k{}^c \qquad (4)$$

Activation energies have been found to range between 72 and 40 kJ/mol (8,10). A study by Moldenius and Sjugren suggest constants of a = .67, b = .23. and c = 2.2 for 15% consistency (solids content) pulp, with an activation energy of 45 kJ/mol (10). Other studies have suggested an order of reaction for the chromophore concentration of 4 - 5 (7). No literature studies have been made for the second stage peroxide reaction that is used in industry, and little has been said about the effect of mixing on the kinetics of the reaction.

Peroxide Decomposition

One of the most important factors in the use of hydrogen peroxide is its decomposition reaction illustrated by Equation (3) above. This decomposition is catalyzed by transition metals such as iron, copper, and especially manganese (2,5,6,11). The metal-catalyzed decomposition of hydrogen peroxide has been extensively studied with the result that manganese is by far the most active catalytic agent toward decomposition (5,6). Under certain conditions, this loss may represent as much as one third of the peroxide's oxidative capacity (2). In the Georgia Tech lab even larger losss in oxidation potential has been seen. For pulp bleaching, this represents a significant loss in bleaching potential, because these transition metals are present in the bleach sytem.

The primary source of transition metals in mechanical and chemical pulp bleaching processes is the wood itself. As an example, wood can frequently contain 100 ppm of manganese, which is the most active catalyst to decomposition (5). Transition metals are present because they are present in the nutrients which support tree growth (6). Transition metals also occur in process water, equipment from corrosion, and chemical additives to the pulping process. As a result, without metal control, peroxide is wasted and unnecessary costs arise to achieve high brightness levels.

Control of tranisition metal-induced decomposition of hydrogen peroxide can be achieved using chelating agents such as ethylene-diatriaminepentaacetic acid (EDTA), diethylene-triaminepentaacetic acid (DTPA), and others (2,5,6). These chelating agents complex the transition metal ions so that they are unable to achieve contact with the hydrogen peroxide and so cause its decomposition. Once the metals are chelated out of the system, the bleaching rate is increased and higher brightness levels may be achieved.

Historically, DTPA was the chelant of choice in peroxide bleaching plants (6). Its oxidative stability is higher in comparison to other chelating agents, so when carried over to the bleach tower, it does not decompose as readily as other agents. Colodette et al (5) determined that the decomposition of H2O2 is completely inhibited by the addition of small amounts of the sodium salt of DTPA in the pH range 9.8 - 11, which is the same pH range as that used in alkaline peroxide bleaching.

Basciano and Heimberger (6) found that in traditional tower peroxide bleaching operations, HEDTA and EDTA have demonstrated improvements in metal removal and brightness response.

Typical applications of chelant range from 0.2 - 0.4 % charge on bone dry fibers, dependent on incoming metal ion concentration. The concentration of metal ions in a wood sample may be determined via atomic absorption spectroscopy (6). In this kinetic study, a heavy chelation step was used with 1% DTPA charge on bone dry fibers before the pulp was bleached.

Use of Silicates

Sodium silicate functions as a peroxide stabilizer, source of alkali, and as a buffer in peroxide bleach systems (2). Like chelating agents, silicate absorbs some of the metal ions and acts as a metal surface passivator (11). Anywhere from between 2 and 7 points of brightness increase can result from addition of sodium silicate to the bleach system. Typically, 41° Baume grade sodium silicate is used.

Silicates also function to increase the bleaching rate. Ali et al (11) found that in the range of 25 - 90°C, brightening response was increased by silicate addition. Also, silicate slows darkening reactions caused by high alkali concentrations at low peroxide concentrations near the end of the bleach tower (11). More about alkali darkening is mentioned below.

Alkali Darkening

As the peroxide concentration begins to run low, the alkali concentration in the bleach system remains high. High alkali concentrations cause darkening of the pulp through the reaction of chromophores back to their colored forms (2,9). Figure 4 shows a typical peroxide bleaching kinetic curve at 12% consistency and 70°C. As seen by the curve a maximum brightness of 57 is reached in 90 minutes, then the brightness starts to decrease. This is explained by the high consumption of peroxide due to increased reaction rate at 70°C. Once the peroxide is consumed, OH- ions revert the chromophores in the lignin back to their colored forms. These chromophores are not the same as the original color bodies in the pulp, and they are known as leucochromophores (9). Thus competing reactions take place where alkali helps form perhydroxyl anions which

remove chromophores while at the same time reacting with lignin to form leucochromophores. The point where leucochromophore formation dominates is the point where brightness starts to decrease. This is the point at which the hydroxyl ion concentration is increased more that the peroxide anion concentration (10). Leucochromophores are removed as they are created by the perhydroxyl anion until there is no more perhydroxyl anion.

One result of alkali darkening is that the pulp must be stabilized after the bleaching process (2). The pH is reduced to between 5 and 6 by either sulfuric acid or sulfur dioxide. Sulfur dioxide also destroys residual hydrogen peroxide by the reaction

$$H_2O_2 + H_2SO_3 \quad \rightarrow \quad H_2O + H_2SO_4 \qquad (5)$$

This reaction is necessary when a subsequent sodium hydrosulfite (reduction) stage is utilized. This keeps the peroxide from oxidizing the hydrosulfite.

Experimental

The work in this study is aimed at showing the effect of mixing on the pulp bleaching kinetics. Previous kinetic studies only bleached under stirred conditions at low consistencies where interfiber mass transfer is negligible, or in plastic bags maintained at constant temperature, where mass transfer would severely limit the reaction rate (7,8,10). This study bleached in both a well mixed batch reactor and plastic bags under the same conditions at medium consistency to show the effect of mixing on the rate of reaction.

Thermomechanical pulp was obtained from a southern thermomechanical pulp mill for use in these experiments. Unbleached TMP pulp had an initial brightness of 50, and sodium hydrosulfite bleached TMP had an initial brightness of 57.

A CRS bleaching reactor shown in Figure 5 was used as the well-mixed batch reactor. All the pulp was chelated at 1.6% DTPA charge at 60°C for 30 minutes prior to bleaching to complex metal ions. For each bleach run 20 grams of bone dry pulp was put into the reactor with the proper amount of distilled water. The reactor vessel was passivated with sodium silicate and nitric acid prior to the set of bleaching experiments. Once the temperature in the reactor was brought to either 59°C or 68°C, a solution of sodium hydroxide and sodium silicate was put into the bleach liquor storage cylinder. Then, a solution containing the proper amount of hydrogen peroxide was put into the bleach liquor storage cylinder. Air pressure was used to push the bleach liquor into the reactor, and the watch was started. The stirrer motor was set at 315 rpm for the duration of the bleach run. At the end of each time period, the reactor was opened and sulfuric acid was used to end the reaction by bringing the pH to 6.0. In all reaction runs, a peroxide charge of 2% on bone dry fibers was used, along with 2% NaOH, and 3% Na2SiO3. For the kinetic results, 7% consistency was used.

Peroxide concentrations at the end of each bleach run were measured via iodometric titration of the bleach liquor with potassium iodide and sodium thiosulfate (2), and alkali concentration was measured via titration with HCl using phenylphthalein as an indicator. The pulp was washed with tap water and stored for 24 hours. Handsheets were then made according to standard methods. The pulp brightness was measured 24 hours later with a brightness meter, and all brightness results are reported as %G.E.

In the plastic bag experiments, again 20 grams of bone dry pulp was placed in a bag with distilled water. This bag was placed in a water bath for one hour for the temperature to achieve the setpoint temperature of the well-mixed runs. Then the sodium hydroxide and sodium silicate were added, along with the hydrogen peroxide. The bag was sealed and squeezed vigorously to mix the pulp and chemicals together. Once the reactants were added to the bag, the watch was started. The bag was put into the constant temperature bath for the remainder of the retention time.

The bags used as unmixed batch reactors for the first stage in peroxide bleaching were also compared to brightening kinetics for the second stage of peroxide bleaching. A P1 first peroxide stage was conducted by applying 1% H2O2, 1% NaOH, and 1.5% Na2SiO3 to pulp at 7% consistency for 90 minutes at 60°C. The resulting brightness from this stage was 55. This pulp was then bleached in plastic bags in the constant temperature water bath in the same manner as described above at 59°C

Another set of experiments run in the CRS reactor was designed to observe the alkali darkening behavior with time. These experiments were run exactly as the peroxide brightening experiments, except that no hydrogen peroxide was injected into the reactor. Sodium hydrosulfite-bleached TMP with an initial brightness of 57 was used for this set of experiments.

Finally, the effect of consistency under high shear mixing was studied briefly. The same amount of pulp and bleaching chemicals as described above were added to the CRS reactor at 59°C. For the first 15 seconds of the reaction, the reactor motor speed was set at 1200 rpm to achieve high shear mixing (14). Then for the rest of 5 minutes the reactor motor was turned off. This experiment was run at both 7% consistency and 14% consistency. This experiment resulted in brightness levels of 59.3 and 60 % G.E. brightness, respectively.

Results

In order to generate meaningful kinetic data from these experiments, it is necessary to calculate the absorbtion coefficient from the brightness value for each data point. The absorption coefficient, k is used as a direct measure of chromophore concentration in the pulp, in m^2/kg. It is calculated from the Kubelka-Munk equation (3):

$$k/s = \{(1-Br)^2/200Br\} \qquad (6)$$

where nomenclature is defined at the end of this paper. The value s is the light scattering coefficient which remains constant throughout the pulp. This value was estimated to be ~20 kg/m^2 following standard Tappi methods.

Because the perhydroxyl anion OOH- is the active bleaching agent in this system, a rate law should include its concentration rather than the total hydrogen peroxide concentration. Looking again at Equation (1),

$$H_2O_2 + OH^- \quad \rightleftharpoons \quad OOH^- + H_2O \qquad (1)$$

an equilibrium can be written as

$$K_p = [OOH^-]/[H_2O_2][OH^-] \qquad (7)$$

From Teder and Tormund, the value of $1/K_p = 100$ (12). The total titrated amount of H2O2 in the system is given by (7)

$$[H_2O_2]_{tot} = [H_2O_2] + [OOH^-] \qquad (8)$$

From rearrangement of Equations (7) and (8), the concentration of OOH⁻ can be calculated by

$$[OOH^-] = [H_2O_2]_{tot}[OH^-]/\{1/K_p + [OH^-]\} \quad (9)$$

Now the rate law may be described.

Most of the literature concerning H2O2 bleaching kinetics describe a rate law using the total H2O2 concentration (4,7,8,9,10). The rate law developed here is based on perhydroxyl anion concentration, because it is the true bleaching agent. Figure (6) shows the chromophore concentration vs time at 59°C and 68°C. This was calculated by Kubelka-Munk theory from brightness/time data appearing in Figure (7). As shown by the figure, there are two distinct regions of chromophore elimination. There is a fast region from 0 to 5 minutes where most of the brightening takes place. Since no data was taken before 5 minutes, it is unknown as to when the exact point the fast brightening region stops. This same phenomenon may be observed in bleach chemical concentration kinetics, Figures (9) and (10). This phenomenon is also observed in oxygen bleaching of kraft and sulfite pulps (14), where a region of "fast lignin" removal is followed by a region of "slow lignin". This facilitates the need to break the kinetics into 2 regions, fast and slow chromophore removal. Rate data appears in Table 1, showing the calculated rate of reaction for chromophore removal, perhydroxyl anion concentration, and hydroxide ion concentration. Each rate of reaction was calculated from slopes of concentration vs time correlations taken for either the fast or the slow region of reaction. These rates were then correlated in power law form as

$$\ln(-r) = \ln A - B/T + a \ln[OOH^-] + b \ln[OH^-] + c \ln C_k \quad (10)$$

using a regression technique in the Minintab statistical software package. The resulting kinetic equations for chromophore removal are

$$-r_{k\ fast} = 1 \times 10^{11} \exp(-1073/T) [OOH^-]^{1.0} C_k^{9.73} \quad (11)$$

$$-r_{k\ slow} = 1 \times 10^{37} \exp(-17206/T) [OOH^-]^{4.7} [OH^-]^{-5} C_k^{1.5} \quad (12)$$

with an r^2 of .954 for the slow region and 1 for the fast region. In comparison of this work to literature data, the activation energy is 38 kJ/mol compared with 45 (10) and 72 (8) kJ/mol. For the fast region, the activation energy is only 8.9 kJ/mol. This indicates that the stirred system has a lower resistance to mass transfer than an unstirred system. Also, the low activation energy of the fast region compared to the slow region indicates that there may not be a separate "fast lignin" form in the pulp, instead, the lignin and the bleach chemicals in this first stage contact each other much more rapidly due to rapid diffusion of chemicals to the surface of the pulp. Once the surface lignin is reacted, there are less chemicals to penetrate into the pulp fibers and react with the remaining lignin, thus the reaction rate is much slower. The order of reaction for OH- in Equation (12) appears odd, but this equation may be rearranged recalling Equation (9) to yield

$$-r_{k\ slow} = 1 \times 10^{27} \exp(-17206/T)[H_2O_2]_{tot}^5 C_k^{1.5} \quad (13)$$

The orders on the chemical species may also be analyzed. The order on the absorption coefficient k for the fast portion of the reaction indicates the high rate of elimination and mass transfer. The order on perhydroxyl anion (1.0) is in line with some literature predictions (7). The regression analysis threw out OH- concentration entirely, and the order on this value was less than one for rate Equation (12). This would indicate error in the regression analysis, but rearrangement in Equation (13) threw out OH⁻ entirely because of the interplay between OH⁻, H₂O₂, and OOH⁻. Typical values for the order of [OH⁻] in the rate law range from .2 to 5 (7,8,9,10). The reason for the sharp order here could be the result of sharp decline in the concentration of hydroxyl anions (Figure 8) at the beginning of the reaction. This skews the data enough to give this negative reaction order. The order of reaction for [OH⁻] should in reality be very small, which it is upon rearrangement. Also the high order on Ck in Equation (11) is explained by the rapid mass transfer taking place in the beginning of the reaction.

The results of the alkali darkening experiments appear in Figures 11 and 12. These results also show a fast initial region followed by a slow region. Once again this may indicate a region where there is little resistance to mass transfer because lignin to bleach contacting is better initially. What is interesting to note about these results is that there seems to be little temperature dependence of the reaction. According to principles of mass transfer, the mass transfer rate should increase proportionally with temperature. These results indicate that mass transfer is not the limiting phenomenon in alkali darkening. This could be due to alkali swelling of the fibers, and a resultant loss of diffusion limitation (14).

Results Concerning Mixing Experiments

The goal of comparing mixed to unmixed bleaching data is to show qualitatively how peroxide bleaching can be limited by poor mass transfer. Figures 13 and 14 show the distinct difference between the rate of bleaching in a mixed reactor and an unmixed reactor with all other conditions constant. As shown by Figure 13 the rate of the slow reaction region is approximately equal for both the mixed and unmixed systems, because the slopes are parallel. The rate for the fast region in the mixed reaction is much faster than that for the unmixed reactor. This indicates the importance of good mixing in the first moments of the reaction. Mixing is not quite as important after the initial fast rate is complete, however. In the industrial bleaching facility, a mixer is used prior to the bleaching tower. From Figure 14 this mixer is the most important piece of equipment in the bleachplant for ensuring good brightening and better product quality. Without good mixing, high brightness levels can never be reached.

The final mixing experiment was to run pulp at two different consistencies under fluidized conditions. Under fluidization, pulp and bleach form into one phase, so mixing becomes ideal. According to Moldenius (10) as the consistency is increased the rate is increased. This could be due to free radical formation and action as a bleaching reagent (10), or it could be due to less liquid-phase mass transfer need. Under fluidized conditions, the rate should be the same. As described above, pulp was bleached for 5 minutes at 2% H_2O_2 charge at both 7 and 14% consistency. The first 15 seconds of the reaction was run under fluidized conditions. After each experiment the pulp brightness was measured. The results were that brightness went from 50 to 60 % G.E. brightness in both cases, so the rate of brightening was the same. Thus, mass transfer is broken down by fluidization, and pulp consistency does not affect the rate under fluidized conditions. More experiments are needed to confirm this hypothesis.

The final experimental results compare the first stage of peroxide bleaching to the second stage. Figure 15 shows chromophore elimination in P1 and P2 stages run under the same conditions as described earlier. Note that the second peroxide stage proceeds at a much slower reaction rate than does the first stage. This could be due to the removal of all the chromophores in the "fast

lignin". It is more likely due to the slow diffusion of bleach chemicals into the fibers after the initial lignin is converted in the first peroxide stage. There is still a small region of fast reaction in the second stage, it is just not quite as sharp as the first stage. This indicates that there is still initially some area of high lignin to bleach contact, but it is substantially lower than in unbleached pulp. More work could be done to develop an entirely new kinetic rate equation for the second peroxide stage, because this study shows that its rate law may differ significantly from the first stage bleaching rate law.

Conclusions

Major conclusions from this experimental study include:

1) The rate of reaction of hydrogen peroxide bleaching of TMP can be broken down into a fast region and a slow region, where mass transfer dictates the shift in reaction rate.

2) The activation energy for kinetics in a mixed reactor is lower than that for unmixed kinetics reported in literature.

3) The activation energy for the fast region of bleaching is significantly lower than for the slow region, indicating a higher rate of mass transfer.

4) The fast region of reaction in a mixed reactor is much faster than the fast region in an unmixed reactor.

5) The rate of reaction of the slow region is unaffected by mixing.

6) Fluidization of the reaction significantly reduces mass transfer limitations, so that the rate of reaction for pulps of different consistencies becomes equal.

7) The rate of brightening in a second peroxide stage is slower than in a first peroxide stage.

Acknowledgement

Thanks are due to International Paper Company Foundation, Fluor Daniel Foundation, and the Georgia Tech Pulp and Paper Foundation for their support of this work.

Notation

A	preexponential factor
B	Activation energy over ideal gas constant
C_k	Chromophore content in pulp, m^2/kg
K_p	equilibrium constant defined in eq. (7)
T	temperature, K

References

1. D. H. Andrews and R. P. Singh, "Peroxide Bleaching." *The Bleaching of Pulp.* 1979. pp 211 - 253

2. W. G. Strunk, "Peroxide Bleaching." *Pulp and Paper Manufacture: Mechanical Pulping.* 1989. pp. 238 - 251.

3. D. W. Reeve, "Bleaching Chemistry." *Pulp and Paper Manufacture: Alkaline Pulping.* 1989. pp. 425 - 469.

4. E. Strand, R. Koponen, L. Edwards, S. Moldenius, and E. Viljakainen, "Optimization of Peroxide Bleaching Systems." *1987 Pulping Conference.* p. 497.

5. J. L. Colodette, S. Rothenberg, and C. W. Dence, "Factors Affecting the Hydrogen Peroxide Stability in the Brightening of Mechanical and Chemimechanical Pulps. Part I: Hydrogen Peroxide Stability in the Absence of Stabilizing Systems." *JPPS.* V14, N6, Nov, 1988. p. 126.

6. C. R. Basciano and S. A Heimburger, "Importance of Chemical Pretreatment on the Hydrogen Peroxide Brightening of Mechanical Pulps." *1989 Pulping Conference.* p. 657.

7. G. C. Hobbs and J. Abbot, "Peroxide Bleaching Reactions Under Alkaline and Acidic Conditions." *J. of Wood Chem. and Tech.* 11(2), 1991. pp. 225 - 246.

8. M. Lundqvist, "Kinetics of H2O2 Bleaching of Mechanical Pulp." *Svensk Papperstidning.* n1, 1979. p. 16.

9. J. Abbot and Y. A. Ginting, "Development fo Kinetic Models for Alkaline Peroxide Bleaching." *JPPS.* V 18, N3. May, 1992. p. 85.

10. S. Moldenius and B. Sjogren, "Kinetic Models for H2O2 Bleaching of Mechanical Pulps." *J. of Wood Chem. and Tech.* 2(4), 1982. pp. 447 - 471.

11. T. Ali, M. Fairbank, D. McArthur, T. Evans, and P. Whiting, "The Role of Silicate in Peroxide Brightening fo Mechanical Pulp. Part II: The Effects of Retention Time and Temperature." *JPPS.* V14, N2. March, 1988. p. 23.

12. A. Teder and A. Tormund, " The Equilibrium Between Hydrogen Peroxide and the Peroxide Ion - A Matter of Importance in Peroxide Bleaching." *Svensk Papperstidning.* N4, 1980. p. 106.

13. P. Axegard, S. Moldenius, and L. Olm, "Basic Chemical Kinetic Equations are Useful For an Understanding fo Pulping Processes." *Svensk Papperstidning.* N5, 1979. p. 131.

14. J. Hsu, PhD Thesis. 1988.

15. B. Stromberg and R. Szopinski, "Pressurized Hydrogen Peroxide Bleaching for Improved TCF Bleaching." *1994 Intl. Pulp Bleaching Conf.* p. 199.

Table 1
Correlated Rate Data

Rate Data for Chromophore Elimination

59°C

t	-r k	k, kg/m2	[H2O2], M	[OOH-], M	[OH-], M	ln(-r)	lnk	ln[OOH-]	ln[OH-]
0	0.346	4.973	0.04428	2.05E-05	0.0464	-1.06132	1.604023	-10.7933	-3.07046
5	0.037961	3.244	0.02	3.5E-06	0.0175	-3.2712	1.176807	-12.5629	-4.04555
10	0.020868	2.983	0.0165	2.23E-06	0.0135	-3.86954	1.09293	-13.0148	-4.30507
20	0.008781	2.938	0.013	1.56E-06	0.012	-4.73516	1.077729	-13.3709	-4.42285
30	0.003426	2.895	0.012	1.32E-06	0.011	-5.67636	1.062985	-13.538	-4.50986
60	-0.00355	2.875	0.008333	6.67E-07	0.008	#NUM!	1.056053	-14.2211	-4.82831

68°C

t	-r k	k	[H2O2]	[OOH-]	[OH-]	ln(-r)	lnk	ln[OOH-]	ln[OH-]
0	0.377	4.973	0.04428	2.05E-05	0.0464	-0.97551	1.604023	-10.7933	-3.07046
5	0.056711	3.0875	0.01475	1.7E-06	0.0115	-2.86979	1.127362	-13.2872	-4.46541
10	0.027828	2.775	0.0135	1.42E-06	0.0105	-3.58171	1.020651	-13.4667	-4.55638
20	0.007405	2.762	0.01025	8.2E-07	0.008	-4.9056	1.015955	-14.014	-4.82831
30	-0.00164	2.649	0.009	6.3E-07	0.007	#NUM!	0.974182	-14.2776	-4.96185
60	-0.01343	2.925	0.0065	3.57E-07	0.0055	#NUM!	1.073294	-14.8442	-5.20301

Rate Data for [OOH-]

59°C

t	-r ooh-	k	[H2O2]	[OOH-]	[OH-]	ln(-r)	lnk	ln[OOH-]	ln[OH-]
0	3.40E-06	4.973	0.04428	2.05E-05	0.0464	-12.5917	1.604023	-10.7933	-3.07046
5	4.63E-07	3.244	0.02	3.5E-06	0.0175	-14.5859	1.176807	-12.5629	-4.04555
10	1.49E-07	2.983	0.0165	2.23E-06	0.0135	-15.7185	1.09293	-13.0148	-4.30507
20	4.8E-08	2.938	0.013	1.56E-06	0.012	-16.8511	1.077729	-13.3709	-4.42285
30	2.48E-08	2.895	0.012	1.32E-06	0.011	-17.5136	1.062985	-13.538	-4.50986
60	7.98E-09	2.875	0.008333	6.67E-07	0.008	-18.6463	1.056053	-14.2211	-4.82831

68°C

t	-r ooh-	k	[H2O2]	[OOH-]	[OH-]	ln(-r)	lnk	ln[OOH-]	ln[OH-]
0	3.76E-06	4.973	0.04428	2.05E-05	0.0464	-12.4911	1.604023	-10.7933	-3.07046
5	2.54E-07	3.0875	0.01475	1.7E-06	0.0115	-15.1849	1.127362	-13.2872	-4.46541
10	8.13E-08	2.775	0.0135	1.42E-06	0.0105	-16.3251	1.020651	-13.4667	-4.55638
20	2.6E-08	2.762	0.01025	8.2E-07	0.008	-17.4653	1.015955	-14.014	-4.82831
30	1.33E-08	2.649	0.009	6.3E-07	0.007	-18.1323	0.974182	-14.2776	-4.96185
60	4.27E-09	2.925	0.0065	3.57E-07	0.0055	-19.2726	1.073294	-14.8442	-5.20301

Rate Data for [OH-]

59°C

t	-r oh-	k	[H2O2]	[OOH-]	[OH-]	ln(-r)	lnk	ln[OOH-]	ln[OH-]
0	5.78E-03	4.973	0.04428	2.05E-05	0.0464	-5.15335	1.604023	-10.7933	-3.07046
5	0.00102	3.244	0.02	3.5E-06	0.0175	-6.88829	1.176807	-12.5629	-4.04555
10	0.000416	2.983	0.0165	2.23E-06	0.0135	-7.78453	1.09293	-13.0148	-4.30507
20	0.00017	2.938	0.013	1.56E-06	0.012	-8.68077	1.077729	-13.3709	-4.42285
30	0.000101	2.895	0.012	1.32E-06	0.011	-9.20503	1.062985	-13.538	-4.50986
60	4.1E-05	2.875	0.008333	6.67E-07	0.008	-10.1013	1.056053	-14.2211	-4.82831

68°C

t	-r oh-	k	[H2O2]	[OOH-]	[OH-]	ln(-r)	lnk	ln[OOH-]	ln[OH-]
0	6.98E-03	4.973	0.04428	2.05E-05	0.0464	-4.96471	1.604023	-10.7933	-3.07046
5	0.000744	3.0875	0.01475	1.7E-06	0.0115	-7.20297	1.127362	-13.2872	-4.46541
10	0.000301	2.775	0.0135	1.42E-06	0.0105	-8.10961	1.020651	-13.4667	-4.55638
20	0.000121	2.762	0.01025	8.2E-07	0.008	-9.01625	1.015955	-14.014	-4.82831
30	7.14E-05	2.649	0.009	6.3E-07	0.007	-9.54659	0.974182	-14.2776	-4.96185
60	2.89E-05	2.925	0.0065	3.57E-07	0.0055	-10.4532	1.073294	-14.8442	-5.20301

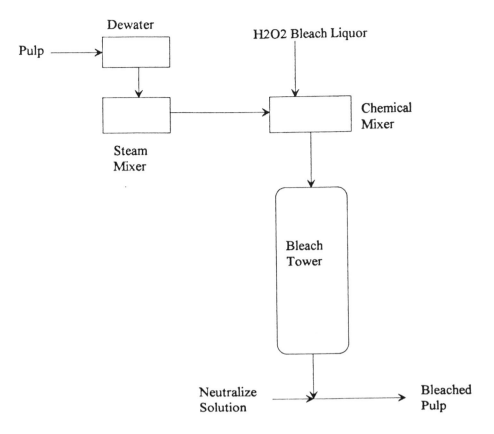

Figure 1. Single stage peroxide bleaching system.

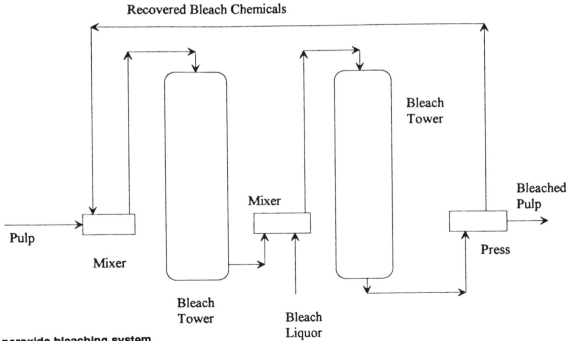

Figure 2. Multistage peroxide bleaching system.

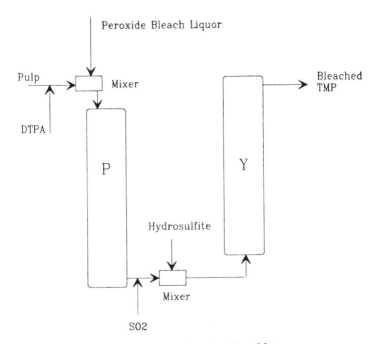

Figure 3. Two stage oxidative/reductive bleaching.

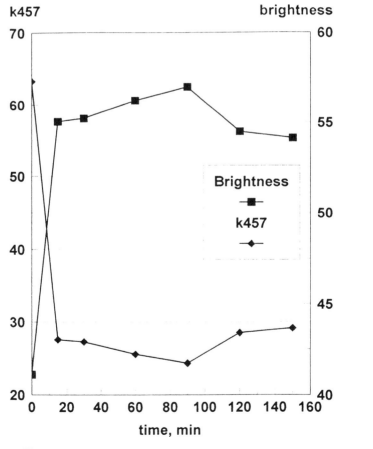

Figure 4. Peroxide brightening kinetics at 70°C.

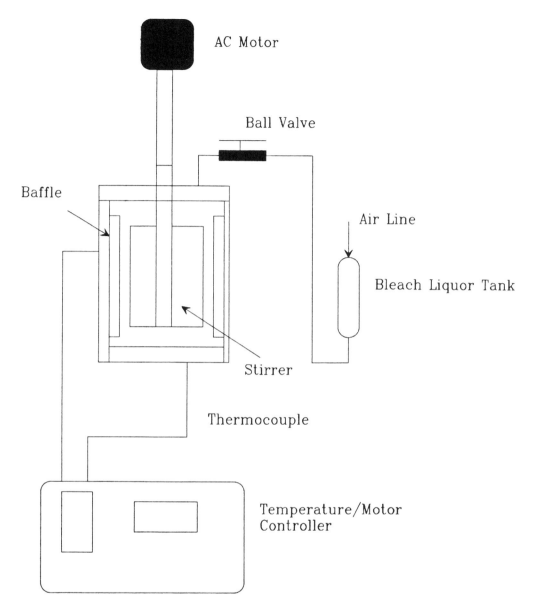

Figure 5. Schematic of CRS reactor system.

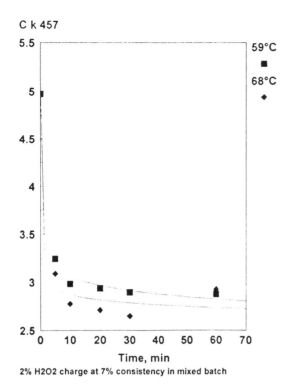

2% H2O2 charge at 7% consistency in mixed batch

Figure 6. Chromophore elimination kinetics.

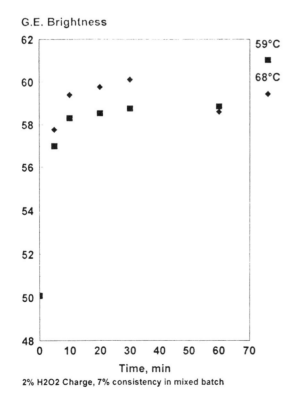

2% H2O2 Charge, 7% consistency in mixed batch

Figure 7. Brightness development kinetics.

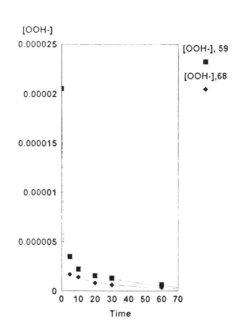

Figure 8. Perhydroxyl ion profile.

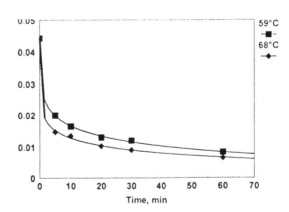

Figure 9. Peroxide concentration profile.

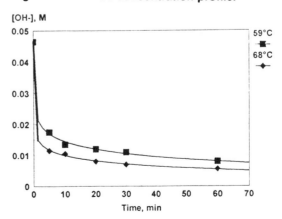

Figure 10. Alkaline concentration profile.

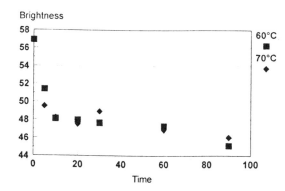

Figure 11. Alkali darkening brightness loss.

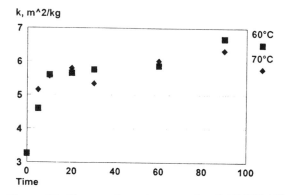

Figure 12. Chromophore increase in alkali darkening.

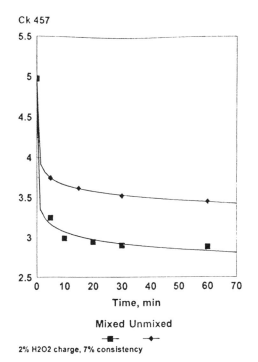

Figure 13. Mixed vs. unmixed kinetics.

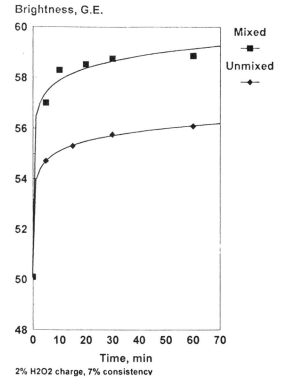

Figure 14. Mixed vs. unmixed kinetics.

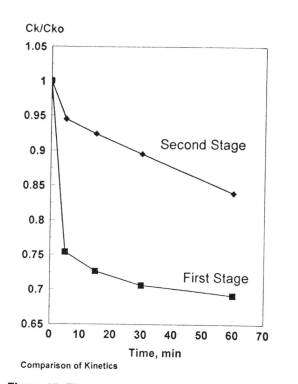

Figure 15. First reactor vs. second reactor
kinetic comparison.

Enzymatic Bleaching of Pulps With the Laccase-Mediator-System (LMS)

H.P. Call and Ingo Mücke

Lignozym GmbH, Aronold-Sommerfeld-Ring 28, 52499 Baesweiler, Germany

The authors recently published a technically feasible approach to delignify lignocellulosic material using laccase from Trametes versicolor in cell free systems [1]. LIGNOZYM's laccase-mediator (redox) concept overcomes the performance constraints of other known cell free systems. By combining the enzyme and a low molecular, environmentally save redox mediator, strongly oxidizing co-mediator(s) are generated, which specifically degrade lignin without attacking the cellulose fiber. By treatment of different kinds of pulps (hardwood-, softwood-, kraft-, sulphite-, Organosolv-pulps, pulps from annual plants etc.) with LIGNOZYM's laccase-mediator system (LMS) a kappa reduction of up to 70% can be observed in a single step. With respect to enzyme and mediator dosage recent improvements with different pulps (hardwood/softwood) are presented. It is possible to start the enzymatic treatment at high or very high levels (> 30). In several consecutive steps a lignin removal of 50 - 70 % can be obtained in each step. No "passivation" of the pulp had been observed. LIGNOZYM's laccase/mediator system (LMS) operates at a pulp consistency of 1 to 20 %, a pH range of 4 to 6.5 (optimum pH 4.5), and at temperatures of 40 to 65 °C (optimum 45 °C) with a retention time of 1 - 4 hours. Additionally oxygen as a co-substrate has to be provided in a pressurized system, e.g. hydrostatic pressure of a conventional upflow tower is sufficient. LIGNOZYM's laccase/mediator concept provides a completely new pulp bleaching system which can be combined with existing bleaching sequences in order to give access to chlorine free pulp under a broad variety of mill situations. An implementation seems possible with a limited investment, e.g. for an efficient MC-mixing device (laccase/mediator/oxygen), pH adjustment and an upflow tower of at least 15 m height. First results of a 1-week pilot plant trial are presented demonstrating the technical feasibility of the LMS.

INTRODUCTION

The largest processor of renewable raw materials, the pulp and paper industry, has until now, only used enzymes to a limited extent. There is, however, a traditional application of amylases in starch conditioning for paper coating, and an increasing use of lipases for pitch control.

On the other hand, the separation of lignin from cellulosic fibers in pulping and bleaching, the major possible application target of enzymes in this industry, is still in the beginning stage. This is not surprising due to the fact that polymers, lignin and cellulose, were developed during the evolution of plants for constructive and long term preservation purposes. Processes using harsh physico-chemical conditions to attack lignocellulose and to separate lignin and cellulose during pulping had already been developed. The specific lignin removal should be the main objective of enzyme application in this industry.

Recently LIGNOZYM presented the principle of a new biotechnological/enzymatic technology: The Laccase-Mediator-System(LMS) [1-2]. Recent improvements obtained with various pulps, plus the results of a 1-week pilot plant trial, are presented here.

THE LACCASE-MEDIATOR-SYSTEM (LMS)

Only a few microorganisms in nature are able to attack, modify or destroy the rigid organic polymer lignin. The main producers of lignolytic enzymes, lignin peroxidase (LiP), manganes peroxidase (MnP) and laccase, are white rotting fungi. Two of the most important fungi are *Phanerochaete chrysosporium* and *Coriolus (Trametes) versicolor*.

Growing on wood, these fungi secrete a number of oxidative enzymes, and some unidentified substances (mediators), into their environment. Together, they effect a slow but continuous degradation of lignin. Unfortunately in the absence of the living organism the various peroxidases and laccases are unable to perform a significant kappa reduction, indicating that single enzymes cannot mimic a complete biological system. Small improvements can be achieved by the addition of low molecular aromatic compounds [3-4].

Despite the disappointing experience with isolated lignin degrading enzymes LIGNOZYM has continued its previous projects using enzymes in combination with chemical mediators [5-7]. LIGNOZYM's plan was to develop an effective duplicate of the situation in nature compatible with technical processes.

Combining the oxidoreductase laccase from *Coriolus (Trametes) versicolor* and a special group of mediators, especially N-OH-, N-oxide-, oxime- or hydroxamic acid-compounds, a lignin removal of 50 - 70 % can be achieved in a short term application (1 - 4 h) depending on enzyme and mediator dosage and the type of pulp used.

Whereas the treatment of pulp with laccase alone doesn't result in any degradation of lignin but just in its structural change (oxidation) or repolymerization LMS

Table 1 Contribution of Reaction Partners to the Delignifying Effect of the LMS, Measured as Kappa After Extraction With Caustic

Dosage of enzyme	Dosage of mediator	Dosage of oxygen	Effect *
-	-	-	18.0
-	+	+	17.7
-	-	+	17.6
+ (↓)	+	+	17.6
+	+	+	7.8

(↓) inactivated by heat treatment

* kappa after extraction

general conditions:

extended cooked softwood pulp; 10 % consistency, pH 4.5

and 4 h retention time; 20 kg mediator/to and/or

2 kg enzyme/to and/or 10 bar oxygen pressure

causes a significant kappa reduction at reasonable treatment times. Table 1 demonstrates that no reactions occur if one compound (enzyme, mediator, oxygen) is missing or an enzyme is inactivated.

Figure 1 shows the net reaction of laccase, demonstrating that a one-electron substrate oxidation is coupled to a 4 electron reduction of oxygen.

In Figures 2 and 3 our present understanding of the reaction is given as a model. Laccase contains four atoms of copper per molecule and requires oxygen as a co-substrate for action, which has to be provided, even in a technical process. While oxidizing the chemical mediator, a substrate of the enzyme, laccase is generating a strongly oxidizing co-mediator in the presence of oxygen, which is in turn the real bleaching agent. For size exclusion reasons the enzymatic conversion of the mediator will mainly take place outside of the fiber, while the strongly oxidizing co-mediator can penetrate the fiber performing the reaction towards lignin.

APPLICATION OF THE LMS IN THE DELIGNIFICATION OF PULP

Recently LIGNOZYM presented for the first time the laccase-mediator-concept as a technically feasible approach for delignification of pulps [1,2]. In the meantime, optimization trials with a number of hard- or softwood or bagasse (kraft- or sulphite pulps), especially with respect to a better mixing, pH-control or addition of additives (e.g. Mg2+; EDTA) led to a better understanding and an enhanced performance.

LIGNOZYM's laccase-mediator-system operates at a pulp consistency of 1 to 20 % (optimum 10 to 15 %), a pH range of 4 to 6.5 with an optimum at pH 4.5 and at temperatures of 40 to 65 °C (optimum 45 °C) with a retention time of 1 - 4 hours dependent on pulp

source and lignin content. Oxygen as a co-substrate must be provided in a pressurized system, for instance, hydrostatic pressure of a conventional upflow tower is sufficient.

By dosage of additives like EDTA and/or Mg2+ an enhanced rate of lignin removal could be observed (Figure 4). The effect of additives is dependent on the pulp and will not improve the performance in general.

Since LIGNOZYM's first presentation the LMS has been proven with a variety of pulps. The comparison of delignification obtained with different soft, hardwood and bagasse pulps, under identical test conditions, is summarized in Figures 5 through 9. For that reason, all pulps were treated for 4 hours at 45 °C and 10 bar oxygen pressure, applying 2 kg of enzyme per to of pulp and mediator dosages of 5, 10 or 20 kg/to. For many of the pulps a 1 or 2 h retention time would be sufficient for a good performance. The results give a clear indication for the general applicability of LIGNOZYM's concept.

The best performance of the LMS (obtained until now), applied to a swedisch oxygen bleached softwood kraft pulp, is shown in Figures 10a and 10b as a function of residence time and mediator dosage (enzyme dosage: 2 kg/to).

Another example demonstrates the applicability of the LMS to bagasse pulps, before and after oxygen stage (Figure 11 and Figure 12).

From results in Figures 4 through 12 one can see that, in many cases, good results in delignification can be obtained with 1/2 to 1/4 of the original published mediator concentration (20 kg/to), the main cost factor of the LMS.

PILOT PLANT TRIAL

A one-week pilot plant trial was performed during June and July 1994 in the ASAM-pilot plant in Baienfurt, Germany [8], to demonstrate the technical feasibility of the new LMS-technology.

After disintegration and screening, the pulp enters the 4-stage bleach plant (normally O-Z-E-P, except here L-E-Q-P had reactors in different order) at the first double wire screen press, where the oxygen stage was used as a pressurized L-stage and the Z-stage as Q-stage. Double wire screen presses designed for high outlet consistencies and recirculation of filtrates are installed after each stage. The variable piping system allows a counter current flow of bleach filtrates.

During our trials the filtrates were recirculated in three very narrow, nearly closed cycles in counter-current flow: the acidic filtrates of the L- and the Q-stage in single closed loops; the alkaline E- and P-stage filtrates together.

With respect to pH and temperature optimal conditions obtained in lab-trials (pH 4.5 and 45 °C) were chosen for the pilot plant trials. The 8m-oxygen tower was run as a pressurized reactor with a limitation of pressure to 2 bars at the head of the tower, simulating the hydrostatic pressure of conventional towers (25 - 30 m) in existing mills. The residence time was fixed with two hours. Start-up problems had to be solved during the first two days (the plant had been shut down over a six month period), and adjustments (dosages of enzyme and mediator, pH- and temperature control etc.) had to be tested in order to obtain a continuous run free of interruptions and break-downs.

During the trials two oxygen delignified softwood kraft pulps of different suppliers (see Table 2 for characteristics) were treated under conditions shown in Figure 13. The pulp was fed with 100 kg dry pulp/h at 10% consistency. Pulp samples were taken every hour in each stage and analyzed for pulp flow, dry substance pH, kappa, viscosity and brightness to control the run. At the same time samples of the recirculation water were taken and analyzed for pH, transition metals and COD. Strength properties were determined within the laboratories of Haindl.

Figures 13 through 20, demonstrate results obtained during the trial. An overview of conditions in the different stages are given in Figure 13.

DELIGNIFICATION OF PULP A

Pulp A (characteristics see Table 2) was treated in a sequence L-E-Q-P with 2 kg enzyme/to and 13 kg mediator/to. The development of kappa-reduction and brightness in the L- and E-stage in comparison to the delivered pulp is shown in Figures 14 and 15. A diminished brightness after LMS-treatment is normal behavior for a 1-step application prior extraction. A constant delignification rate of > 55% could be obtained within a few hours. The strength properties of the pulp after the whole sequence (L-E-Q-P) remained almost unchanged (Figure16).

After reduction of mediator dosage to 8 kg/to a kappa reduction of > 50% was still obtained (see first step in the L-E-L-E-Q-P sequence; Figure 20), indicating a better mixing / oxygen supply compared to lab-trials. Interestingly, viscosity was unaffected by the second L-E-stage. Brightness was enhanced (34.6 %) and kappa reduced (34. 5%) by this treatment. Results of the first and the second L-E-stage are compared in Table 3.

DELIGNIFICATION OF PULP B

Taking the results with pulp A into account, pulp B (data in Table 2) was treated with the reduced mediator dosage from the beginning of the test. Unfortunately it became necessary to abort this trial due to damage to a double wire screen press prior to the the final performance. At that time kappa was reduced to 6 (44 % of delignification) with no loss of viscosity after enzyme treatment (Figure 17) and no loss of strength after L-E (Figure18), despite the fact that viscosity had dropped by 100 ml/g in the E-stage. No data from the P-stage are available due to the damage incurred.

Table 3   Comparison of Results Obtained in the First and in the Second L-E-Treatment

	Kappa	Viscosity	Brightness
After L-E	100 %	100 %	100 %
After L-E-L-E	- 34.5 %	- 3 %	+ 34.6 %

conditions:
pulp A, 2 x 2 kg enzyme/to and 2 x 8 kg mediator/to

SUMMARY OF RESULTS FROM THE PILOT PLANT TRIAL

Figure 19 summarizes the significant results obtained with both pulps during the pilot plant trial in Baienfurt. Delignification of > 50 % could be obtained in a single step, even if the mediator dosage was reduced by factor 0.6. It should be kept in mind that a sequence was run for one day only, because the focus was to eludicate the behavior of the L-stage. For that reason, and due to the residence time and mixing effects in the final stages, it was impossible to obtain a stable performance over all stages in that short time.

As a result of the successful demonstration of its technical practicability, LIGNOZYM is convinced that its new enzyme-based technology is a valuable biotechnological contribution to the immediate and particular demands of the pulp industry.

Table 2 Pulps Used in the Pilot Plant Trial

Pulp	Origin	Pre-treatment	Kappa [ml/g]	Viscosity [%ISO]	Brightness
A	Sweden	Oxygen	11.7	830	36.5
B	Sweden	Oxygen	10.7	870	39.5

Bleachability of Pulps

The results of bleachability (Q-P) of pulp samples taken from the trials after L-E was tested in different laboratories are summarized in Figure 20. Due to the good bleachability of pulps delignified with LIGNOZYM's LMS, a production of a TCF-quality with good strength properties is technically feasible in combination with state-of-the-art bleaching technology. Two unusual facts observed in the post-bleaching trials are important to note:
(1) the high stability of the bleaching liquor and (2) the high residual peroxide concentration at the end of the treatment (often in the range of 30 - 70 % of the dosage).

Strategies for Further Optimization

Results from the pilot plant trial had indicated further optimization potential, such as, reduction of mediator and enzyme dosage. With reduction of mediator (=substrate) dosage the calculated oxygen demand for the enzyme reaction (< 0.2 kg O2 / kg mediator), which is about one order lower than in a conventional O-stage, will be reduced further. In combination the inactivation of enzyme due to the highly active co-mediator is diminished, a lower dosage can be applied. Four strategies are now under examination:

1) enhancemant of performance due to an improved mixing
2) *in situ* generation of mediator by addition of suitable co-mediators
3) protection of enzyme from undesired inactivation during the process
4) chemical/biotechnological improvement of mediator chemistry

Advantages of the Laccase-Mediator-Concept

Following is a summary of the characteristics of the new laccase-mediator-system for enzymatic pulp:

• The results obtained are very reproducible.

• The system provides a wide range of possibilities with respect to pulp substrate, technical environment for application and final pulp quality.

• The principle applicability for a variety of softwood, hardwood and bagasse pulps derived from different cooking processes are demonstrated.

• The technical feasibility are demonstrated in pilot plant scale.

• TCF-pulp can be obtained in high quality (brightness and strength).

• The use of existing mill facilities is possible with limited investment.

CONCLUSION

LIGNOZYM's technology is a new, very effective enzymatic bleaching technology. LIGNOZYM's enzymatic bleaching system (LMS) is an alternative to existing bleaching stages, suitable for combination with established technologies. The LMS offers the possibility to improve the flexibility of bleaching sequences regarding consumption of chemicals and final pulp quality.

LIGNOZYM demonstrates the technical feasability of the new LMS-technology in a pilot plant trial successfully. Results indicate a high potential for further optimization with respect to dosage of enzyme and mediator.

LIGNOZYM's new enzyme-based technology is a valuable biotechnological contribution to the urgent and sparticular demands of the pulp industry.

LITERATURE CITED

1. **H.P. Call, I. Mücke** 1994 NCB-Conference, Proceedings (1994).
2. **H.P. Call, I. Mücke,** Microbiology and Enzymology for Pulp and Paper Industries, 1994, Espoo (1994).
3. **R. Bourbonnais et al,** *FEBS Let.* **267**, 99 (1990)
4. **W.L. Olsen et al,** *EP,* 345 715 (1989)
5. **H.P. Call,** *EP* 327 576 (1987)
6. **H.P. Call,** *DE* 40 08 893 (1990)
7. **H.P. Call,** *WO* 92/20857(1992)
8. Kraftanlagen Heidelberg, ASAM Pilot Plant confirms Laboratory Test Results (1990).

Net Reaction of Laccase:

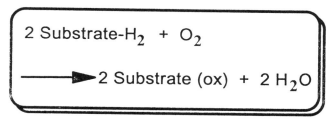

Figure 1

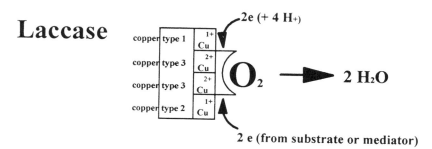

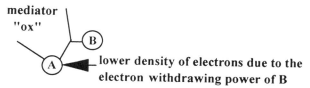

Figure 2

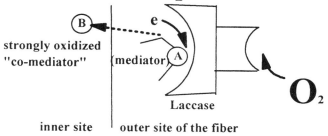

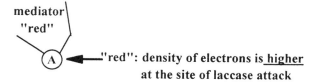

Figure 3

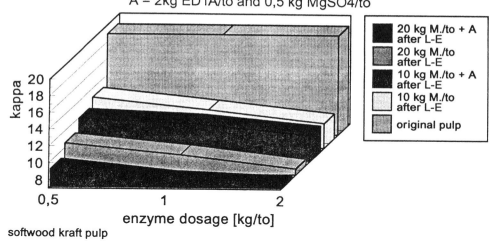

Influence of Additives on the Dosage of Mediator and Enzyme
A = 2kg EDTA/to and 0,5 kg MgSO4/to

softwood kraft pulp

Figure 4

Comparison of Delignification [%]
softwood kraft pulp of different origins

	kappa origin	A 20 kg M./to	B 10 kg M./to	C 5 kg M./to
SW1	31,0	67,7		
SW2	23,1	48,5		
SW3	19,5	60,0	39,5	
SW4	29,0	65,5	50,0	
SW5	21,6	49,5	38,0	31,9
SW6	19,0	49,5	37,9	25,8
SW7	21,8	49,1	39,0	
SW8	13,4	57,5		
SW9	15,2	59,2	48,7	32,9
SW10	14,2		50,7	
SW11	22,7		50,2	
SW12	19,0	59,5	47,3	

A/B/C: 20/10/5 kg mediator/to and 2 kg enzyme/to
standard conditions

Figure 5

Comparison of Delignification [%]
oxygen pretreated softwood kraft pulp of different origins

	kappa origin	A 20 kg M./to	B 10 kg M./to	C 5 kg M./to
SW13	15,5	58,7	52,9	
SW14	10,6	54,7	51,9	38,7
SW15	15,7	53,5	48,4	
SW16	7,6	59,2		
SW17	15,0	67,7	67,7	
SW18	11,0	58,2	54,5	50,0
SW19	12,7	56,7	50,4	41,3
SW20	15,2	54,6	45,4	
SW21	15,2	54,6	48,7	30,9
SW22	14,0	56,4	50,0	40,0
SW23	10,8	50,9	46,3	38,9

A/B/C: 20/10/5 kg mediator/to and 2 kg enzyme/to
standard conditions

Figure 6

Comparison of Delignification [%]
other pulps of different origins

	kappa origin	A 20 kg M./to	B 10 kg M./to	C 5 kg M./to
sulphite pulps				
SW24	19,7	71,1	59,9	42,6
SW25	11,8		63,6	54,2
SW26	17,5	71,4		
SWO2 27	11,0	57,3	54,5	40,9
ASAM-Pulp				
SW28	18,7	59,4	48,7	
Bagasse				
bagasse	9,3	54,8	52,2	49,5
bagasse-O2	5,6	51,8	51,8	41,1

A/B/C: 20/10/5 kg mediator/to and 2 kg enzyme/to
standard conditions

Figure 7

Comparison of Delignification [%]
hardwood kraft pulp of different origins

	kappa origin	A 20 kg M./to	B 10 kg M./to	C 5 kg M./to
HW1	13,6	40,4	38,2	
HW2	10,0	50,0	49,0	
HW3	13,0	38,5	36,5	31,5
HW4	14,9	69,1	60,4	
HW5	15,2	69,1	63,2	
HW6	12,5	45,6	44,8	
HW7	15,2		43,4	42,1
HW8	9,0		53,3	38,9
HW9	11,3	36,3	32,7	32,7
HW10	11,5	40,0	34,8	33,0

A/B/C: 20/10/5 kg mediator/to and 2 kg enzyme/to
standard conditions

Figure 8

Comparison of Delignification [%]
hardwood kraft pulp of different origins

	kappa origin	A 20 kg M./to	B 10 kg M./to	C 5 kg M./to
HW-O2				
HW11	5,4	35,2	31,5	27,8
HW12	6,8	39,7	41,2	33,8
HW13	7,6	28,9	27,6	
HW14	10,0	33,0	32,0	32,0
HW after EOP	5,5	29,1		
HW-sulphite	15,3	77,8	72,5	58,2

A/B/C: 20/10/5 kg mediator/to and 2 kg enzyme/to
standard conditions

Figure 9

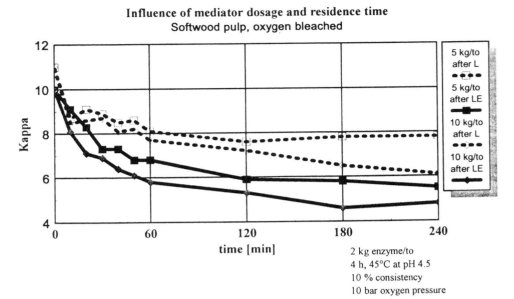

Figure 10a

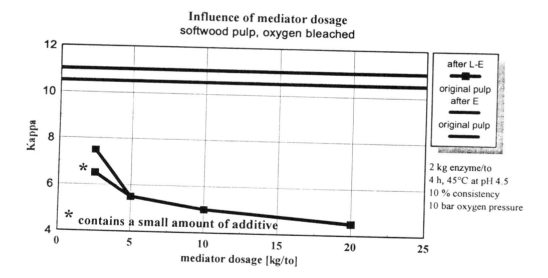

Figure 10b

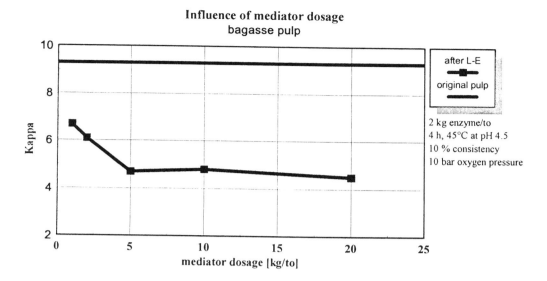

Figure 11

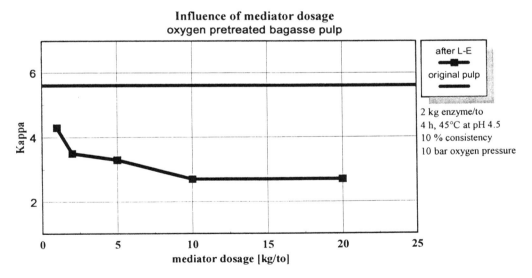

Figure 12

Set-up and Conditions in the Pilot Plant Trial with the LMS

	L-stage	E-stage	Q-stage	P-stage
consistency [%]	10	10	5	10
temperature [°C]	45	60	60	75
pH [-]	4,5	~11,5	5	11,2
residence time [min]	120	60	30	210
pressure [bar]	2			
dosage	enzyme: 2 kg/to mediator: variable	NaOH via pH	0,2 % DTPA	3% peroxide NaOH via pH

Figure 13

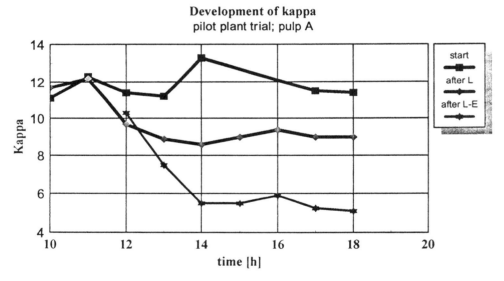

Figure 14

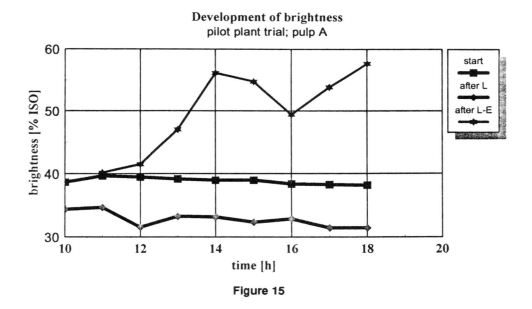

Figure 15

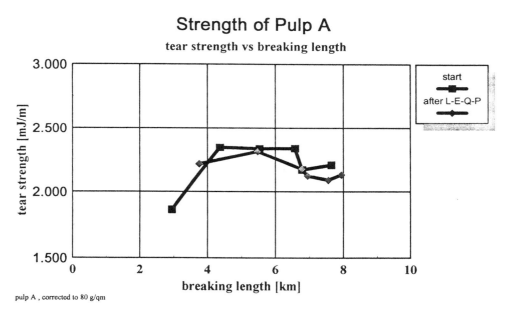

Figure 16

Development of Kappa, Viscosity and Brightness of Pulp B

sequence	kappa	viscosity [ml/g]	brightness [% ISO]
origin	10,7	870	39,5
after L	8,2	856	34,2
after E	6,0#	755	49,7

values still droping at the end of the day; the trial had to be terminated due to a damage of a double wire screen press

Figure 17

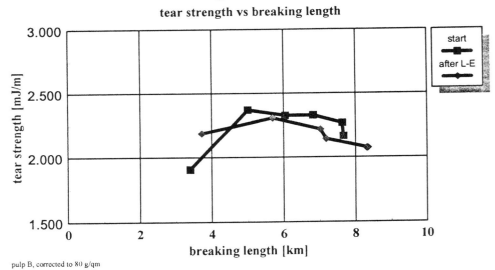

Strength of Pulp B
tear strength vs breaking length
3.000
2.500
2.000
1.500
tear strength [mJ/m]
0
2
4
6
8
10
breaking length [km]
start
after L-E
pulp B, corrected to 80 g/qm

Figure 18

Summary of Results from the Pilot Plant Trial with the LMS

sequence	pulp	dosage of enzyme /mediator [kg/to]	degree of delignifi-cation [%]	max. brightness [% ISO] in P
L-E-Q-P	A	2 / 13	56,6#	76,5#
L-E-L-E -Q-P	A	2 x 2 / 2 x 8	50,6 / 67,7 (34,5)	82,7#
L-E-Q-(P)	B	2 / 8	44,2#	

values still raising at the end of the day

Figure 19

Summary of post-bleaching trials with a P1-stage performed in laboratories of customers ( )

sequence	pulp	conditions	drop in viscosity [ml/g]	max. brightness [% ISO]
L-E-(Q-P)	A	unknown	50	86,6
L-E-(Q-P)	A	75°C ; 180' 3% P	n.d.	84,5
L-E-(Q-P)	B	75°C ; 45' 1 % P	20	74,2
L-E-(Q-P)	B	95°C ; 45' 3,5% P	20	84,5
L-E-(Q-P)	B	95°C ; 360' 3,5% P	95	89,3

Figure 20

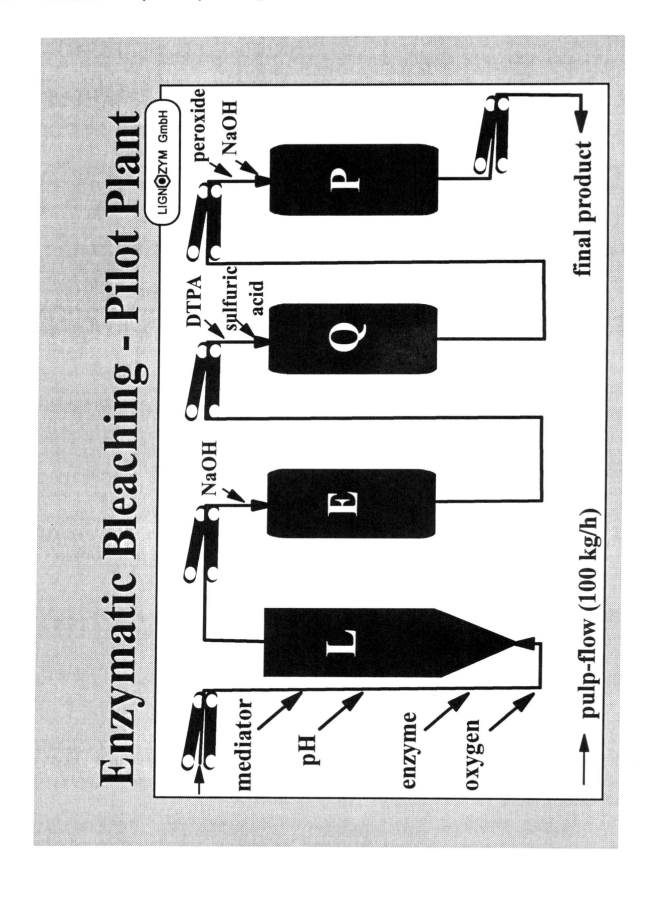

Enzymatic Bleaching - Pilot Plant

Kraft Pulp Bleaching: Laboratory Studies of Totally Chlorine-Free Systems

Gunilla Saltin
Mo Och Domsjö AB, Örnsköldsvik, Sweden
and
Lou Edwards
Chemical Engineering Department, University of Idaho, Moscow, Idaho

Several different bleaching sequences were compared in the laboratory to determine the best sequence for converting an existing, conventional five-stage bleach plant to totally chlorine free (TCF) bleaching. Using hydrogen peroxide and ozone as bleaching agents as well as xylanase enzyme treatment, over 20 different sequences were evaluated with respect to final brightness and strength (tear and tensile index). Two different softwood kraft mill pulps were used: a conventionally cooked pulp and a pulp produced using modified continuous cooking (MCC). Both pulps had been oxygen delignified and chelated with DTPA.

The position of the ozone stage in the bleaching sequence was found to have the largest effect on pulp strength and final brightness. The strongest pulp with the highest final brightness was obtained when the ozone stage was positioned between two hydrogen peroxide stages. The bleaching of the pulp caused a drop in tear index of approximately 65% and an increase in tensile index of approximately 20%. This may indicate a high level of interfiber bonding.

By positioning the enzyme stage prior to an ozone stage, the tear index of the bleached pulp was improved by about 40% while the tensile index was essentially unaffected. The impact of enzyme treatment on pulp brightness was small at brightness levels above 80% ISO (on the order of one brightness point). At lower brightness levels the impact of enzyme treatment was greater (approximately 5 points). Refining of the pulp prior to hydrogen peroxide bleaching or enzyme treatment did not increase the final brightness.

INTRODUCTION

Due to environmental regulations, chlorine free bleaching agents are being investigated as alternatives to chlorine and chlorine dioxide. Much interest has focused on hydrogen peroxide and ozone. Enzyme treatment has also been proposed as a way to lower the chlorine charge in a conventional bleach plant (1, 2, 3). For example, an enzyme stage has been reported to save approximately 10 % of the active chlorine per ton pulp for softwood pulp and slightly more for hardwood pulp (1).

Recently, enzyme treatment was reported to increase the brightness of softwood kraft pulp bleached using ozone and hydrogen peroxide by 9.7 points (4). This substantial brightness gain could lead to large chemical savings which would reduce the need for ozone and/or hydrogen peroxide. An enzyme treatment could also affect the selectivity of ozone and hydrogen peroxide bleaching thus improving pulp strength.

The object of this research was to investigate the effect of various ozone, hydrogen peroxide and enzyme treatments on the brightness and strength

properties of softwood kraft pulp. The bleaching sequences and the residence times were based on conditions in an actual five stage conventional bleach plant. Thus, the number of stages was limited to five (five existing washers). This limitation results from the need to convert the existing, conventional bleach plant to totally chlorine free bleaching.

MATERIALS AND METHODS

Pulp Samples

Two commercially produced softwood kraft pulps were used in the brightness and strength investigation. Both pulps had been oxygen delignified in the mill. The characteristics of the pulps are given in Table 4.1.

Pulp Bleaching Procedures

The pulp was chelated with 0.4% DTPA on o.d. pulp at a pH between 4.5-6.5 at 90°C for 30 minutes prior to bleaching or enzyme treatment (Q stage).

In hydrogen peroxide bleaching (P), the hydrogen peroxide and the sodium hydroxide were mixed with the pulp in a Hobart mixer. DTPA (0.1% on o.d. pulp) and the required dilution water were also added to the pulp and mixed well. The bleaching was

---

University of Idaho, Moscow, Idaho. Dr. Saltin is now with Mo Och Domsjö AB, Örnsköldsvik, Sweden.
University of Idaho, Moscow, Idaho.

performed at medium consistency in plastic bags at 90°C for 100 minutes for the first P stage in a sequence and for 150 minutes for the second P stage. A 1:1 hydrogen peroxide:sodium hydroxide ratio was used. Residual hydrogen peroxide was determined using iodometric titration.

The ozone bleaching (Z) was performed at low consistency in a modified Waring blender at room temperature and pH 2-3. The concentration of ozone in air generated by the ozone generator was approximately 1.4 wt%. The maximum pulp sample size was 10 o.d. grams thus limiting the reaction time to approximately 2 minutes for a 1% ozone charge on o.d. pulp. The amount of unconsumed ozone was determined by iodometric titration.

A commercially available xylanase enzyme, Pulpzyme™ HB from Novo Nordisk Bioindustrials, was used for the enzyme treatment (X) and a 0.1% charge on o.d. pulp was used in all experiments. The stock solution used for the enzyme treatment was diluted using a TRIZMA buffer solution of pH 8.3 at 25°C. The sample required for the correct charge was taken from this mixture and added to the pulp in a Hobart mixer. The buffer solution was also used for dilution to ensure a constant pH during the enzyme treatment. The treatment was performed at medium consistency in plastic bags at 50°C for 150 minutes. To determine the effect of the enzyme stage, a reference treatment was performed using denatured enzymes (x) instead of active enzyme but keeping all other conditions the same.

Refining (r) of the pulp was performed to specified number of revolutions in a PFI mill. The pulp was washed after every bleaching stage and enzyme treatment stage using distilled water and a dilution factor of approximately 8 to ensure that the pulp was well washed. The pH of the pulp was adjusted prior to washing to approximately 5.5 to avoid pH effects on the brightness readings.

Physical Testing

All physical testing followed the Tappi standard test methods (5): Kappa number (T 236 cm-85), forming handsheets for physical testing of pulp (T 205 om-88), brightness (T 525 om-92), physical testing of pulp handsheets (T 220 om-88), tear index (T 414 om-88), tensile index (T 494 om-88), and pulp freeness

(T 227 om-92). Strength tests were performed on unbeaten pulp.

RESULTS AND DISCUSSION

Repeatability

The repeatability of ozone bleaching was determined by bleaching eight samples of chelated pulp with 1% ozone on o.d. pulp. On the average, 88.5% of the charged ozone was consumed. The standard deviation of ozone bleaching was ± 0.48 brightness points (95% confidence level for the mean). The hydrogen peroxide bleaching repeatability was determined by bleaching four pulp samples with 2.5% hydrogen peroxide on o.d. pulp and 2.5% sodium hydroxide on o.d. pulp for 100 minutes at 90°C. Approximately 40% of the hydrogen peroxide was consumed. The standard deviation of hydrogen peroxide bleaching was ± 0.44 brightness points (95% confidence level for the mean).

To increase the accuracy, the first stage bleaches or enzyme treatments and, wherever possible, additional stages were made in large batches thus ensuring the same starting material for comparable sequences.

The repeatability of the physical testing procedures (tear and tensile index, pulp freeness) was not determined but assumed to be the same as reported by the Tappi Standards (4.2% for tear index, 5% for tensile index and 12 mL for freeness). The repeatability for the measurements are defined in T 1206 (Precision Statement for Test Methods).

Pulp Brightness

Since the incoming Kappa numbers of both unbleached pulps were fairly low, brightness was used as a measure of the bleaching efficiency, even after the first bleaching stage. The Kappa number measurement is less accurate at low values. However, it is somewhat disadvantageous to use the brightness as a measurement of the bleaching efficiency especially if a delignifying agent is used rather than a brightening agent, since the Kappa number can be directly correlated to the lignin content of the pulp.

Ten different bleaching sequences were evaluated using the conventional kraft pulp. The resulting brightness is shown in Figure 4.1. Brightness was not measured after enzyme stages since they have no direct brightening effect. Thus, the legend in Figure 4.1 refers to the first, second and third brightening stages, not the first, second and third stage in the sequence.

As can be seen from Figure 4.1, the most efficient bleaching sequences are PXZP and PZXP with 82.2 and 82.3% ISO respectively. Placement of the ozone stage between the two peroxide stages produces a higher brightness pulp than placing the ozone stage either first or last. This result is true for both conventional kraft with AQ and MCC pulp (Figure 4.1 and 4.3). When ozone is the first bleaching stage, caustic extraction prior to a subsequent peroxide stage would likely improve the final brightness.

It is interesting to note that at the higher brightness (above 80% ISO), the difference in brightness between the enzyme treated pulp and the reference sequence is smaller than at lower brightness levels. The difference in brightness between PZXP (82.3% ISO) and PZxP (81.0% ISO) is 1.3% ISO which is close to the accuracy of the experiments. This result can be compared to XZPP (75.1% ISO) and xZPP (69.6% ISO) with a difference of 5.2 brightness points. This trend is also illustrated in Figure 4.2 where the ozone charge was varied to obtain different final brightness levels.

The same result, although less pronounced was also obtained for the MCC pulp as can be seen in Figure 4.3. The difference between PXZP (79.1% ISO) and PxZP (78.3% ISO) is 0.8 points while the difference between XZPP (71.9% ISO) and xZPP (68.7% ISO) is 3.2 points.

An interesting experimental observation is that in all cases when one or two peroxide stages followed an ozone stage, no peroxide residual could be maintained. In other cases 30-60% residual peroxide was always present. Even with chelation (0.4% DTPA on o.d. pulp) followed by a wash after the ozone stage, no residual was present in a subsequent P stage. It should be noted that no magnesium sulfate was used in the P stages following an ozone stage. It is possible that a peroxide residual would have been obtained if this additive had been used (10).

It is realized that the 1% ozone charge used in the experiments presented above is probably on the high side when considering actual charges to be used in a mill due to the large amounts of excess oxygen generated.

Pulp Strength

Unbeaten tear and tensile index were chosen as measures of pulp strength over the viscosity measurement due to the dubious results obtained when this test is used on ozone bleached pulp (8). When pulp is treated with a strong oxidant in acid medium, the cellulose chains are susceptible to degradation if the oxidation is followed by an alkaline treatment. Since the viscosity determination is carried out using an alkaline solution, the reported viscosity does not necessarily represent the pulp strength compared to the strength of pulps not treated with oxidant in acid medium. An unbeaten strength comparison among different bleaching sequences for conventional softwood kraft pulp is shown in Figure 4.4. The numbers in Figure 4.4 refers to the bleach sequences listed in Table 4.2. A similar comparison for MCC pulp is shown in Figure 4.5.

The first observation from Figures 4.4 and 4.5 is that all the bleaching sequences cause about a 65% drop in tear index and about a 20% increase in tensile index. This may indicate a high level of interfiber bonding strength since this is beneficial for tensile index but will cause a drop in tear index when increased beyond a certain minimum level (9).

The next observation from Figures 4 and 5 concerns bleach stage sequencing. When ozone is applied between the peroxide stages, the tear and tensile are about 40% and 6% higher respectively compared to sequences in which the Z stage is first.

It can also be seen in Figures 4.4 and 4.5 that in those sequences where the enzyme treatment precedes the ozone stage (sequences 13 and 15), the pulp is stronger (tear about 30% higher and tensile about 5% higher) than in the sequences where the enzyme was denatured (14 and 16). For sequences 17, 18 and 19, 20 where the enzyme treatment precedes a peroxide stage, the enzyme treated pulp has slightly lower strength than the reference sequence (i.e. with denatured enzyme). However, the strength differences in sequences 17-20 are insignificant.

The pulp tensile strength properties corresponding to variations in ozone charge in the PZP sequence (see Figure 4.2) are shown in Figure 4.6. Tensile index increases with higher ozone charge while the tear index drops dramatically with all levels of ozone charges as shown in Figure 4.7.

Effect of Refining on Enzyme Treatment and Hydrogen Peroxide Bleaching

The xylanase enzyme catalyzes the hydrolysis of xylan. The xylan may be reprecipitated on to the cellulose fibers at the end of the kraft cook when the hydroxide concentration is reduced or may be bound to the lignin in the lignin-carbohydrate complex. Different attempts to explain the mechanism of the enzyme treatment have been made, but the exact mechanism of the hydrolysis is yet unknown. Pedersen et al. (1) extracted pulp with dimethylsulfoxide (DMSO), a compound known to remove reprecipitated xylan, prior to enzyme treatment. The effect of the enzyme treatment was still seen after the DMSO treatment showing that the enzyme treatment affects redeposited xylan not removed by the DMSO or that another fraction than the redeposited xylan is affected by the enzyme treatment. It can also be noted that the large molecular size of the xylanase enzyme can make it difficult for the enzymes to penetrate the fiber matrix to any greater extent and react with the lignin-carbohydrate complex (6). Viikari et al. (7) found that enzyme treatment of pulp produced in the lab using a flow-through cooking method that excluded xylan reprecipitation was ineffective and concluded that the major effect of enzyme treatment is on the reprecipitated xylan.

If it is correct that the size of the enzymes inhibits them from reactions with the xylan bound to the lignin in the lignin-carbohydrate complex, the effect of the enzyme treatment would be enhanced it these xylanase molecules were made more accessible. These complexes should become more accessible if the pulp is refined prior to enzyme treatment since refining opens up the fiber structure. Refining experiments were conducted using a conventionally cooked, western softwood pulp since there is a more even alkali profile in the MCC case, thus causing a lower degree of hemicellulose reprecipitaion. The pulp had been oxygen delignified in the mill and was chelated in the lab prior to any bleaching treatment or refining. The pulp was refined to 500 PFI revolutions and to 5000 PFI revolutions (corresponding to a CSF of 645 mL and

355 mL respectively), enzyme treated and bleached using hydrogen peroxide in two different sequences. It is realized that the freeness of the pulp refined to 5000 revolutions is very low, but this number of revolutions was chosen as the extreme case to insure maximum xylan exposure. The results from the refining and enzyme treatments are shown in Table 4.3.

As can be seen from Table 4.3, the brightness is not enhanced by refining the pulp prior to the enzyme treatment. The reason for the low final brightness after the 5000 revolution refining is the decrease in light scattering coefficient due to the intense refining (11). It is clear that the enzyme treatment cannot compensate for this decrease by increasing the xylanase accessibility. However, even the mild refining of 500 revolution (little change in light scattering coefficient) did not enhance the enzyme treatment. The cause of this effect may be that the xylanase fragments bonded to the lignin in the lignin-hemicellulose complex exposed by the refining process are resistant to the enzyme treatment. The reason for this resistance may be that the increased accessibility of the xylans in the lignin-carbohydrate complex is insufficient for the large-sized xylanase enzyme.

CONCLUSIONS

Bleaching softwood kraft pulps with over 20 different TCF sequences using ozone, hydrogen peroxide and enzyme treatment resulted in a maximum brightness gain of approximately 45 brightness points when the PZXP sequence was used. The unbeaten pulp tear index decreased by approximately 65% but the tensile index increased by about 20% after bleaching which may indicate an increased level of interfiber bonding.

By positioning the ozone stage between peroxide stages, the selectivity of the bleaching sequence was enhanced resulting in higher pulp strength and higher brightness compared to placing the ozone stage first or last in the bleaching sequence.

It was not possible to maintain a peroxide residual when the P stage followed an ozone stage, not even when a chelation stage was used after the ozone stage and prior to the peroxide stage.

The brightness gain obtained by using an enzyme stage is largest when the brightness level of the bleached pulp is low. Above 80% ISO, the brightness gain from an enzyme stage is on the order of one brightness point. Tear index increased from about 35% of the original tear to about 45% of the original tear with enzyme treatment but the change in tensile index was statistically insignificant.

Using a commercially available enzyme, it was not possible to reproduce the brightness gains reported by Eriksson and Yang (4). The highest gain obtained in this work by using active enzymes compared to denatured enzymes was approximately 5 points and this was obtained only at brightness levels in the range 60 - 70% ISO. This is different from the almost 10 points obtained by Eriksson and Yang (4) resulting in a final brightness of 81% ISO. It is possible that the different enzyme used by Eriksson and Yang compared to this investigation is the cause of this discrepancy or it may be due to the different softwood species used.

Refining the pulp prior to hydrogen peroxide bleaching or enzyme treatment did not increase the final brightness. This may imply that hydrogen peroxide bleaching is not mass transfer limited. It is proposed that refining removes the xylan molecules on the fiber surface that are affected by the enzyme treatment.

It should be noted that the brightness levels and pulp strengths reported here may not be obtained on a mill scale. The low consistency ozone stage has the advantage of homogenous mixing conditions in the lab. It is not implied that a low consistency ozone stage should be used on a larger scale. However, it is expected that the same trends will be obtained irrespective of the ozone stage consistency.

ACKNOWLEDGMENTS

The authors would like to thank Professor William McKean of the Pulp and Paper Technology Department at the University of Washington for his assistance and for the use of the pulp and paper laboratory at the UW. Part of the equipment used for the experiments was generously made available by Dr. Jerry Crosby of the Weyerhaeuser Co. Financial support from the National Council for Air and Stream Improvement (NCASI) and Novo Nordisk Bioindustrials Inc. is gratefully acknowledged.

LITERATURE CITED

1. Pedersen, L. S., Kihlgren, P., Nissen, A. M., Munk, N., Holm, H. C., Choma, P. P. *1992 Pulping Conference*, Boston, MA, November 1-5, 31-37.

2. Tolan, J. S.*1992 Pulping Conference*, Boston, MA, November 1-5, 13-17.

3. Skerker, P. S., Beeman, N., Labbauf, M. M., McCarthy, P., Farrell, R. L.*1992 Pulping Conference*, Boston, MA, November 1-5, 27-29.

4. Eriksson, K-E., L., Yang, J. L., *1993 Environmental Conference*, Boston MA March 28-31, 627-632.

5. *Tappi Test Methods 1992-1993*, Tappi Press 1992.

6. Pedersen, L. S., Elm, D. D., Nissen, A. M., Choma, P. P. *1991 International Pulp Bleaching Conference*, Stockholm, Sweden, June 11-14, 107-121.

7. Viikari, L., Sundquist, J., Kettunen, J., *Paperi ja Puu*, 73, 5, 384-389 (1991)

8. Hartler, N., Granlund, V., Sundin, J., Tubek-Lindblom, A. *1991 International Pulp Bleaching Conference*, Stockholm, Sweden, June 11-14, 75-92.

9. Voelker, M. H. in *"The Bleaching of Pulp"*, R. P. Singh Ed., Tappi Press 1979, 339.

10. Szopinski, R. Personal communication, May 1993.

11. Rydholm, S. A. *Pulping Processes*, Interscience Publishers, 1965, 845.

Table 4.1. Characteristics of unbleached oxygen delignified pulp samples.

Cooking Method	Western Softwood kraft pulp Conventional with AQ	Southern Pine kraft pulp MCC
Kappa number	10.2	11.2
Brightness, % ISO	37.5	35.4
Freeness, mL	700	740
Tear Index, mN·m^2/g	23.7	23.9
Tensile Index, N·m/g	38.7	25.5

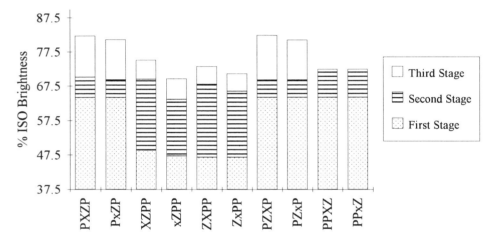

Figure 4.1. Bleaching results using the conventional kraft pulp. A 1% ozone charge was used. 2.5% and 2% hydrogen peroxide were charged in the first and second P stages respectively. All charges are % on o.d. pulp.

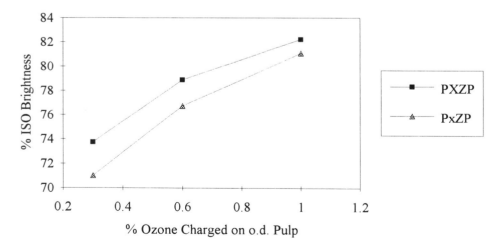

Figure 4.2. Brightness when the ozone charge is varied in the PXZP and PxZP sequences using conven-tional kraft pulp. 2 and 2.5% hydrogen peroxide on o.d. pulp were used in the first and second P stage respectively.

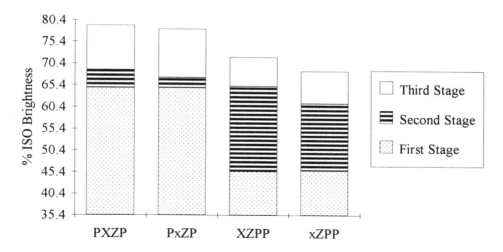

Figure 4.3. Bleaching results for the MCC pulp. Experimental conditions as in Figure 4.1.

Table 4.2. Sequence numbering scheme used in Figures 4.4 and 4.5. Chemical charges as given in Figure 4.1. Bleaching conditions are given in the "Pulp Bleaching Procedures" section.

Sequence #	Sequence
13	PXZP
14	PxZP
15	XZPP
16	xZPP
17	ZXPP
18	ZxPP
19	PZXP
20	PZxP

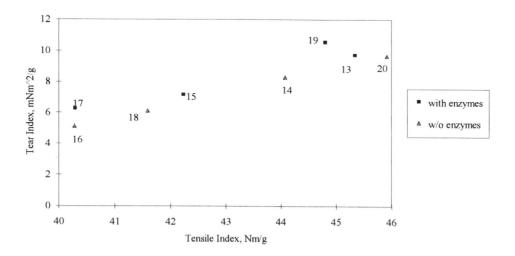

Figure 4.4. Pulp strength comparison among different bleaching sequences for conventionally cooked kraft pulp. The legend is given in Table 4.2.

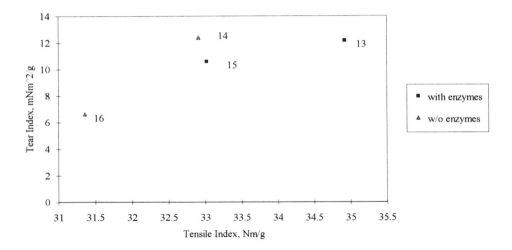

Figure 4.5. Pulp strength comparison among different bleaching sequences for MCC pulp. The legend is given in Table 4.2.

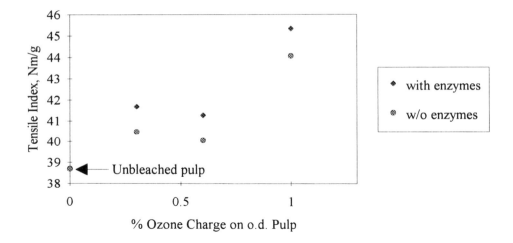

Figure 4.6. Tensile index when the ozone charge is varied in the PXZP and PxZP sequences using conventional kraft pulp. 2 and 2.5 % hydrogen peroxide on o.d. pulp were used in the first and second P stage respectively.

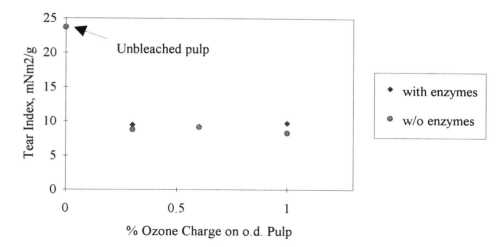

Figure 4.7. Tear index when the ozone charge is varied in the PXZP and PxZP sequences using conventional kraft pulp. 2 and 2.5 % hydrogen peroxide on o.d. pulp were used in the first and second P stage respectively.

Table 4.3. Result of refining and enzyme treatment. The hydrogen peroxide charges were 2.5 and 2 % on o.d. pulp in the first and second P stage respectively. The initial pulp brightness was 32.3 % ISO for the first four sequences and 36.7 % ISO for the following four.

Sequence	No. of PFI revolutions	Final Brightness, % ISO
rXP	5000	46.6
XP	0	54.4
xP	0	50.9
rP	5000	45.9
PrXP	500	67.5
PXP	0	68.8
PxP	0	66.8
PrP	500	67.5

Follow up of the Acid Change in Ozone Bleaching: Process Optimization by Acid Control

Michael X. Meng and Jeffrey S. Hsieh

Pulp and Paper Engineering Program, School of Chemical Engineering
Georgia Institute of Technology, Atlanta, GA 30332

In order to optimize the bleaching performance with proper acid pretreatment and to better understand the acid (or pH) effect on both delignification and the pulp quality, the acid change during ozone bleaching is investigated in this paper. The results show that the mineral acid added into the system in the acid treatment is consumed while the organic acids are produced during the bleaching. The determination of the acid amount before and after normal bleaching indicates that there are net productions of acid. The amount of acid produced is directly proportional to the ozone consumption under fixed bleaching conditions. The ozone bleaching is, therefore, a self-catalyzed process with regard to the hydrogen ion: the oxidation by ozone needs hydrogen ion and it actually consumes acid, so that the efficiency and the rate of the delignification are directly determined by the acid amount in the system; on the other hand the process generates extra acid at the same time. The data are then correlated with both the kappa number and pulp viscosity. It seems that the more acid produced, the better delignification obtained. However, at the same extent of delignification a high acid production always accompanies a lower viscosity. The optimization of the process by acid or pH control, thus, should be balanced between the delignification efficiency and the fiber protection.

Traditional pulp bleaching processes using chlorine-containing compounds release more or less toxic substances into the environment [1]. One group of such toxic matters is well-known as the absorbable organic halides (here denoted by AOX), which would accumulate once released and be hardly degraded by current technology. Many studies, both in laboratory and industrial scales, have been devoted to develop new bleaching technologies that produce reduced level or none AOX. Accelerated by the EPA's proposal to specifically limit AOX releasing level from paper mills, the totally chlorine free (TCF) bleaching processes have become an extremely important issue in pulp and paper industry.

Ozone bleaching is one of such newly-developed bleaching processes and it has been investigated for many years. While much fundamental work has been done to understand the nature of the technology as reviewed by Liebergot et al [2, 3, 4] and Byrd Jr. et al [5], the process has been successfully demonstrated as an integral stage in ECF and TCF sequences, in North America and Europe [6, 7, 8, 9, 10, 11]. A clear understanding of the process, however, is still needed for the best utilization of the technology under various conditions. For example, minimization of the fiber degradation while delignifying and brightening the pulp has always been the central topic in ozone bleaching. Since all operation parameters affects the bleaching performance to a certain extent, it is expected that the process optimization can only be achieved upon such understanding of the bleaching nature.

Among many other operation variables, pH of the pulp slurry has been found to play an important role in ozone bleaching. Many studies [12, 13, 14, 15, 16, 17, 18, 19, 20, 21] have shown that the optimum pH range is 2-3. In this pH range, the most efficient delignification is achieved with a minimal loss in pulp viscosity. Some researchers have attributed this effect to three factors [12]: 1) a higher oxidation potential of ozone at lower pH; 2) less decomposition of ozone at lower pH and 3) a pH-dependent difference of reactivity of carbohydrates with ozone. Bouchard et al [22], on the other hand, concluded that it was the result of the pH effect on ozone solubility, and made the correlation between the pH and the observed reactivity. These observations suggest that it is necessary to further clarify the role of pH or hydrogen ion in ozone bleaching. As Allison [23, 24] has recently pointed out, further fundamental studies are required to explain why low pH promotes ozone-lignin reactions so that the bleaching process can be optimized.

One thing that has nearly been ignored in previous studies is the direct involvement of hydrogen ions in ozone-bleaching reactions. From the point view of electrochemistry, the way that hydrogen ions participate in bleaching reactions may determine the oxidation efficiency of ozone. The reduction of ozone could proceed either by $O_3 + 6H^+ + 6e = 3H_2O$ or $O_3 + 2H^+ + 2e = H_2O + O_2$. Thermodynamically, hydrogen ion has different impacts on these two semi-reactions, and thus on the overall delignification performance. It can be easily seen that the bleaching efficiency would be down by 67% should the bleaching reaction switch from the first pathway to the second. This indicates a potential for further optimization of the ozone delignification by means of acid control. Meanwhile, it is natural to assume that bleaching through different pathway will result in different extent of carbohydrates degradation. And this brings another potential of minimizing the loss of the fiber strength. For the first time, therefore, the acid change during ozone bleaching is studied in the present paper. The experimental data is then correlated to the delignification efficiency and the change in pulp viscosity. As the results, some guidelines to further optimize the ozone bleaching are outlined.

EXPERIMENTAL

Oxygen-delignified southern pine pulp from a local paper mill was used as the starting sample. This O-pulp has a kappa number of 14.6 and a viscosity of 11.6. The present study has three sets of experiments done at different pH levels and with pretreatment by different acids. For each set, the pulp was diluted to 2-3% consistency and its pH was then adjusted with appropriate acid to the desired value while the slurry was agitated. After the pH value has become stable for 2-3 hours, the pulp was dewatered to 30-35% consistency and the filtrate was also saved. The amounts of the dewatered pulp and the filtrate for each experiment were calculated according to the desired consistency level and the total amount of born dry pulp. The initial pH value or the acid concentration in the bleaching liquor in each experiment was evaluated from either the pH determination of the filtrate or direct titration with standard NaOH solution, being monitored by both color-indicator and potential measurements.

The ozone bleaching was carried out in a CRS 1015 Reactor from CRS Reactor Engineering, Sweden. Figure 1 is the schematic diagram of the bleaching system. Ozone gas was generated with an Ozone Generator Model GL-1 (from PCI Ozone and Control Systems). The outlet flow of the ozone gas (in fact, it is a mixture of ozone and oxygen) was then compressed through a Metal-Diaphragm Compressor (from Sera Seybert & Rahier) into the storage tank made of stainless steel. The ozone concentration was monitored by Ozone Monitor Model HC (from PCI Ozone and Control Systems) during its generation and later checked by titration after a certain amount of mixture was allowed to flow through an absorbing module that contained excess KI. After the reactor was loaded with required amount of pulp, the operating consistency was adjusted by adding the filtrate saved from the acid treatment. The temperature control system and the mixing system were turned on and allowed to stabilize before the ozone was charged into the reactor, when timing was started. The amount of the ozone for each experiment was calculated for specific charge and controlled by the pressure drop off the ozone storage tank. The mixing had different patterns depending on the consistency: For the bleaching at medium consistency (MC, 10-15%), the agitation speed was 1,200 rpm in the first minute to fluidize the slurry and then 300 rpm for the rest of the reaction; For the bleaching at either high-consistency (HC) or low-consistency (LC), only gentle mixing of 300 rpm was

utilized throughout the whole process. By the completion of the desired bleaching, the mixing was stopped and the residual gas mixture was released through the absorbing module containing KI and sulfuric acid. The amount of ozone left could thus be determined by the titration with standard sodium thiosulfate solution.

Immediately after the bleaching experiments, acid concentrations were measured by either direct titration or pH measurement. For the bleaching carried out at lower pH level such as 2, the direct titration of the bleaching liquor was performed through monitoring by both indicator and potential measurement. Whenever possible, the bleaching liquor was previously separated from the pulp slurry. The pulp slurry for bleaching at high-consistency, i.e. 30%, however, had to be used without separation. The amount of the liquor in this case was calculated through the amount of wet pulp and its consistency. For the bleaching done at higher pH levels, it became not practical to perform the titration. Fortunately only sulfuric acid-treated pulps were bleached at pH = 4.0. The activity of hydrogen ion can thus be determined through pH measurement since the acid dissociation in the bleaching liquor is completed. The acid concentration was further evaluated by using the ion activity coefficient with Debye-Hückel equation [25]:

$$- \log f_i = 0.509 \, Z^2 \, [\, I^{1/2} / (\, 1 + B\mathring{a} \, I^{1/2}) \,] \qquad (1)$$

where f_i is the ion activity coefficient; Z is the charge number of the ion and B is a constant depending on temperature and the solvent nature. For aqueous solutions at 298K, B = 0.328. å is a parameter representing the size of the ion, in angstrom. å = 9 for hydrogen ion. I is the ionic strength:

$$I = (1/2) \, C_i Z_i^2 \qquad (2)$$

where C_i is concentration of ion i in moles per liter. The acid concentration was thus:

$$[acid] = [H^+] = (10^{-pH}) / f \qquad (3)$$

The pulps were further subject to washing and then the testings of kappa number and viscosity. Both these testings were performed according to TAPPI standards. Throughout the study, the total amount of pulp in each bleaching was fixed at 30 grams born dry pulp. Temperature was constantly 298K. Ozone concentration was also fixed at 11%(wt). The variables included pH, ozone charge and pulp consistency.

RESULTS AND DISCUSSION

Acid change in ozone bleaching was first found in a preliminary study in which the experiments were carried out in a manner described earlier [26, 27]. The reaction system was open, with the ozone gas continuously flowing through the system under a driving pressure of 15 psi. The initial acid (sulfuric) concentration in bleaching liquor for these experiments was fixed at 0.050N. The acid change can be seen in the titration curves shown in Figure 2 for the liquors after bleaching. The results indicate that the total acid concentrations, determined by the second end-point in these curves at the addition of 10 ml NaOH (0.500N) standard, remain unchanged in all cases. The curves, however, show a range with a stable reading of conductivity, implying that a group of weak acids other than sulfuric acid is produced during the bleaching. As some researchers have identified [28, 29, 30], carboxylic acids are the main product group in the ozonation of lower molecular cellulose and poplar lignin. The first end-point in the titration curve is corresponding to the residual concentration of sulfuric acid. The difference between two end-points, in other words, gives the concentration of such weak acids produced during the bleaching.

The change in acid (or alkaline) concentration in different oxidative bleaching processes have been well documented except for ozone [31]. In bleaching with chlorine dioxide and oxygen, the delignification is mainly achieved through oxidation reactions that either produce equimolar hydrochloric acid or consume equimolar alkaline. In chlorine stage, about half of the chlorine charged undergoes oxidation that again yields equimolar hydrochloric acid. The overall acid change for all three sequences, therefore, is the increase in acid amount, as summarized in Table 1.

Table 1. Acid Change in Bleaching Sequences

Sequence/Oxidant	pH Change	Acid Change
C/Cl$_2$	Decrease	Increase
D/ClO$_2$	Decrease	Increase
O/O$_2$	Decrease	Increase
Z/O$_3$	NA*	No change*

*: Predicted from the balance of lignin oxidation and ozone reduction.

On the contrary, no experimental result so far has been reported on acid change for ozone bleaching. The literature only gave either final or initial pH, without information of the change in pH and especially in acid concentration. If it is assumed that equimolar weak acids are produced by the oxidation of lignin by ozone, the total concentration of acids in the system should not change since the reduction of ozone itself will consume equimolar acid, regardless of its reaction pathway:

$$O_3 + 6H^+ + 6e = 3H_2O \qquad (4)$$

$$\text{or} \qquad O_3 + 2H^+ + 2e = H_2O + O_2 \qquad (5)$$

The transformation of mineral acid into organic acids through the bleaching, somehow, could result in a slight increase in pH because less product acid is dissociated.

In practice, however, this pattern may change due to the complexity of the reactions. For instance, ozone also reacts at least 1) with the water soluble products of the ozone-lignin reactions, and 2) with cellulose. These reactions may have different impact on acid change. Since the hydrogen ion, thus the acid concentration for a certain type of the acids, affects on bleaching performance and is directly involved in bleaching reactions as shown by equations (4) and (5), the acid change in return will affect the bleaching.

The results of acid change in normal ozone bleaching (pH = 2.0, adjusted with sulfuric acid) are presented in Figure 3. The data are presented in total mili-moles (10^{-3} mole) of the acid change verses the ozone consumed in the system (30 grams b.d. pulp). It indicates that the acid amount in the system is actually increased. Both consistency and ozone consumption significantly affects the acid production. At a given consistency, however, the acid change is directly proportional to the ozone consumed. In the range of high consistency (20-30%), nearly half-molar acid is produced upon one-molar ozone consumed. This significant change in acid amount, a deficiency from the prediction based on ozone-lignin reactions, suggests that the bleaching reactions in ozone stage undergo different reaction mechanism from other operations listed in Table 1 with regard to the oxidation process. One possibility is that ozone reacts with some products of ozone-lignin reactions, and produces even lower molecular weight matters. The disintegration process of these bleaching products probably leads to the opening of more acidic functional groups in the structure so that the overall acid change becomes positive. Another possible approach is that ozone reacts with cellulose. As Bes et al [28] have found, the ozonation of lower molecular weight celluloses results in net production of a strong acid and a group of weak acids. A positive acid change (net production of acid), therefore, indicates that while most ozone directly attacks lignin, yielding kappa number reduction, some of it is in fact wasted by reacting with 1) lose-lignin-species that is partially oxidized and is disconnected from the fiber; and 2) the cellulose, also causing the decrease in pulp viscosity.

The data in Figure 3 also indicate that the acid change is clearly a function of the operating consistency. The acid change reduces marginally if consistency decreases from 30 to 20%. However, it drops dramatically at medium consistency (10%), with briefly one-tenth molar production upon one-molar ozone consumed. This abrupt change may imply that the oxidation pathway by ozone has changed.

For the same experimental runs, the results of kappa number after Z stage are shown in Figure 4 against the ozone consumed. Since 30 b.d. pulp was consistently used in every experiment, an ozone consumption of 6.25 milimole is equivalent to 1%(wt) on b.d. pulp. As many other researcher have found, the kappa number continues to decrease with the increase in ozone consumption. The efficiency of delignification, however, gradually proceeds flat. In other words, relatively more ozone at higher ozone charge is consumed by the reactions leading to positive acid change. It is also found that the pulp viscosity changes in a similar manner, seen in Figure 5.

Compare the data in Figure 4 and 5 to these in Figure 3, respectively, one can see that same effect of the consistency appears in Figure 3 and 5. The decrease in consistency from 30 to 20% only results in a marginal increase in either acid production or viscosity drop. Further reduction of consistency to 10%, however, leads to a dramatic change in both cases. This, to some extent, implies that the acid-producing reactions have more to do with the viscosity drop. Same concept is shown by the data in Figure 6. With the increase in ozone consumption, the ratio of acid production to the kappa reduction increases greatly. It is most likely in proportion to the ozone consumed. The effect of pH and acid type also indicates that this ratio increases if more hydrogen ion is available for the reactions. Nevertheless, if the acid production is the result of the ozone-lignin reactions, this ratio should remain as a constant.

Consequently, the acid production are correlated to the pulp viscosity directly. In despite of the change in consistency, all data points fall on an unified curve, as in Figure 7, for the sulfuric treated pulps with pH = 2.0. It is thus obvious that the depression of the acid-producing reactions in ozone bleaching will benefit the overall process in two ways. Firstly under same charge level more ozone will be available for the ozone-lignin reactions so that the delignification will be improved. Secondly, the viscosity drop will be reduced for better pulp strength.

The effect of the acid type used in treatment, as well as the initial pH value, has also been investigated in the present study. Some results are shown in Figure 8. For the pulps treated with sulfuric acid but adjusted to different initial pH levels, the bleaching with same ozone consumption results in different amount of acid change. Increasing pH from 2.0 to 4.0, the acid production decreases by 80%. From equations (4) and (5), the decrease in acid production can be attributed to the lower concentration of hydrogen ion in the system. The driving force for the oxidation reactions, no matter how they proceed, is reduced accordingly. With same initial pH (2.0), the bleaching for the pulps treated with acetic acid also produce less acid. For a given ozone consumption, the acid increase is approximately 50% of that in sulfuric environment. This is probably due to the effect of the buffer capacity of the acetic acid solutions. The change of the pH during bleaching will be then greatly inhibited in the presence of the acetic acid. The self-enhancement of the acid-producing reactions by the hydrogen ion no longer affects the process to the same extent in sulfuric system. In fact, the buffer behavior of the acetic systems can be further illustrated by Figure 9 in which the acid production data obtained for the bleaching at different consistency levels are plotted against ozone consumption for the acetic system. It can be seen that while the ozone consumption still affects the acid change as it did in sulfuric acid environment, the effect of consistency vanishes.

The effect of pH and acid type on delignification is shown in Figure 10. In sulfuric system, the increase in pH from 2.0 to 4.0 suffers the lower delignification efficiency. The kappa number after Z stage at the same ozone consumption is higher by 2.5 units. Since acid production at pH = 4.0 is lower, which means that less ozone is wasted in acid-producing reaction, the amount of ozone used for ozone-lignin reactions should be more. This states that the oxidation efficiency of ozone greatly decreases with the increase in pH, suggesting that the pathway of ozone-lignin reactions has changed. For example, it might be from schematic (4) to (5). With all experimental conditions fixed, the higher the concentration of hydrogen ion (or the lower the pH), more ozone will undergo the favorable pathway. The effect of pH can thus be summarized as follows: with the increase in pH, the portion of the ozone involved in acid-producing reactions decreases and the ozone consumed on lignin increases. The overall bleaching efficiency, however, decreases probably because the bleaching reaction gradually switches from (4) to (5).

For the pulps treated with acetic acid and adjusted to pH = 2.0, the bleaching show no difference in delignification from the sulfuric acid treated pulps (Figure 10). The acid production, meanwhile, reduces by approximately 50%. If considering that the portion of ozone wasted in acid-producing reaction is reduced accordingly, the oxidation efficiency of ozone in delignification reactions is, in fact, lower than that for sulfuric acid treated pulp.

To study the effect of pH and acid type on bleaching selectivity, the experimental results are summarized in Figure 11 as the function of the ozone consumption. The bleaching selectivity here is defined by the ratio of viscosity drop to the kappa reduction, $dV/dK_a\#$. The lower the $dV/dK_a\#$'s value, the better the fiber is protected. The results in Figure 11 show that the bleaching in acetic environment constantly has better selectivity. This is in good agreement with the findings of Mbachu and Manley [19]. It is also the results of the lower acid production. The utilization of acetic acid in ozone bleaching, however, has to consider its higher charge and thus the cost. To adjust an aqueous solution from neutral to pH = 2.0, the corresponding concentration of acetic acid is 0.6-0.7 M, or about 42 g/L. On the contrary, only 0.015M sulfuric acid (or 1.47 g/L) is needed for the same purpose.

Similar to Figure 7, the pulp viscosity is correlated with acid production for the bleaching at 30% consistency but with different pH and acid type in Figure 12. It indicates that the pulp viscosity is an unified function of acid change only if the pH and acid type are fixed. This implies that while the pattern of ozone-lignin reactions changes with the change in pH and acid type, the pattern of the ozone-cellulose reactions are also strongly affected. It seems that the ozone-cellulose reactions, as the ozone-lignin reactions do, switch from (4) to (5). At the same level of acid change, the lower pulp viscosity obtained at lower pH, or with acetic treated pulps, indicates that the fiber is damaged to a greater extent if ozone undergoes low-effective pathway (5).

CONCLUSIONS

As the summary, it seems that the ozone-lignin reactions in ozone bleaching do not affect the acid balance in the system. While hydrogen ion is directly involved and consumed in the delignification process, equal-molar acid is produced at the same time. The acid form may be transformed from mineral into organic acids. These product acid usually have lower pK_a values. If no side-reaction took place, the concentration of free hydrogen ion would decrease along the delignification. The final pH of the pulp slurry could be slightly higher than the initial value because of the lower degree of dissociation of the organic acids produced. The driving force of the ozone-lignin reaction would diminish eventually.

In practical processes, the overall acid change is positive, meaning a net production of the acid. This acid production has more to do with the ozone-cellulose reactions. The effect of hydrogen ion (or acid) on bleaching performance is double-folded: It does not only participate in and drive the ozone-lignin reactions, it also affects the pattern of the reactions. The higher the concentration of hydrogen ion (or lower pH), the more ozone will be utilized at its full potential of oxidation toward lignin. The efficiency of delignification, therefore, is higher. However, hydrogen ion also accelerates the ozone-cellulose reactions. The overall process, thus, can become self-catalyzed. This explains why there is an optimal pH range for ozone bleaching. If pH drops too much, delignification may be more effective but it is subject to more viscosity loss. If pH is higher, on the other hand, up to 67.7% of the ozone's oxidation power could be wasted which the bleaching selectivity may not be superior to these obtained in the optimal pH range.

LITERATURE CITED

1. Shrinath, S. A. and Bowen, I. J., "An overview of AOX regulations and reduction strategies". *1993 TAPPI Pulping Conference Proceedings*, TAPPI press, Atlanta, 1993, p. 1.

2. Liebergot, N.; van Lierop, B. and Skothos, A., "A survey of the use of ozone in bleaching pulps, part 1". *Tappi Journal*, **75**(1), 45(1992).

3. Liebergot, N.; van Lierop, B. and Skothos, A., "A survey of the use of ozone in bleaching pulps, part 2". *Tappi Journal*, **75**(2), 117(1992).

4. Liebergot, N.; van Lierop, B. and Skothos, A., "The use of ozone in bleaching pulps". *1992 Environmental Conference Proceedings*, TAPPI press, Atlanta, 1992, p. 1105.

5. Byrd Jr., M. V.; Gratzl J. S. and Singh, R. P., "Delignification and bleaching of chemical pulps with ozone: a literature review". *Tappi Journal*, **75**(3), 207(1992).

6. Gottlieb, P. M.; Nutt, W. E.; Miller, S. R. and Macas, T. S.: "Mill experience in high-consistency ozone bleaching of southern pine pulp". *1993 TAPPI Pulping Conference Proceedings*, TAPPI press, Atlanta, 1993, p. 1183.

7. Gottlieb, P. M.; Nutt, W. E.; Miller, S. R. and Macas, T. S.:"Mill experience in high-consistency ozone bleaching of southern pine pulp". *Tappi Journal*, **77**(6), 117(1994).

8. Helander, R. and Nilson, B., "Development and progress in ozone bleaching at the Skoghill mill". *1994 International Bleaching Conference Proceedings*, Vancouver, Canada. June 13-16, 1994, p. 289.

9. Kappel, J.; Brauer, P. and Kittel, F., "High-consistency ozone bleaching technology". *1993 TAPPI Pulping Conference Proceedings*, TAPPI press, Atlanta, 1993, p. 1173.

10. Kappel, J.; Brauer, P. and Kittel, F., "High-consistency ozone bleaching technology". *Tappi Journal*, **77**(6), 109(1994).

11. Nutt, W. E.; Wachus, S. W.; Griggs, B. F. and Pikulin, M. A., "Development of an ozone bleaching process". *1992 TAPPI Pulping Conference Proceedings*, TAPPI press, Atlanta, 1992, p. 1109.

12. Hosokawa, J.; Kobayashi, T.; Kubo, T. and Kimura, Y.; "Effects of thickness and pH of pulp sheets on the properties of pulp bleached with ozone". *Japan Tappi*, **30**(4), 226(1976).

13. Jacobson, B.; Lindblad, P. and Nilvebrant, N., "Lignin reactions affect the attack of ozone on carbohydrates". *1991 International Bleaching Conference Proceedings*, SPCI, Stockholm, Sweden. June 11-14, 1991, p. 45.

14. Lindholm, C., "Effect of pulp consistency and pH in ozone bleaching - 2. Lignin removal and carbohydrate degradation". *The Proceedings of International Oxygen Delignification Conference*, TAPPI press, Atlanta, 1987, p. 155.

15. Lindholm, C., "Effect of pulp consistency and pH in ozone bleaching - 3. Bleaching of oxygen-delignified Kraft pulp". *Nordic P&P Res. J.* 3(1), 44(1988).

16. Lindholm, C., "Effect of pulp consistency and pH in ozone bleaching - 5. Various pretreatment and additives in LC and HC bleaching". *Cellul. Chem. Technol.* 23, 44(1989).

17. Lindholm, C., "Effect of pulp consistency and pH in ozone bleaching - 6. Strength properties". *Nordic P&P Res. J.* 5(1), 22(1990).

18. Lindholm, C., "Some effects of treatment consistency in ozone bleaching". *1991 International Bleaching Conference Proceedings*, SPCI, Stockholm, Sweden. June 11-14, 1991, p. 3.

19. Mbachu, R. A. D. and Manley, R. S-J., "The effect of acetic and formic acid pretreatment on pulp bleaching with ozone". *Tappi Journal*, 64(1), 67(1981).

20. Rutkowski, J. and Szopinski, R., "Investigation on bleaching of sulfate pine pulp with ozone". *Cellul. Chem. Technol.* 18, 323(1984).

21. Singh, R. P., "Ozone replaces chlorine in the first bleaching stage. Advances in ozone bleaching - Part I". *Tappi Journal*, 65(2), 45(1982).

22. Bouchard, J.; Nugent, H. M. and Berry, R. M., "The role of water and hydrogen ion in ozone bleaching of Kraft pulp at medium consistency". *1993 TAPPI Pulping Conference Proceedings*, TAPPI press, Atlanta, 1993, p. 1093.

23. Allison, R. W., "Effects of temperature and chemical pretreatment on pulp bleaching with ozone". *The Proceedings of 1985 International Pulp Bleaching Conference*, CPPA, Technical Section & TAPPI, Quebec, Canada. June 18-21, 1985. p. 47.

24. Allison, R. W., "Potential of ozone in Kraft pulp bleaching". *Appita*, 44(6), 405(1991).

25. Butler, J. N., Ionic Equilibrium: A Mathematical Approach. Addison-Wesley Publications Co.. Reading, Mass..1964. pp.471-472.

26. Su, W. and Hsieh, J., "The effect of lignin content on ozone bleaching at medium consistency condition". *1992 TAPPI Pulping Conference Proceedings*, TAPPI press, Atlanta, 1992, p. 1085.

27. Suren, A.; Hsieh, J. and Su, W., "The effect of pretreatment on ozone bleaching at medium consistency condition". *1993 TAPPI Pulping Conference Proceedings*, TAPPI press, Atlanta, 1993, p. 1103.

28. Bes, R. S. et al; "Enhancement of poplar cellulose susceptibility to cellulase enzyme hydrolysis by ozonation". *Ozone Sci. Technol.* 11, 217(1989).

29. Euphrosine-Moy, V. et al; "Degradation of poplar lignin with ozone". *Ozone Sci. Technol.* 13, 239(1991).

30. Nompex, Ph. et al; "Ozonation of selected molecules constituting cellular matter". *Ozone Sci. Technol.* 13:265(1991).

31. TAPPI, "The Bleaching of Pulp: A Project of the Pulp Bleaching Committee", Pulp Manufacture Division. 3rd Edition. Ed. R. P. Singh. TAPPI Press, Atlanta. 1979.

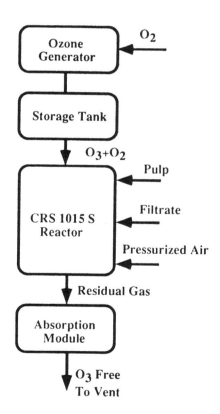

Figure 1. The schematics of the ozone bleaching system

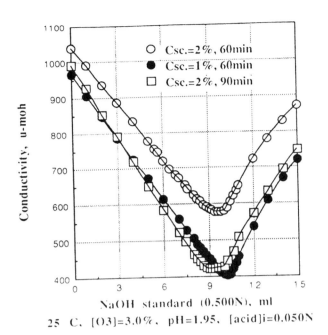

25 C, [O3]=3.0%, pH=1.95, [acid]i=0.050N

Figure 2. Titration curves of Z effluents
(100ml) in preliminary experiments

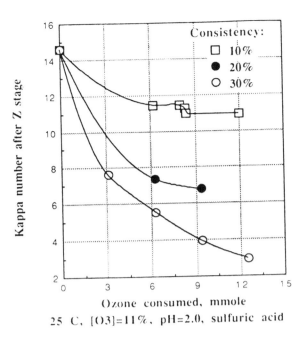

25 C, [O3]=11%, pH=2.0, sulfuric acid

Figure 4. Effect of ozone charge on
kappa number change

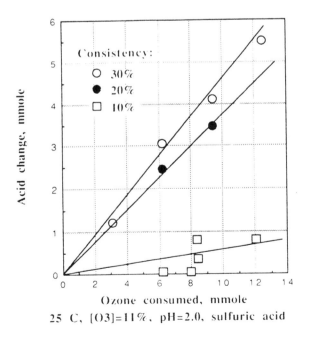

25 C, [O3]=11%, pH=2.0, sulfuric acid

Figure 3. Acid change in ozone bleaching

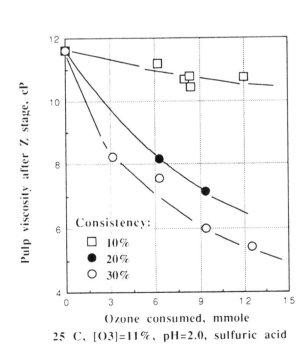

25 C, [O3]=11%, pH=2.0, sulfuric acid

Figure 5. Pulp viscosity vs. ozone charge

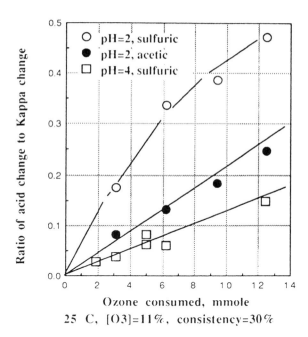

Figure 6. The ratio of acid change to Kappa reduction vs. ozone consumption

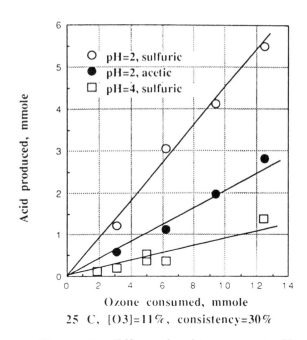

Figure 8. Effect of acid type and pH on acid change

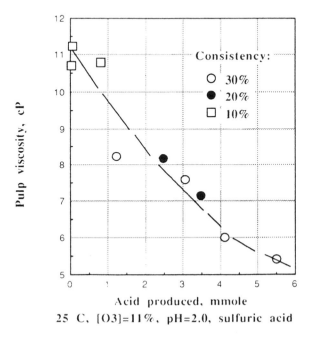

Figure 7. Effect of acid change on viscosity

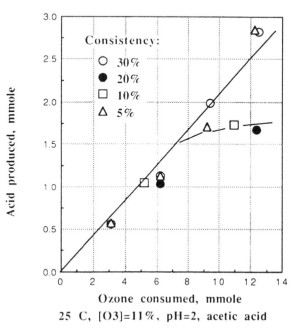

Figure 9. Acid change in ozone bleaching for the pulps treated with acetic acid

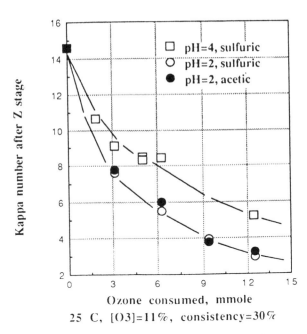

25 C, [O3]=11%, consistency=30%

Figure 10.   Effect of pH and acid type
on delignification during ozone bleaching

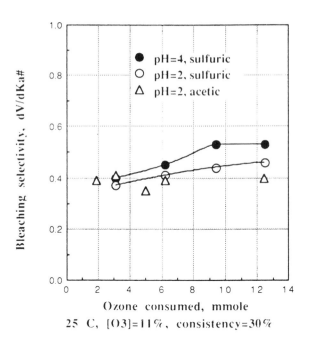

25 C, [O3]=11%, consistency=30%

Figure 11. Effect of pH, acid type and
ozone charge on bleaching selectivity

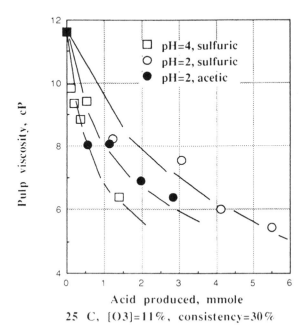

25 C, [O3]=11%, consistency=30%

Figure 12.   Effect of pH and acid type
on pulp strength

High Concentration Ozone: System Design and Economics

Jeff Rounsaville, Debra Breed
Ingersoll-Rand Company (IMPCO), 150 Burke St., Nashua, NH 03060

Seiji Nakamoto
Sumitomo Precision Products Co., LTD., 1-10, Fuso-Cho, Amagasaki, Hyogo 660, Japan

James Griggs
Dresser-Rand Company, 100 Chemung St., Painted Post, NY 14870

High concentration ozone gas offers advantages in pulp bleaching for both high and medium consistency systems. Until recently the ability to generate and compress high concentration ozone was not economically feasible at large scale. The development and commercial application of high concentration ozone generators and rotary screw compressors, in combination with proven mixing technology, provides a system for mills to apply ozone in a single medium consistency stage. This paper addresses the design considerations for such a system, introduces advances in ozone generation and compression and analyzes the impact of these on overall economics for mill scale ozone application.

INTRODUCTION

Ozone bleaching has progressed from a laboratory and pilot plant curiosity to now include eight operating commercial installations [1] in both medium (8-14%) and high (>35%) pulp consistency applications. Interest in ozone is growing. Many mills have begun to consider ozone as an alternative in ECF and TCF bleaching sequences. In looking at these alternatives there has been the need for basic information outlining the chemical supply side of ozone and the relative economics of this chemical. The primary purpose of this report is to address these issues by providing the building blocks for an ozone system and by examining major system variables impacting overall economics.

OZONE SYSTEM COMPONENTS

The primary components in any ozone system include:
- Oxygen System
- Ozone Supply System
- Process Equipment
- Off-gas Handling
- Instrumentation & Control
- System Housing

Table 1 provides a further breakdown and a brief summary for each of these components. A more detailed description for each component is included in this text followed by a discussion on key issues to address in evaluating the economics of an ozone system.

OXYGEN SYSTEM

The oxygen system is the feed source for ozone generation. Ozone is generated by converting $O_2 \rightarrow$ within a generator. Ozone can be generated from a feed source of air to a source of nearly pure oxygen. To meet the ozone capacity demand of a pulp mill will require a high concentration of oxygen in the feed gas for a manageable set of economics. Generally, there are two options available to meet this demand: Vacuum Swing Adsorption (VSA) at 90-93% O_2 purity or Cryogenic at 98 or 99.5% O_2 purity[3]. At these high concentrations (>10% ozone), the oxygen feed purity will impact the power demand of the generator slightly as illustrated in Figure 1.

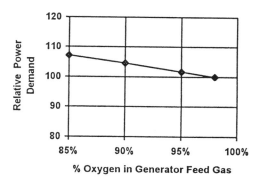

Figure 1: Generator Power Demand Impact of Oxygen concentration

The selection of an oxygen source will be a broad mill decision, which may have already been addressed. The

Table 1: Components of an Ozone System

Component [9]	Function	Design Basis
Oxygen System	Feed source for ozone generator, can be a cryogenic (97-99% O_2) oxygen facility or on site VSA/PSA (90-93% O_2) oxygen source.	O_2 delivery lb or kg/ day
Ozone Supply: ➤ Ozone Generator	Ozone is generated using a corona discharge in an oxygen-rich feed stream to convert $O_2 \rightarrow O_3$. Generators for pulp applications are generally designed to deliver a 6→14% concentration of ozone in the oxygen feed stream. Such concentrations can be supplied from the latest generation of tube or plate type generator designs.	O_3 delivery lb or kg/ hr
➤ Cooling water supply	Ozone generator efficiency is greatly dependent on the rate at which heat can be removed and therefor cooling water availability can directly impact specific mill economics. In many mills the addition of a chiller will be necessary for optimum economics.	Flow, gpm or lpm
➤ Power supply	Converts incoming electrical power to the frequency and voltage required to produce a corona discharge.	Generator kVA
➤ Ozone Compressor	➤ Medium Consistency System: The gas from the generator, must be compressed to achieve a gas volume below 35%*, or a phase ratio below 0.54*[2], at the mixer. Rotary screw or Liquid ring compressors can be used. ➤ High Consistency System: Gas compression is typically not required, if generator, discharging 0-10 psi, is located in reasonable proximity to the Contactor.	Delivery Pressure Total gas flow, SCFM or Nm^3/min
Process Equipment: ➤ Mixer/ Contactor	➤ Medium Consistency System: Generally utilizes a high shear type mixer operated under pressure (up to 150 psig) to achieve gas to pulp mixing. ➤ High Consistency System: Generally pulp at high consistency (40-45%) is fluffed and sent to a Contactor where ozone is introduced at near atmospheric conditions.	Pulp capacity ton/day & gas volume (%) Pulp capacity & Time
➤ Retention Vessel	The initial reaction of ozone with pulp is fast so that most of the reaction occurs during mixing or contacting. As the ozone is consumed, the reaction rate decreases, requiring a short retention vessel to consume the residual ozone.	Time (minutes)
➤ Gas Separator	Due to the high volume of carrier gas all systems require a device to separate the pulp fibers from the residual gas prior to gas destruct.	Exit gas volume SCFM or Nm^3/min
Off-Gas Handling: ➤ Gas Destruct Unit	Destroys residual ozone and some hydrocarbon byproducts in the off-gas, leaving primarily O_2, some N_2 (from O_2 source and entrained air) CO_2, and trace amounts of CO and hydrocarbons.	Off-gas flow SCFM or Nm^3/min
➤ Gas Compressor	The gas can be recompressed to supply an O_2 source for other mill applications or can be looped back to feed the ozone generator.	Suction & Discharge Pressure, Temp; Total gas flow, SCFM or Nm^3/min
Instrumentation & Control	Monitoring and control of ozone system operation including generation, application of ozone to pulp and off gas management.	Process system type & size, control system type
System Housing	The ozone generator should be located within a protected enclosure. This equipment can be remotely located from the Process Equipment but it should be as close as possible to minimize ozone and pressure losses through piping runs.	footprint, ft^2 (or m^2)

* *phase ratio* = (gas volume, at system pressure) ÷ (pulp stream volume)

 gas volume % = (gas volume, at system pressure) ÷ (gas volume, at pressure + pulp stream volume)

oxygen supply for ozone generation will constitute one of the mill's largest demands for oxygen. But, about 98% of the oxygen entering the ozone generator can be recovered after the reation, and can be reused for other mill applications or recycled back to feed the generator. Generally, recycling recovered oxygen back to the generator can require substantial additional capital for removal of moisture, CO_2, CO and trace hydrocarbons. The final selection should be a mill specific decision based on overall utilization of oxygen, to provide a complete analysis of broad economic and system flexibility impact. Figure 2 [3,4] illustrates some mill-wide applications which could be supplied from the oxygen rich exhaust gas of an ozone system.

Figure 2: Cumulative Mill Oxygen Demand

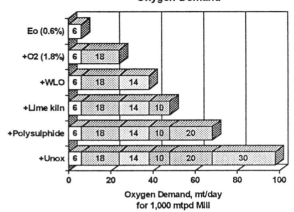

In most instances utilizing ozone, it is assumed that a mill will have installed oxygen delignification and white liquor oxidation, or has plans to do so when implementing ozone. Therefore, the total base demand of oxygen from E_o + O + WLO will be at least 3.2% of production or 32 mton/day for a 1,000 mt/d mill. The total demand may even reach upwards of 100 mt/day. The amount of oxygen exhausted from an ozone system will vary depending on the concentration of ozone and the amount of the exhaust gas recycled to the generator as shown below.

Figure 3: Oxygen Available for Re-use (1,000 mt/d mill, 6 kg/t ozone)

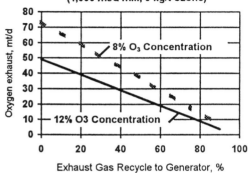

OZONE SUPPLY

Ozone Generator

The oxygen supply, made up of recycled generator exhaust gas plus fresh oxygen or solely from the O_2 supply source, is fed to an ozone generator. A portion the oxygen stream is then converted from $O_2 \rightarrow O_3$ in the presence of an electrical corona discharge. Most of the energy applied in the production of ozone, about 90%, is dissipated as heat. Since the rate of ozone decomposition increases directly with temperature, the key to efficient generation of ozone at high concentration is the ability to effectively remove the heat of generation. Thus, all ozone generators resemble heat exchangers to a large degree.

There are two basic configurations of ozone generators, shell-and-tube or plate type units. The shell-and-tube generators are the most common. (Refer to Figure 4)

FIGURE 4: Tube-Type Ozone Generator

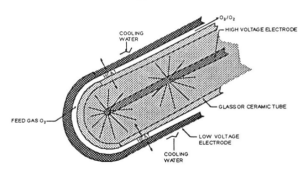

A shell-and-tube unit consist of a cluster of metalized glass or ceramic (advanced design) dielectrics which are carefully inserted into a stainless steel tube, composing the discharge cell. A typical generator may contain over 900 of these cells, to produce about 1,400 kg/day[8] of ozone. A high voltage electrode is inserted inside the glass tube, and the current is discharged across the gap to the stainless steel low voltage electrode. Oxygen feed gas is passed through the gap between the tubes and a portion of the oxygen is converted to ozone. Cooling water circulates around the outside of the stainless steel tube to remove the heat generated in the formation of ozone.

For the plate type generator, the discharge cell consists of two flat metal plates which comprise the high and low voltage electrodes. Each face has a thin ceramic coating which functions as the dielectric layer. (Refer to Figure 5) A typical full size generator may contain over 700 cells to produce about 1,800 kg/ day of ozone.

FIGURE 5: Plate-Type Ozone Generator

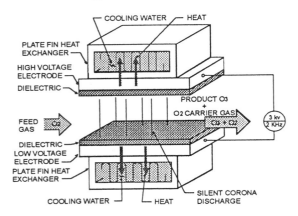

In a plate type generator the oxygen feed gas passes between the two plates for the generation of ozone. Since the gap between the plates is very narrow, a lower voltage is used, reducing the heat input to the generator. The plate-type enables the circulation of cooling water behind both electrodes, providing a high efficiency of heat removal.

Cooling Water

As mentioned previously, the ability to quickly remove the heat of generation enables higher ozone concentrations. Therefore, the temperature of the cooling water will have a direct impact on the capacity of a generator.

Most large-scale ozone generators can use cooling water up to 30°C (86°F). But, the effect of these high temperatures can be a reduction of as much as 40% of the design capacity, as illustrated in figure 6, when high concentration ozone is desired. Because of this it is

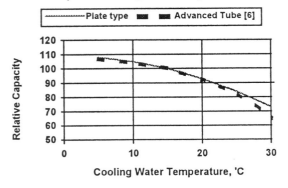

**Figure 6: Generator Capacity
Impact of Cooling Water Temperature**

recommended that the water temperature to the generator be in the range of 10°C (50°F) for efficient use of generator capacity. The trade-off between ozone capacity and the capital for a chiller should be compared. In most cases the addition of a chiller to decrease cooling water temperature and thus increase the output of the generator will be the best economic option.

Power Supply

As previously stated, ozone is generated by passing oxygen gas between a high voltage and a low voltage electrode. A portion of this oxygen is converted to ozone by the discharge of electricity between the electrodes. This process is known as "silent" or corona discharge. High voltage and high frequency are required to convert oxygen to ozone. The power unit of an ozone generator is designed to convert the incoming power supply from the mill's power source to the voltage and frequency levels required to generate ozone. The power unit typically employs transformers and rectifiers to achieve this task.

Frequency and Voltage. The effective input power is proportional to the frequency and approximately to the square of the voltage in the discharge unit. The relationship between these factors is described as the power density, and increasing the power density increases the amount of ozone generated High power density can be achieved by applying:
1.) high voltage and low frequency or
2.) low voltage and high frequency.
Higher voltage input generates more heat, which in turn places a greater burden on cooling efficiency, dielectric reliability and maintenance. Therefore, it follows that option 2, low voltage and high frequency, will provide the best efficiency for ozone production and reliability of the discharge cells.

Harmonic Current Distortion. The power unit converts commercial frequency power into high frequency power. Semiconductor circuitry is used to convert the incoming sine wave voltage. The resulting waveform is rectangular and includes harmonic contents.

If the fundamental frequency current is assumed to I_1, each harmonic current is expressed as follows:

$$I_n = I_1 (nq \pm 1) \quad n = 1, 2, 3, - - - - -$$
$$q = 6 \text{ (in case of 6-pulse rectifier)}$$
$$12 \text{ (in case of 12-pulse rectifier)}$$

<u>Harmonic Current - Impact on Other Equipment.</u>
Power factor improvement equipment uses capacitive
loads, which have a low impedance to harmonic current
induced in the power supply grid. As the flow of
harmonic current increases, other equipment within the
mill's power grid absorbs the harmonic current as an
excess heat load. Furthermore, the harmonic current,
which is expressed as the product of impedance of the
electric power system by the harmonic current, distorts
the voltage waveform of the voltage grid. This wave
distortion may cause malfunction of control equipment.

The 5th harmonic current is the largest of all. One
method of harmonic suppression is to adopt a 12-pulse,
or more, rectifier. To suppress the harmonic of the 11th
order and higher, which is induced with 12-pulse
rectification, a LC filter or an active filter can be used.

Though guidelines about the limitation of harmonic
current are continually being examined in virtually
every country, IEEE-519 is considered to currently be
one of the leading guidelines and regulations, and
conforming to IEEE-519 is desirable.

<u>Power Factor Improvement.</u> Ordinarily, the power
factor at the inverter input is less than 80%, causing a
large amount of lagging reactive power not to be useful.
To overcome the lagging reactive power, more current is
needed to supply the same effective power to the ozone
generator. Since most equipment capacity is determined
by current, this situation can cause an overload to the
equipment. To reduce the lagging reactive power,
condenser banks are connected to the line at the inverter
input, resulting in an apparent power reduction.

Ozone Compression

Ozone bleaching of pulp has been accomplished
commercially at high (40%) and medium (10-14%) pulp
consistency. (Refer to discussion of Process Equipment)
The consistency of the bleaching stage will determine
the need for compression of the ozone gas.

In the case of a high consistency pulp system, which
operates near atmospheric pressure, the location of the
generator to the pulping process will determine if there
is a compression requirement. Typically, compression
will not be required, as the generator can operate at a
pressure sufficient to ovecome the losses in the gas lines
to the process.

When working in a medium consistency pulp system, it
is necessary to compress the O_3/O_2 gas mixture from a
pressure of 3-10 psig leaving the generator to 150-175
psig entering the process. This compression is

necessary to maintain a small relative gas volume for
effective mixing. Measurement of this volume can be in
terms of phase ratio (V_g/V_p). Two pilot installations
reported effective phase ratio's to be:
0.33 (not accounting for entrained air)[5] or up to
0.5-0.55 (accounting for entrained air)[2].

For this report we will limit the phase ratio in a medium
consistency system to 0.5 and estimate air entrainment
to be about 5% of the pulp volume. Figure 7 then
illustrates the impact of system pressure on the gas/pulp
phase ratio. It is important to also evaluate the stock
pump feeding the system, when a pressure is selected.

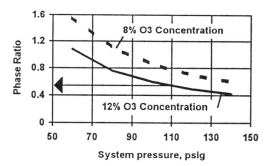

Figure 7: Compression Requirement
Medium Consistency Z Stage
(6 kg/t O3, 5% air entrainment, 1000 mt/d)

Depending on the concentration of ozone in the carrier
gas and the dose required, wide variations of operating
pressures can be necessary. This dictates the use of
positive displacement rather than dynamic compressors.
Additionally, since ozone decomposes rapidly as
temperature increases, isothermal compression is
required, which further reduces the available options for
compressor selection. While a reciprocating compressor
is well suited to the wide fluctuations of operating
pressures, its adiabatic compression process yields
discharge temperatures of 200-300°F (93-149°C)
depending on the compression ratio per stage.

The traditional method of compressing ozone employs a
liquid ring compressor (figure 8) which is a rotary
compressor with some positive displacement
characteristics. The compression process, while not
necessarily isothermal, delivers gas at a highly
suppressed discharge temperature which is the result of
intimate contact between the gas and sealing water.
Generally, discharge temperatures for liquid ring
compressors are 10-20°F. higher than sealing water
temperature

Figure 8: Liquid Ring Compressor

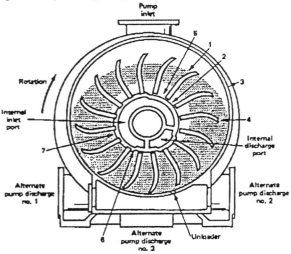

Cross section diagram of a liquid piston rotary compressor.

A typical compression loop employing a liquid ring compressor includes the compressor, a discharge separator to separate the sealing water from the discharge gas, a circulating water cooler to remove the heat of compression from the sealing water, and a water filter to remove particulates prior to reintroduction into the compressor housing. The sealing water is driven in its closed loop by the gas discharge pressure. Compression ratio and differential pressure protection are provided by a gas bypass valve.

The advantages of using a liquid ring compressor over a reciprocating compressor are:
> Greatly reduced discharge temperatures,
> Reduced maintenance,
> One shaft seal to atmosphere.

Liquid ring compressors do however have some inherent disadvantages, most notably:
> Limited pressure rise capability of approximately four compression ratios per stage,
> High specific horsepower due to poor compression efficiency.

The ideal oxygen/ozone compressor should then contain the benefits of the liquid ring compressor but also improve on the previously listed disadvantages. The single screw compressor is an option which meets these requirements.

Like the liquid ring compressor, the single screw compressor uses water to seal and cool the compressed gas. The water separation and cooling loop are similar. The major difference between the two systems is the method of compression. The liquid ring compressor

obtains gas volume reduction (hence pressure rise) by the interaction of a forward leaning impeller and an elliptical housing. Water and gas are trapped between the impeller blades. As the rotor turns, the water moves in and out due to the casing shape. The inner ring of the water volume thus produces a piston like effect, resulting in a pressure increase.

FIGURE 9: Single Screw Compressor

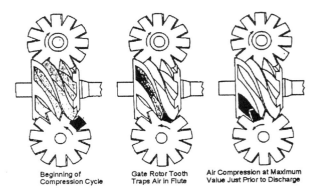

| Beginning of Compression Cycle | Gate Rotor Tooth Traps Air in Flute | Air Compression at Maximum Value Just Prior to Discharge |

The single screw compressor obtains pressure rise by the interaction of a main screw and inter meshing gate rotors, as illustrated by figure 9. The individual screw flutes have a tapered depth which are deep at the suction end and shallow at the discharge end. The main screw to housing seal is liquid while the individual flutes are sealed by the meshing gate rotor teeth. Internal leakage is minimized, hence compression efficiency is high.

The single screw compressor, like the liquid ring, offers the advantage over reciprocating compressors of reduced discharge temperature. The single screw compressor has demonstrated a temperature rise even lower than that associated with liquid ring units.

In addition, the single screw compressor offers the following advantages: (Refer also to Table 2)
> Low specific horsepower due to improved compression efficiency,
> Compression ratios up to 20 in a one stage,
> No "surge" concern, hence simple controls,
> Compact design.

Table 2: Efficiency Comparison Single Screw vs Liquid Ring
(Typical)

P2/P1 Ratio (r)	5.85	6.47	7.07	7.68
Liquid Ring IE	55	53	53	47
Single Screw IE	75.9	75.8	72.4	71.6
% Improved SS vs LR	38%	43%	37%	52%

(IE equals isentropic efficiency)

PROCESS EQUIPMENT

Ozone is a powerful oxidizing agent that reacts rapidly when in contact with pulp. The key to a powerful ozone system is to effectively and rapidly mix ozone with pulp. In the case of a medium consistency (8-14%) pulp system this is accomplished using a high intensity mixer followed by a short retention tube, both pressurized to provide a manageable gas volume fraction. A typical medium consistency system is illustrated in figure 10.

FIGURE 10: Medium Consistency Z Stage

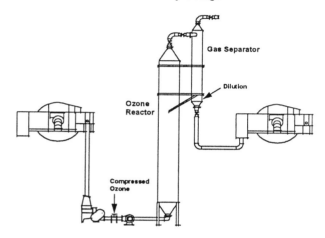

For the high consistency (35-45%) system contact is generally carried out after the pulp is fluffed, to expose the maximum fiber surface area. Since the gas volume is not a major concern in high consistency system contact can be made under atmospheric conditions. A typical high consistency system is shown in figure 11.

FIGURE 11: High Consistency Z Stage

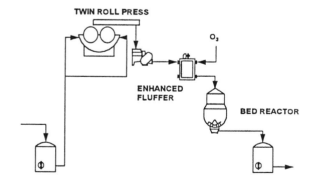

Ozone Charge
There are a number of other reports that specify the conditions and configuration of the pulp side of an ozone system. To stay focused on the gas delivery and handling system the only concern is therefore how much ozone is required for each system. In PAPRICAN's

pilot and laboratory facility [2] a comparison was made between medium and high consistency systems. This comparison concluded that for a dose up to a 5 kg/ton (0.5%) on pulp there was little difference between medium and high consistency system efficiency (Δkappa/ ozone charge) and ozone selectivity. Further, this work concluded that the split addition of ozone, without intermediate washing, in a medium consistency system was not an effective means to increase the ozone charge, and thus delignification power of the system. Also it is well known that ozone will react with any solids carried over from the post oxygen washers. So for the medium consistency system an ozone dose of 6 kg/t has been selected as a typical medium consistency application level.

For the medium consistency system at a 6 kg/mt ozone charge a high ozone concentration (>10%) is demanded, as illustrated by figure 12.

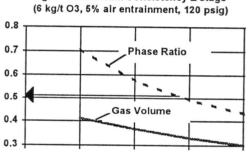

Figure 12: Medium Consistency Z stage
(6 kg/t O3, 5% air entrainment, 120 psig)

In the case of high consistency, a dose of 11 kg/t was selected to represent a pulp with acceptable strength properties and some carryover of oxygen solids and a more powerful delignification stage.

For a high consistency system the case for high concentration ozone is made by examining the reaction kinetics for this atmospheric system. As illustrated by figure 13, data accumulated on laboratory evaluations at higher concentrations the reaction of pulp with ozone is faster and more efficient.

FIGURE 13: Laboratory Reaction Kinetics

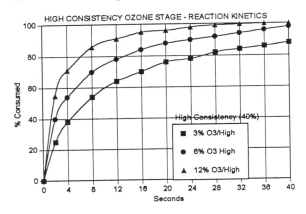

OFF-GAS HANDLING

Since 85% or more of the gas entering the process is non-reactive, it is imperative to remove this gas from the pulp stream before the next bleaching operation. Also, since the tail of the ozone reaction is very long, there is a good possibility that trace amounts of ozone will be present in the off-gas stream. Therefore, the gas separated from the process must undergo some treatment prior to recycle, reuse (in other mill applications), or venting.

Typical for pulp bleaching operations is the use of a thermal destruct unit, with some type of heat exchanger to help cool the gas prior to exiting. With thermal units, it is important to remove the particulate matter from the gas stream, to assure that pulp fibers are not carried to the destruct chamber. This means that separation techniques for both High and Medium Consistency bleaching operations must be designed to remove any entrained fiber from the gas stream. This is particularly more difficult in medium consistency operations, where the gas must be expanded and the velocities are conducive to carrying fiber.

Figure 14: Ozone Recirculation After Pulp

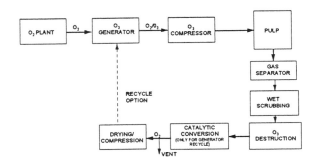

The off-gas from the process is very rich in oxygen, contianing as much as 98% of the oxygen initially fed to the ozone generator. Following destruct, the gas can be reused in other areas of the mill (as listed in figure 2), recycled to the ozone generator, or vented. In any case, a small purge is necessary. Each of these processes has some different equipment requirements.

Venting. Unless the cost of oxygen used for feeding the generator is very inexpensive, the option of venting the spent gas after destruct is likely not economical. Even in the case of a high ozone concentration, the oxygen in the vent line can reach 100 lbs/OD ton of pulp. For a moderately sized mill, this can easily amount to over half a million dollars per year.

Reuse. Most mills considering the use of ozone as a prime bleaching agent may have an oxygen delignification stage. Additionally, an Eo stage will be operational, and coupled with the use of oxygen for white liquor oxidation, or aeration of water treatment, provide enough opportunities to make recompression of the off gas an economically viable alternative, with little excess. This is particularly true if the ozone generator is operated at high concentration providing low oxygen use at the front end. This option requires only ozone destruction and off-gas compression to implement. Three considerations are key to selecting an off gas compressor.

➢ *Suction Pressure and Temperature:* The pressure of the gas leaving the destruct unit and entering the compressor is critical to the selection of the compressor. This will determine the size and power required based on the compression ratio.

➢ *Process Conditions:* The destination of the gas determines the pressure requirement at the point of reuse, typically line pressure plus 10 psig and any pressure required for the reuse application. The gas can also be compressed and sent to storage for utilization as required.

➢ *Compressor Location:* The location of the compressor needs to be known in order to evaluate the additional discharge pressure required to satisfy system pressure losses.

Recycle - When oxygen costs are very high, the generator output is not capable of high concentration, or there are not sufficient alternate uses for the spent gas another option is to recycle the gas back to the generator. Due to the stringent feed gas quality required by most ozone generators, the recycle option can be costly.

Moisture, hydrocarbons, particulates, CO_2 and CO must be removed prior to the reintroduction to the generator. This removal is generally accomplished in two steps. First, by catalytic conversion of trace hydrocarbon to CO_2. The CO_2 is then typically managed by a small vent purge in the recycle loop. An other option is to remove the CO_2 by absorption but, this can be a more costly alternative. Moisture in the presence of nitrogen can lead to nitric acid, so that it is essential to remove moisture prior to generator reuse. Therefore, the second step is moisture removal by a combination of refrigerant and desiccant gas drying [7]. In addition there needs to be a small bleed (<10%) of gas from the system to avoid excessive build up of inert compounds, such as CO_2 and N_2. Since the gas re-entering the generator will have a lower oxygen content, the generator will need to produce a higher concentration of O_3/O_2. The lower oxygen content results from the dilution effect of N_2 built up from the O_2 supply and from air entrained by the pulp. Therefore, additional generator capacity will be necessary to provide the same concentration at a given mass flow.

INSTRUMENTATION AND CONTROL

Typically, the ozone pulp process will demand a certain mass flow of ozone on pulp at a given concentration. The simplest control strategy is then to fix the feed flow to the generator. Then, measure the ozone concentration in the gas stream exiting the generator, and adjust the power input to the generator to yield the desired concentration and dose on pulp. This method has the added benefit of maintaining a specific gas volume to the process, particularly important with medium consistency gas mixing.

ENCLOSURES

Ozone Generators are usually furnished with two basic components, the discharge unit and the power supply. The requirements for enclosures are typically more stringent for the power supply, since the transformers and other electrical equipment exhibit sensitivity to dust and particulate contamination. Therefore power supply units normally require an enclosed, temperature and atmospherically controlled building.

The discharge units, on the other hand, are normally sealed vessels, and therefore do not usually require an environmentally controlled unit. But although they do not necessarily require an enclosure, an enclosure is still recommended. This becomes increasingly evident during installation and maintenance, especially in an environment such as a pulp mill. When assembling tube-type generators at installation, care must be taken to avoid airborne particulate from accumulating in the generator body. The plate type generator is generally delivered factory tested, pre-assembled and sealed to minimize on-site preparation.

ECONOMICS

There are several options for a mill to consider when evaluating the purchase of an ozone system, particularly for the ozone generator. These options include:
> A Mill Capital Investment
   - Equipment & base engineering
   - Installed Package
> A Leasing option
   - Equipment package
   - Installed package or
> Purchasing ozone "over-the-fence".

The lease option usually will have a buy-out ability and could be extended to include a broader range of the total ozone system. The "over-the-fence" purchase generally ties the oxygen and ozone supply with a third party supplying capitalization, operation and maintenance for both systems. Specifics for the "over-the-fence" supply can vary from mill to mill depending on how services such as, electricity, cooling water, exhaust oxygen reuse and real-estate are negotiated between the supplier and mill. In all cases it is important to make a complete comparison of all three options to determine the best selection for a particular mill site.

To complete a comparison it is important to consider all elements of an Ozone System listed in table 1. In particular, there are key variables in the total system that can have significant impact on both the capital and operating cost analysis These components are listed below, in table 3.

Table 3: Key Cost Components

Component	Range	Cost Impact (base case)
Cooling Water Temperature	5 - 30°C	Capital (15°C)
O_3 Concentration	8 - 14%	Capital (8 or 12%)
Oxygen Cost	$0.02 - 0.06/ lb ($0.044 - 0.132/ kg)	Operating ($0.03/ lb)
Exit gas Re-use	1.Exhaust Vented 2.Exhaust Credited 3.Total Mill Demand	Operating
Electricity Cost	$0.02 - 0.12/kWh	Operating ($0.06/kWh)
Air Entrainment	5-10% (of pulp volume)	Capital & Operating (5%)
O_2 Feed purity	90-99% (O_2 supply) 85-95% (recycled)	Capital & Operating (98%)

Capital Investment

A typical capital investment for a single ozone system, not including pulp process equipment, can be in the $10-15 million dollar range for a 1,000 ton/day pulp mill. To supply a mill demand of 6-11 kg O_3 /mton of pulp will generally require multiple ozone generating units, as illustrated by figure 15, since the capacity of a single generator is only 1,400 [8] - 1,800 kg/day. Therefore, the major component of capital for an ozone system is likely to be the ozone generator. The possible exception would be the case of a high consistency pulp bleaching system where there may also be a significant investment required for the process equipment, not addressed in this report.

FIGURE 15: Ozone Gas Supply System

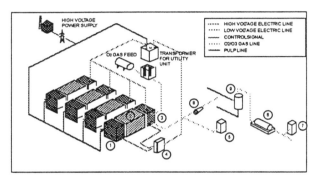

Since the ozone generator represents a major portion of the capital investment, sizing of these units and uptime will be important considerations. In the Cooling Water section of this report, figure 6 illustrates the value of minimizing cooling water temperature to the generator, as the impact of this variable alone can alter capacity by 40%. Another key variable to generator capacity is the ozone concentration, which can also have a dramatic impact on capacity, as shown in figure 16. In selecting a generator it is important to be sure that a consistent definition for ozone concentration is being used. Typically, O_3 concentration = O_3 (weight)/ Total gas weight ($O_3 + O_2 + N_2$...). But, sometimes O_3 concentration can be defined as $O_3/(O_3 + O_2)$ or even O_3/O_2, with all three descriptions yielding very different gas products.

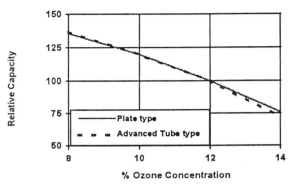

Figure 16: Generator Capacity
Impact of Ozone Concentration

In addition the amount of air entrainment and oxygen feed gas purity will also have a slight effect of diluting the ozone concentration. The total capital for the ozone generating system can be broken down into primary components of cost, as seen in table 4, with the generator leading the list at 60-70% of the total capital investment.

Table 4: Capital Breakdown

Components	Cost
Generator, Power Unit, Cooling Utility Unit	60-70%
Chiller, O_3/ O_2 Compressor, O_3 Instruments	5-10%
Off-Gas Handling, O_2 Compressor (option)	5-15%
Installation, Housing, spares	15-20%

Capital Check List

The items to consider when putting together an ozone system can be broken down into a checklist. In comparing different systems it is important to remember that supply package content can vary significantly from source to source. Therefore, in order to do a complete comparison, it is necessary to evaluate each machine on an equal basis. Things to account for during checking are listed in table 6.

Table 6:

Generator	√
➤ Type	
➤ Uptime	
➤ Ozone Charge & Concentration demand	
➤ Maintenance Spares	
➤ Housing Requirements	
➤ Installation time/cost	
Generator Cooling Water	√
➤ Temperature (generator size impact)	
➤ Chiller	
➤ Circulation pump(s)	
➤ Piping & Valves	
Generator Power Supply	√
➤ High Frequency Transformer	
➤ Power Factor Adjustment	
➤ Harmonic Filter	
Oxygen Supply	√
➤ Purity	
➤ Mill Wide O_2 Utilization	
Compression	√
➤ Number and size	
➤ Control Requirements	
➤ Consumed Power	
➤ Cooling requirement	
Off-Gas Handling	√
➤ Gas/ Fiber Separation	
➤ Wet Scrubber	
➤ Ozone Destruction (all systems)	
➤ CO/ Hydrocarbon Conversion (Recycle case)	
➤ Gas Vent or CO_2 Absorption (Recycle case)	
➤ Gas recompression?	
Auxiliaries	√
➤ Process O_3 Control Monitor(s)	
➤ Ambient O_3 Monitors	
➤ Control Valves & Piping	
➤ Instrumentation and Gauges	

OPERATING COSTS

The operating cost of ozone systems have been the subject of much debate. This debate is primarily caused by different bases for comparison, including direct purchase of product ("over-the-fence"), varying utility rates, or accounting methods for oxygen feed and/or exhaust gas. But, this comparison does not need to be complex if a step by step comparison is done. Table 3, provides a list of key variables effecting the cost of ozone, that should be examined in each study.

Accounting For Oxygen

In beginning the operating cost analysis, the first decision to consider is how to account for the oxygen carrier gas exhausted from the ozone pulp process. As discussed in this report there are basically three options, described below and illustrated in figures 18 and 19. (Figures 18 and 19 were developed based on the base costs listed in table 3, key components include oxygen at &0.03/ lb and electricity at $0.06/ kW-hr.)

➤ Exhaust vented: In this case the oxygen rich carrier gas exhausted from the ozone process is vented to the atmosphere. The total available oxygen that will be exhausted, at various rates of gas recycle to the ozone generator, are shown in figure 17. The case of venting all of this exhaust gas to the atmosphere is not likely to be the best set of economics and also needs to be examined as an additional source of air emissions.

Figure 17: Oxygen Exhaust Gas

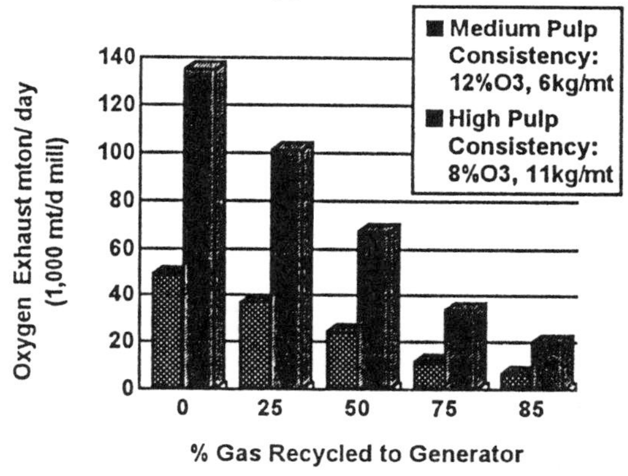

➤ Exhaust Credited: In this case, all of the exhausted carrier gas from the ozone process, generally containing more than 85% O_2, is sent to supply other mill applications. The total cost of the reused oxygen is then credited to the ozone stage and expensed to other mill applications. For this option only the cost of consumed oxygen <2% is charged as operating cost for the ozone generator. This case does assume that the mill can use what ever volume there is available from the exhausted oxygen gas stream, which may in some not be practical for some of the lower levels of gas recycle to the generator. The actual volume of gas available should be examined for a specific mill case (pulp capacity, ozone demand and concentration and generator recycle). An example for 1,000 mt/d of capacity and two ozone demands are shown in figure 17.

➢ Total Mill Demand: This case includes the cost of ozone plus the cost of supplying a minimum 32 mt/ day base load of oxygen to other areas of the mill complex. The 32 mt/day base load covers the approximate oxygen requirement for $E_o + O + WLO$ in a 1,000 mton/ day mill, as illustrated by figure 2. For example, in the case of the exhaust gas being greater than 32 mt/d the net oxygen exhaust is expensed to ozone generation. But, in the case that the ozone process exhaust contains less than 32 mt/d an additional supply of oxygen to make up the difference is added and expensed to ozone generation.

Examples of all three ways of accounting for oxygen are provided in figures 18 and 19, which illustrate a medium consistency (18) and high consistency pulp (19) stage respectively.

Figure 18: Comparing Apples to Apples?
Ozone Operating Cost - Medium Consistency

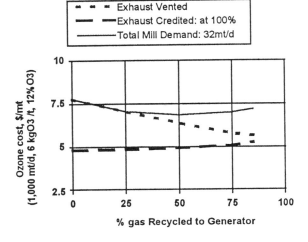

Although figures 18 and 19 show dramatic differences between the three cases, for a given recycle rate, in actuality the cases may constitute the same bottom line impact for a mill. A good approach for accounting for oxygen, and for determining the optimum level of cost and generator recycle, is to first consider whether there are other areas of the mill which can utilize the oxygen-rich process exhaust gas. Then, compare the total cost impact to the mill for all sources of oxygen. The final analysis must also include the capital cost for the off-gas handling system. Recall that the capital may be significantly higher in the case where generator recycle is required.

Figure 19: Comparing Apples to Apples?
Operating Cost - High Consistency

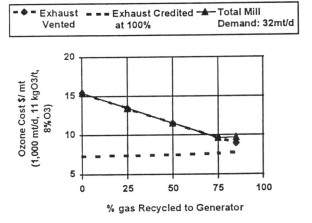

It should be noted that Figures 18-21 are based on the total ozone generating cost for the mill which includes: oxygen (as specified), steam (preheating to O_3 destruct), power (generator, O_3 destructor, compressor, desiccant dryer, recycle gas cooling, Chiller, cold water pump, cooling tower fan, control panel), water, maintenance (plate type generator), manpower (1/3 person/ shift).

The impact of the cost of oxygen is also an important consideration, especially if the oxygen is to be vented. But, in the case where oxygen is reused by either recycle to the generator or in other mill processes oxygen does not have a significant cost impact, as illustrated by figure 20.

Figure 20: Operating Cost - Impact of Oxygen
(Medium consistency system)

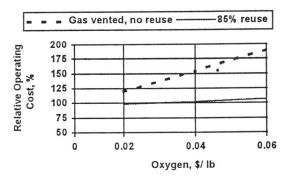

Most important in the accounting method is the cost of electricity, which unlike oxygen, is not directly recoverable by generator recycle or can be reused in other mill applications. Power is the single largest component of ozone cost as illustrated in figure 21. In comparing a mill operated generator to an "over-the-fence" contract the accounting for electricity and oxygen will control the "reported" ozone cost.

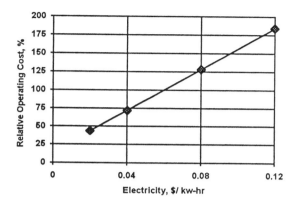

Figure 21: Operating Cost - Impact of Electrical $ (Medium consistency system, Oxygen 85% reuse)

The purity of the generator feed gas will also impact the operating cost by increasing the generator's power demand, as shown in figure 1. The purity of the feed gas will be impacted by the oxygen supply method, and in the case of exhaust recycle further dilution of the feed gas is caused by pulp air entrainment.

Maintenance History

Although the generation of ozone at the scale required for most modern pulp mills is relatively new, the industry has years of experience producing ozone for many other industrial applications. The reliability of these machines is high, a reflection of the precision of their design. Once operational, the units require little operator attention. And since there are no moving parts, the overall maintenance requirement of ozone generators is relatively low.

Ozone generators normally undergo an annual inspection. Identification and replacement of any failed fuses is a key function of this inspection. Tube-type generators, which have stainless steel low voltage electrodes, typically require cleaning during this annual procedure, since metal dust is produced during operation and tends to accumulate.

CONCLUSIONS

➢ High concentration ozone has a place in pulp bleaching applications - enabling effective gas volumes for mixing in medium consistency pulp systems and enhanced reaction kinetics for high consistency systems.

➢ There are design choices available for both ozone generator (plate vs tube design) and ozone compressors (single screw vs liquid ring).

➢ It may be necessary to question the definitions for ozone generation terminology to insure equivalent basis of comparison.

➢ Cooling water temperature vs chiller capacity should be examined to minimize capital investment.

➢ Consistent accounting for oxygen and power are critical to making comparisons between different ozone systems, or capitalization approaches.

➢ A team including: representation from the power house, the pulp mill and finance should work together to engineer the most cost effective ozone installation.

REFERENCES

[1] Govers, T.R. "Ozone in the pulp mill: Alternatives and Cost", Proceedings of the Non-Chlorine Bleaching Conference, Amelia Island, Florida, USA, March 1994.

[2] Berry, Barclay, Prins, Sacciadis, Skothos, Ayala, Magnotta, Breed, Rounsaville, Shackford, "Medium-Consistency Bleaching with High Concentration Ozone Gas in the PAPRICAN Pilot Plant and a Comparison with Laboratory Bleaching", Proceedings of International Bleaching Conference, Vancouver, BC, Canada 1994.

[3] Homer, Horney, Ayton. "Ozone & Oygen Supply for the Bleaching of Pulp", Proceedings of CPPA, Montreal, PQ, Canada, January 1993.

[4] Homer, "An Integrated System for the Production of Oxygen & Ozone for Pulp Mill Use", Proceedings of CPPA Technical Section Pacific & Western Branches, at Jasper Conference, May 1992.

[5] Clark, C., "Ozone Bleaching Merits of High Consistency Operation", Proceedings of AiChE Annual Meeting, November 1993, and reference to: Funk, E., Munro, F., Szopinski, R., Vilpponen, A. Proceedings of Non-Chlorine Bleaching Conference, March 1993.

[6] Lang, H., Erni, P., Liechti, p., "Advanced Ozone Generation Technology to Solve the Oxidation Problems of Today", Proceedings of the International Ozone Association (IOA) Annual Conference, 1993.

[7] Leist, G., "Conventional Long Loop Recycle for Ozone Bleaching of Pulp", Emery-Trailigaz, Proceedings of Non-Chlorine Bleaching Conference, March 1994.

[8] Johnson, l., Johansen, D., Kirby, M., "Oxygen/ Ozone Supply and Integration Economics", Proceedings of the 79th Annual Meeting, Technical Section CPPA.

[9] Neethling, Rice, Kerr, Culp, "Capital and Operating Costs of Ozone Facilities", HDR Engineering CA, Proceedings of American Water Works Association Annual Conference, 1991.

Bleaching of Mixed Office Waste

Patrick E. Sharpe
Kamyr, Inc. R&D Laboratory, Glen Falls, NY 12801

The objective of this study was to determine the feasibility of bleaching a pulp mill sample of mixed office waste (MOW) recycled fiber furnish to greater than 80% ISO brightness. This brightness requirement was set by the demands of the recycled fiber industry. The furnish was a high consistency sample taken before bleaching from a MOW trial that was run at a recycled fiber market pulp mill. The experimental plan was to perform laboratory bleaches on this stock utilizing various chlorine-containing bleaching sequences and total chlorine-free (TCF) bleaching sequences.

Of the sequences studied there were six that produced greater than 80% ISO brightness on the MOW: OZPF (87%), CEDED (86.7%), OpZF (83.2%), ZP (81.3%), ATPFPF (81.2%), and OZEPY (81.0%). It was found that efficient de-inking is necessary for successful bleaching of MOW recycled fiber furnish. Greater than 80% ISO brightness was achievable by bleaching MOW with TCF bleaching reagents.

The future of utilizing recycled fibers in papermaking is dependent upon having an economical source of raw material. MOW would be economical as a fiber source if the furnish could be utilized with minimal sorting.

After sorting MOW would contain various dyed copy papers, dyed file folders, computer printouts, magazines, newspapers, carbon papers, tablet backs, and other types of materials. This requires successful bleaching of many colors and types of dyed fibers, including a small percentage of brown unbleached fibers. The unbleached and dyed fibers have to be bleached to the extent that they would be invisible in the final product.

This future MOW fiber supply would also contain a significant amount of mechanical pulp with a high lignin content which increases the difficulty of bleaching.

EXPERIMENTAL

Mill trials were run at a recycled fiber market pulp mill using MOW as the furnish. Samples of MOW for laboratory bleaching were collected at the mill prior to the bleaching tower.

The MOW samples were deinked and bleached in the laboratory using various chlorine-containing and chlorine-free bleaching reagents. Bleaching conditions are summarized in Table 1. Hydrogen peroxide bleaches contained 0.05% $MgSO_4$, 1.0% Na_2SiO_3, and 0.2% DTPA.

Initial and final ISO brightness, CIE $L^*a^*b^*$ color values, and chemical consumptions were measured. ISO brightness, CIE $L^*a^*b^*$ color values, and kappa numbers were determined by Tappi Test Methods T525, T524, and T236, respectively. BOD and COD were measured for selected effluents.

Deinking was done in a Denver flotation cell at 1% consistency and 60°C using 100 g O.D. samples of pulp. The only chemicals added were 1% NaOH, and Shell Nonatell LX1020 surfactant. The deinking cell was run for 20 to 30 min. until the foam was clean. The deinked pulp was thickened and washed on a Buchner funnel. Deinking was done prior to bleaching.

Species identification and chemical/mechanical pulp ratio were done by using optical microscopy.

RESULTS AND DISCUSSION

Composition of MOW Furnish

The MOW furnish contained 10% mechanical pulp and 90% chemical pulp. The mechanical pulp was a spruce/pine blend. The chemical pulp portion of the furnish consisted of 65-75% southern hardwoods and 25-35% of a spruce/pine/fir mix.

The sampled portion of the MOW starting furnish as it arrived at the mill contained the following paper components by weight percent: 71.0% white, 11.7% dyed, 6.1% brown, 4.3% newsprint, and 5.4% magazine. The 1.5% remaining miscellaneous fraction was outthrows which consisted of plastics, metals, fabric, and other non-paper items which were removed from the process by the drum pulper.

The kappa number of the white paper component was 15.5. This was surprisingly high. Microscopic examination of this white paper component indicated the presence of 5 to 10% mechanical pulp which explained the high kappa number.

If future MOW mills relied on sorting out a portion of undesirable materials from their furnish before bleaching, such high kappa white paper would be difficult to identify and sort out. MOW compositions containing hidden high kappa white paper would be difficult to bleach to their target brightness. This would be an intermittent problem that would make process control difficult.

Easily identifiable and sortable colored fractions would most likely have relatively lower kappa numbers. This furnish had a kappa number of 5.3 for its colored component. This colored component was 100% chemical pulp.

Overall this MOW furnish had an initial kappa number of 20.4 which made it a very difficult furnish to bleach.

Bleaching of MOW Without Deinking

Figure 1 summarizes the results of bleaching the MOW furnish without doing any additional deinking on the sample. An oxidative extraction (Eop) followed by formamidine sulfinic acid (FAS or F); oxygen delignification reinforced with hydrogen peroxide (Op) followed by FAS; and single stage hydrogen peroxide (P) bleaches at 2% and 3% hydrogen peroxide charge were performed on the MOW sample.

None of these bleaches were able to achieve the goal of greater than 80% ISO brightness. Bleaching of the MOW as collected without any further deinking resulted in a maximum final brightness of 65.9% ISO. It was decided that further deinking would be necessary to achieve the required brightness of greater than 80% ISO.

Deinking of MOW Furnish

Table 2 compares the MOW furnish before and after deinking. Deinking the starting pulp increased the ISO

brightness from the initial starting brightness of 58.3% to 63.0% ISO. This is a 4.7 percentage point increase in the brightness. The final deinked brightness of 63.0% ISO achieved 96% of the bleached brightness for the most successful bleach on the original pulp (65.9% ISO) which was not deinked.

Deinking removed nearly all of the remaining ash in the sample. Ash content dropped from 22.6% to 2.1%. The kappa number after deinking was essentially unchanged.

Bleaching of Deinked MOW

The results from bleaching the deinked MOW are presented in Figures 2 through 8.

Chlorine dioxide (D) and sodium hypochlorite (H) were used to bleach the deinked MOW. These results are shown in Figure 2.

At 2.0%, 3.0%, and 4.0% chlorine dioxide the maximum brightness achieved was 70.0% ISO. Sodium hypochlorite at 4.0% worked better than chlorine dioxide and produced a bleached brightness of 77.9%.

However, these single stage bleaches were not successful in reaching the brightness target. It has previously been discovered that hypochlorite becomes less effective as the mechanical pulp content of a MOW composition approaches 10% [1].

Figure 3 shows the effect of chlorination (C) followed by alkaline extraction (E) followed by hypochlorite. The C-E-H sequence produced a brightness of 76.9% These brightnesses were still below the brightness target of 80.0% ISO.

Figure 3 also shows the effect of C-E-D-E-D. The only chlorine-containing sequence to achieve the brightness target was the five stage C-E-D-E-D sequence. A brightness of 86.7% was obtained. The first D stage was 2% chlorine dioxide and the second D stage was 1% chlorine dioxide.

TCF Bleaching of Deinked MOW

To determine the effectiveness of TCF bleaching on the deinked MOW the following sequences were examined: hydrogen peroxide; hydrogen peroxide followed by FAS; and FAS followed by hydrogen peroxide. These results are shown in Figure 4.

Single stage applications of hydrogen peroxide at 2.0% and 3.0% concentrations did not reach the brightness target. The oxidative/reductive sequence of hydrogen peroxide followed by FAS (P-FAS) achieved the highest brightness of 76.9% which was still bellow the brightness target. The FAS-P bleach in which reduction was followed by oxidation produced a slightly lower brightness of 76.3%.

In Figure 5 the results are shown for several TCF oxidative/reductive sequences: Op-FAS, Op-Z-FAS, and Op-Y. None of these sequences achieved 80% ISO brightness. The Op-Z-FAS sequence produced the highest brightness of 78.0%.

The Op-Z-FAS sequence was examined again at 3.0% ozone instead of the 1.5% ozone used in Figure 5. These two sets of results are presented together in Figure 6 for comparison. Using 3.0% ozone the brightness target of 80.0% ISO was achieved. Op-3.0%Z-F produced a final brightness of 83.2% ISO.

Sequences using 3%Z-2%P and O-3%Z-2%P-F produced brightnesses over 80.0% ISO. These results are presented in Figure 7. The Z-P and O-Z-P-F sequences produced brightnesses of 81.3% and 87.0%, respectively.

The O-Z-P stages of the O-Z-P-F sequence were enough to reach the brightness target. After O-Z-P the brightness was 85.3% ISO. The final reductive F stage produced an additional 1.7 percentage points of brightness.

Forsberg and Genco [2] were able to obtain 85% ISO brightness when bleaching MOW using an (EPO)ZP sequence. In this case their starting furnish was different with a higher initial brightness and contained less color with lower L*a*b* values.

The two five-stage TCF sequences that were investigated each achieved the brightness target. O-Z-E-P-Y produced a final brightness of 81.0% ISO. (A-T)-P-F-P-F produced a final brightness of 81.2%. These results are presented in Figure 8.

The final FAS stage in the sequence (A-T)-P-F-P-F was not necessary as (A-T)-P-F-P produced a brightness of 80.2% ISO. The final FAS stage only produced 1.0 additional percentage points of brightness.

The (A-T) stage was a pretreatment. The A represents an acid wash with H_2SO_4 at pH 2.0 to remove metals. This was not effective and a subsequent stage using the chelating agent DTPA (T) was done. The DTPA pretreatment was also ineffective and the iron content remained high at 119 ppm.

Table 3 lists all of the bleaching sequences that exceeded the bleaching target of 80.0% ISO brightness for MOW. In this table the various bleaching sequences are ranked according to their effectiveness.

Six sequences produced >80% ISO brightness on the MOW: OZPF (87%), CEDED (86.7%), OpZF (83.2%), ZP (81.3%), ATPFPF (81.2%), and OZEPY (81.0%).

Dye Removal From MOW By TCF Bleaching

CIE L*a*b* color numbers are listed for the bleached pulps in Table 3. Table 2 lists the initial starting CIE color values after deinking and before bleaching which were L* = 87.4, a* = -0.07, and b* = 7.0. As can be seen from the data, color was removed from these bleached pulps. The b* values were equal to or less than 5.5 which represents a slight yellowish tint that is hardly noticeable and is acceptable to the eye.

A more comprehensive way to examine color removal is to use the dye removal index [3] which objectively expresses the percent color removal from colored fibers. To obtain the dye removal index the CIE L*a*b* color values are used to calculate the distance in color space from an ideal bleach of L* = 100, a* = 0, b* = 0 for the initial unbleached and final bleached samples.

The dye removal index is the difference of these distances in color space expressed as a percent of the distance in color space of the initial unbleached colored sample from the ideal bleach. The dye removal index expresses a percent color removal for bleaching.

The dye removal index was calculated from the CIE L*a*b* color numbers for the successful bleaches which reached the brightness target. The dye removal index numbers are listed in Table 3. The trend seen in the dye removal index was to increase as the brightness increased: as more color was removed the brightness increased. The dye removal index for these bleaches ranged from 74.0 to 88.3%.

Of the six successful sequences CEDED, OZEPY, and ZP were also found to be the three most effective bleaching sequences for removing dyes from colored paper samples as previously reported [3]. The other three bleaching sequences in Table 3 were not investigated in that study.

In this past study it was also discovered when bleaching colored recycled fibers that different colors and types of dyes reacted differently to each type of bleaching chemical. It was also found that to most effectively remove dyes from recycled fiber a combination of bleaching chemicals was required.

In the present study a minimum of two bleaching stages were required to reach the brightness target of greater than 80% ISO brightness.

TCF Bleaching Effluent Analysis

Effluents from several TCF bleaching stages on the deinked MOW pulp were analyzed for BOD and COD contents. Table 4 summarizes the results of the effluent testing on the Op-FAS bleach and the 3%Z-2%P bleach. The bleaching effluents that were tested had acceptable or treatable BOD and COD levels.

CONCLUSIONS

Based on the bleaching results for the MOW samples, the following conclusions were made:

1. Efficient deinking is necessary for successful bleaching of MOW recycled fiber furnish.
2. Greater than 80% ISO brightness is achievable by bleaching MOW with TCF bleaching reagents.
3. Single stage bleaches were not successful at reaching 80% ISO brightness on MOW furnish. A minimum of two bleaching stages are required.
4. The bleaching effluents that were tested had acceptable or treatable BOD and COD levels.
5. Six sequences produced >80% ISO brightness on the MOW:
    OZPF (87%), CEDED (86.7%), OpZF (83.2%), ZP (81.3%), ATPFPF (81.2%), and OZEPY (81.0%).

This is one of a series of papers on bleaching of MOW. Additional TCF bleaching studies have been completed on various compositions of MOW. This work will be reported separately in the future and will include the effect of kappa number on the bleachability of MOW.

LITERATURE CITED

1. Angulo, J., *Tappi J.*, **74**(8):135(1991).

2. Forsberg, P.M., and Genco, J.M., *Tappi J.*, **77**(3):253(1994).

3. Sharpe, P.E., and Lowe, R.W., *Tappi 1993 Pulping Conference Proceedings*, TAPPI PRESS, Atlanta, p.1205.

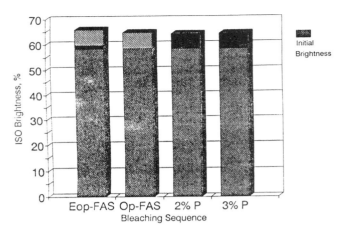

Figure 1. Bleaching of MOW without deinking

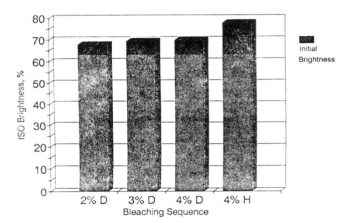

Figure 2. Bleaching of MOW with chlorine dioxide and sodium hypochorite after deinking

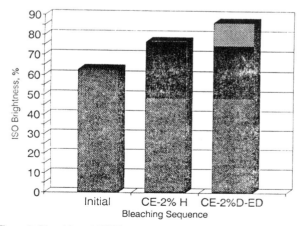

Figure 3. Bleaching of MOW with chlorine-containing sequences after deinking

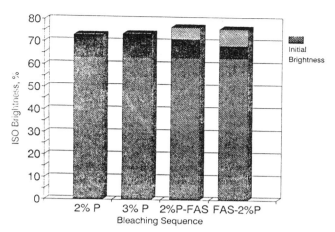

Figure 4. Bleaching of MOW with hydrogen peroxide and FAS after deinking

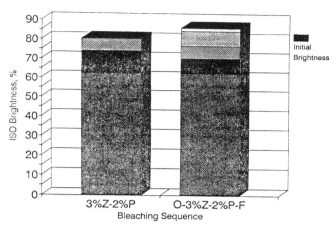

Figure 7. Bleaching of MOW with ZP and OZPF after deinking

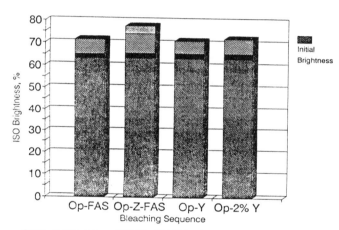

Figure 5. Bleaching of MOW with TCF oxidative/reductive bleaching sequences after deinking

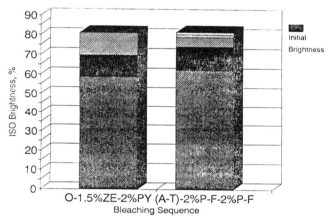

Figure 8. Bleaching of MOW with OZEPY and ATPFPF after deinking

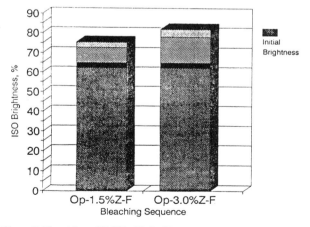

Figure 6. Bleaching of MOW with OpZF after deinking

Table 1.   Summary of bleaching sequence conditions

Condition	Application	Time (min.)	Consistency (%)	Temperature (°C)	Final pH
Hydrogen Peroxide	1 - 3%	120	10	70	9.4 - 11.4
FAS	1%	30	3.5, 10	60	6.5 - 10.4
Ozone	1 - 3%	20	1	20	2.5
Chlorination	4%	60	3.0	45	2.0
Alkaline Extraction	0.4 - 1.7%	60	10	70	10.6 - 12.0
Chlorine Dioxide	1 - 2 %	180	10	70	3.2 - 3.5
Sodium Hypochlorite	2 - 4%	90 - 120	10	45	10.2 - 12.9
Sodium Hydrosulfite	1 - 2%	30	6	60	5.5 - 6.1
Oxygen	90 psig	60	10	95	11.9 - 12.0
Peroxide reinforced Oxygen (Op)	75 psig O_2 2% NaOH/ 1% H_2O_2	90	10	95	10.0 - 11.2
Oxidative Extraction (Eop)	45 → 0 psig O_2 1% NaOH/0.5% H_2O_2	75	10	70	9.8
Acid Wash (A)	4.9% H_2SO_4	30	2	45	2.0
Chelation (T)	0.5% DTPA	30	2	20	7.0

Table 2.   Deinking of MOW

	Starting Pulp	After Deinking
ISO Brightness, %	58.3	63.0
Ash Content, %	22.6	2.1
Kappa No.	20.4	20.9
CIE Color:		
L*	84.5	87.4
a*	-0.45	-0.07
b*	6.5	7.0

Table 3.   Effectiveness of bleaching MOW

Rank Order	Bleaching Sequence	ISO Brightness, %	CIE COLOR			Dye Removal Index, %
			L*	a*	b*	
1.	OZPF	87.0	96.8	-1.2	3.7	87.8
2.	CEDED	86.7	95.9	-1.3	2.4	88.3
3.	OpZF	83.2	95.6	-1.1	4.7	79.5
4.	ZP	81.3	95.3	-1.3	5.5	74.0
5.	ATPFPF	81.2	94.6	-1.7	4.3	75.7
6.	OZEPY	81.0	95.1	-1.4	5.3	74.0

Table 4.   Bleaching effluents for Op-FAS and Z-P sequences

Bleaching Stage	BOD, kg/ODMT	COD, kg/ODMT
Op	14	26
1% FAS	0.55	1.4
3% Ozone	7.2	29
2% Hydrogen Peroxide	6.9	66

Decolorization of Colored Paper Using Chlorine Dioxide to Replace Sodium Hypochlorite

Philip E. Quinnett

Olin Corporation, 1186 Lower River Road, Charleston TN 37310

This is a review of laboratory tests decolorizing ten different standard colored papers comparing chlorine dioxide and sodium hypochlorite. A Northeast U.S. mill requested the tests to help determine a replacement for NaOCl used in broke decolorization. The tests, run at mill-specified conditions, resulted in an average color removal index of 95% or greater for both chemical agents. The response to the chemical agents varied from color to color; however, on average, chlorine dioxide removed color more effectively, with less variation, than sodium hypochlorite.

Chlorine dioxide used in the tests was generated via the 01® Process, a recently developed technology, practical for smaller scale applications; a brief process description is included. A generalized comparison of some common chlorine dioxide technologies is included to assist readers considering chlorine dioxide process utilization at recycled pulp facilities.

Hypochlorite has historically been a preferred chemical for removing color from colored papers because of its ease of use, high effectiveness, good availability, and relatively low cost. Over the last few years, use of hypochlorites in pulp mills has come under scrutiny because of potential environmental concerns; as a result, there is increasing activity evaluating alternative decolorizing chemicals [1-5]. The efficacy of chlorine dioxide is well documented in chemical pulp bleaching and delignification [6-8], but consideration of chlorine dioxide as a viable alternative decolorizing agent has been limited.

We believe ClO_2 has not been considered as a decolorizing agent, to a significant degree, because ClO_2 was considered an impractical small-mill alternative. A major portion of recovered paper deinking facilities for white papers or tissue are relatively small (less than 100,000 tons per year) [9]. For pulp and paper applications, the chlorate-based technologies for ClO_2 have been the primary alternatives considered. In the past, all ClO_2 production technologies were associated, to some degree, with these concerns:

a)   Large-sized equipment for production and storage

b) By-products that need to be recycled or utilized,

c) Complex operation.

A complicating factor to the potential replacement of hypochlorite is the expected decline in the availability and quality of recycled paper: "As deinking capacity expands, mills will either have to downgrade their fiber by upgrading their facilities with the best technology or be forced out of business by high fiber costs and/or poor pulp quality" [10]. This movement, driven by a) increasing recycling capacity in response to the regulatory mandates and b) public-expected environmental benefits of paper recycling, will likely continue for the foreseeable future. As the quality of paper declines, highly efficient and simple decolorizing steps must be available to provide mills with the flexibility to respond to variations in incoming raw material quality and still make high quality paper.

The Northeast U. S. mill that supplied the test samples for this study uses sodium hypochlorite to decolorize broke and wanted alternatives that required minimum process modification. In this mill, decolorization is required for re-use of off-spec colored runs and for color-change transitions.

The broke is repulped in paper machine whitewater, decolorizing agent is added, and pulp is held in a tank for approximately one hour. The resultant decolorized pulp is then added directly to a machine chest. The mill was interested in maintaining mill process conditions where pH and temperature are set by the paper machine conditions, and decolorizing agent application was simple.

In order to effectively evaluate color removal, one must establish a standard for assessment. The industry is still searching for a consistent and reliable means to measure color removal, however, several recent methods for assessing color removal have been proposed that may apply to individual mills [1,11]. During 1994 and 1995, two TAPPI Task Groups are actively investigating color control methods and impact:

> The Color Measurement and Control Task Group (Pulp Bleaching Committee) prepared a new Technical Information Sheet -- TIS0606-22 "Measurement and Control of Bleached Pulp Color";

> The Color Control Task Group (Fiber Recycling Committee) is currently evaluating methods to consistently measure and report color removal.

After evaluating the alternatives to assess efficacy of color removal, we selected average color removal index as our primary evaluation tool, with brightness as a secondary evaluation.

EXPERIMENTAL

Pulp Preparation

Samples of ten different standard colored paper as listed in Table I were provided by a mill manufacturing those papers. These samples were representative of some of the more intense colors processed by the mill. For consistency in our lab tests, deionized water was used for all processing since mill white water was not available for the tests. One gram samples of the individual papers were water pulped for approximately 30 seconds in a blender on slow speed. The pulp was then dewatered on a 100 mesh screen. These prepared samples were then used in pulp decolorizing tests or base brightness and color measurements.

Bleach Preparation

Hypochlorite used for this test was purchased household-grade hypochlorite with no additives. The assay was taken daily to assure consistent results. Typical assay was 4.6% available chlorine.

The chorine dioxide used in these tests was generated using a bench-scale O1® ClO₂ Process capable of producing up to 50 pounds ClO₂ per day. For reference, a commercial process flowsheet is shown in Figure 1. The process utilizes 35% chloric acid as the only chemical feed. The chloric acid is catalytically reduced to chlorine dioxide according to the reaction:

$$4HClO_3 + 2H_2O \longrightarrow 4ClO_2 + 2O_2 + 4H_2O. \qquad (1)$$

A platinum-group metal oxide catalyst and inert-acid is maintained in the generator system; chloric acid addition controls chlorine dioxide production. Heat and vacuum are utilized to remove the water from the system as steam [12].

For our tests, vapor ClO₂ generated was dissolved in chilled water and used the day of production. The typical chlorine dioxide solution concentration was six grams ClO₂ per liter.

Decolorizing Procedure

The test samples for decolorizing were prepared at 4% consistency, placed into plastic bags, and brought to a reaction temperature of 50°C in a water bath. Samples were then adjusted to an approximate 6.5 pH with dilute H₂SO₄. The appropriate bleaching agent was then added; NaOCl at 3% available chlorine applied to OD pulp and ClO₂ at 1.14%. This provides comparable oxidation capacity for ClO₂ and NaOCl assuming a five electron transfer for ClO₂ going to Cl⁻. Each sample was hand mixed for approximately 15 seconds and then replaced into the water bath. Samples were removed and mixed at ten minute intervals for a total reaction time of 60 minutes.

Brightness Pad formation and Measurement

After the decolorization procedure, each sample was immediately quenched by dilution to 200 ml. total volume and formed into a brightness pad by filtering through a buchner funnel. The brightness pad was dried in a constant temperature/humidity area for one day. TAPPI brightness, and CIE L*, a*, b* measurements were made on each brightness pad using a standardized Technidyne Micro S-5.

Color Removal Index

A color removal index was calculated from the measured L*, a*, and b* values of the base paper and the decolored sample according to the procedures of Sharpe and Lowe [1]:

R_1 represents the distance from the initial color point to perfect colorless point L* = 100, a* = 0, b* = 0 in L*, a*, b* color space; R_2 represents the distance of the decolorized point to perfect colorless point.

$$R_1 = \sqrt{a_1{}^2 + b_1{}^2 + (100 - L_1)^2} \qquad (2)$$

$$R_2 = \sqrt{a_2{}^2 + b_2{}^2 + (100 - L_2)^2} \qquad (3)$$

Following standard geometric relations, the difference in the distance can be represented by ΔR.

$$\Delta R =$$
$$\sqrt{(a_2{}^2 - a_1{}^2) + (b_2{}^2 - b_1{}^2) + \left[(100 - L_2)^2 - (100 - L_1)^2\right]}$$
$$(4)$$

The value of $(\Delta R/R)100$ is then a measure of improvement in color. Sharpe and Lowe utilized $(\Delta R^2/R^2)100$ as their "Dye Removal Index" because they obtained better correlation to a parallel visual evaluation. While arguments can be made for both formulae, the Color Removal Index (percent color removal) data in this paper is $(\Delta R^2/R^2)100$ to allow comparison to other published data.

RESULTS

To effectively pulp the samples in the lab, we required a consistency of 0.5%. Table I illustrates the effect of pulping the paper samples in water and shows the base brightness and color measurements for the papers tested. While there is some decolorization for the individual samples from the "washing" during the preparation of the pulp. However, as shown in the data from Table III, "washing" had no significant effects on the conclusions of the study. Any washing effects we might see in these tests are not as likely to be seen in mill applications because the dyes that are extracted will be maintained in the water going to the decolorizing process.

Table II shows the brightness and color data for the decolorized samples. The charts attached as Figures 2-11 graphically illustrate the results for the individual colored papers.

Visual Evaluation

We did not perform a scientific evaluation of the samples visually. We did have several people qualitatively review the brightness pads of the decolorized samples. There was general agreement that, with the exception of Goldenrod, Green, Nile Green, and Salmon, there was no significant visual difference between the hypochlorite treated samples and the chlorine dioxide treated samples for each color sample.

Brightness

For color removal, we do not recommend brightness alone as a process control scheme. However, since many mills still control their process based primarily on brightness, we provide this analysis for comparison to color removal index.

The typical 1-sigma standard deviation value for the TAPPI brightness measurement for these samples is about ±0.5. Using 1.0 point brightness as a numerically significant difference in brightness, the following apply:

Chlorine dioxide improved brightness better on Canary, Goldenrod, and Nile Green;

Hypochlorite improved brightness better on Blue, Cherry, Green, Lilac, Pink, and Salmon;

Chlorine dioxide and hypochlorite showed comparable brightness improvement on Beige.

Overall, average brightness improvement was comparable using chlorine dioxide or sodium hypochlorite:

Chlorine dioxide resulted in an average brightness of 81.0 ± 2.7;

Hypochlorite resulted in an average brightness of 80.6 ± 7.3.

The average brightness of the starting papers was 40.0.

When considering average brightness values of a decolorizing agent; the standard deviation can be considered to measure how consistently that agent decolorizes a variable colored furnish. As the standard deviation goes down, one can expect that typical performance in a process with mixed colored furnish to be close to the average value. Consistency of performance has more significance as the variability of furnish quality increases: a lower standard deviation implies that the decolorizing agent will likely have more uniform results with a highly variable pulp source.

Based on the brightness evaluation, chlorine dioxide has comparable average brightening capability and will likely have more consistent results than sodium hypochlorite.

Color Removal Index

Table III summarizes the color removal index with reference to the different process steps. The data are presented both including and excluding the effects of "washing" during the pulping process. The discussion considers color removal index using the base paper as a reference.

Taking an absolute difference in the Color Removal Index (based on ΔR^2) of 1.0 as being significant, the following apply:

Chlorine dioxide decolorizes better on: Goldenrod, and Nile Green;

Hypochlorite decolorizes better on: Blue, Lilac, and Salmon

Chlorine dioxide and hypochlorite performed comparably on Beige, Canary, Cherry, Green, and Pink.

Overall, the average decolorizing performance of chlorine dioxide was better than that of hypochlorite:

Average Color Removal Index for chlorine dioxide was 96.2 ± 1.8

Average Color Removal Index for hypochlorite was 94.9 ± 4.5.

Similarly to brightness data, the standard deviation for these average color removal values can be used to measure how consistent the agent will decolorize highly variable furnish. Based on the average color removal evaluation, chlorine dioxide decolorizes equal to or better than sodium hypochlorite and will have more consistent results.

A significant factor contributing to better average performance and lower data variability for chlorine dioxide was its marked superior response on the Goldenrod and Nile Green papers. Both these papers were decolorized dramatically better by chlorine dioxide than by hypochlorite. In the real world of recovered paper, there are some dyes that are considerably more difficult to remove than others; the frequency you see these colors in a furnish may shape the way you design your process. Sharpe and Lowe, in their presentation of information, focused their evaluations and conclusions on the difficult to remove colors [1]. If however, one wants to consider an overall performance for a random-supplied furnish, we recommend that an average color removal index be used for all tested colors.

CONCLUSIONS

1 In a direct laboratory comparison of ten colored paper samples, chlorine dioxide demonstrated equal or superior average color removal as a drop-in replacement for sodium hypochlorite.

2 For most specific-colored paper samples, chlorine dioxide and sodium hypochlorite are both effective color stripping agents and demonstrate similar decolorization. Depending on the individual

color, one agent may be somewhat more responsive than the other.

3 For two particular colored papers, Goldenrod and Nile Green, chlorine dioxide was substantially better at removing color than sodium hypochlorite.

4 Chlorine dioxide is a very efficient and consistent decolorizing agent for colored papers tested.

CONSIDERING A CHLORINE DIOXIDE PROCESS FOR SECONDARY FIBER MILLS

As reviewed above, ClO_2 process effluents, equipment size, and process complexity, may have been issues that, in the past, kept chlorine dioxide from being considered at some secondary fiber mills. Over the last several years new technologies have been developed to solve or minimize those issues. Table IV lists some generalized comments regarding effluent and equipment for several different chlorate-ion based ClO_2 generation technologies. One can review this chart to help consider what technologies will most effectively address individual mill considerations.

As demonstrated in this paper, chlorine dioxide is a very effective decolorizing agent that warrants consideration, especially from those mills who expect highly variable raw material quality and want the maximum potential to produce high brightness pulp or paper.

ACKNOWLEDGMENTS

I would like to express my thanks to Olin Corporation for their support of this work and the diligent efforts of K. M. Newman in running the tests and developing the data presented.

LITERATURE CITED

1. Sharpe, P. E. and Lowe, R. W., "The Bleaching Of Colored Recycled Fibers"' TAPPI Pulping Conference Proceedings, Atlanta, (1993).

2. Kronis, J. D., "Adding Some Color to Your Wastepaper Furnish", TAPPI Pulping Conference Proceedings, Boston, (1992).

3. Darlington, B., Jezerc, G., Magnotta, V,. Naddeo, R., Waller, F., and White-Gaebe, K., "Secondary Fiber Color Stripping: Evaluation of Alternatives", TAPPI Pulping Conference Proceedings, Boston, (1992).

4. Kulikowski, T., Naddeo, R., and Magnotta, V, "Oxidative Cleaning and Bleaching", TAPPI Pulping Conference Proceedings, Orlando, (1991)

5. Cheek, M. C. , A Practical Review of Paper Decolorizing Methods - Present and Future", TAPPI Papermakers Conference Proceedings, (1991).

6. Kolar, J. J., et. al., "Chemical Reaction of Chlorine Dioxide Stages of Pulp Bleaching", Wood Sci. Technol. 17(2):117(1982).

7. McDonough, T. J., and Schwantes, T. A., "The Effect of D Stage Reaction Time on the Characteristics of Whole Effluents and Effluent Fractions from D(EO) Bleaching of Oxygen Delignified Softwood Kraft Pulp", International Bleaching Conference - Papers, Vancouver, (1994).

8. Mendiratta, S. K., Cawlfield, D. W., Ward, L. R., and Breed, D., "Low AOX Process for Bleaching High Kappa Pulps; O1® Delignification "TAPPI Pulping Conference Proceedings, San Diego, (1994).

9.   American Forest & Paper Association, Recovered Paper Deinking Facilities, April 94.

10.   "Market deinked pulp outlook pales as more mills choose to integrate" Paper Recycler, 5(8):1(1994).

11.   Rangamannar, G., and DeFoe, R. J., "Influence of Colored Papers on the Brightness of Ledger Pulps", TAPPI Pulping Conference Proceedings, Atlanta, (1993).

12.   Cawlfield, D. W., Mendiratta, S., K. U. S. Patent 5,342,601, to Olin Corporation, (August 30, 1994).

13.   Owen, D., Perot, P., Harrington, E., and Scribner, H. C., "A Survey of Chlorine Dioxide Generation in the United States", TAPPI Journal 72(11):87(1989).

14.   Kaczur, J. J., Woodard, K. E., Jr., and Rolison, C. J., III, "Emerging Electrochemical Technologies In Producing Chloric Acid For Chlorine Dioxide Generation", AIChE Forest Products Division Symposium Proceedings, , (1993).

15.   "ERCO Chlorine Dioxide Processes" Product Bulletin of Sterling Pulp Chemicals, Ltd., Toronto Ontario Canada M9B 1R1

16.   "SVP-HP™ Technology", Product Bulletin of EKA Nobel, Inc., Marietta, GA 30062

O1® is a registered trademark of Olin Corporation

Table I: Brightness and Color Data of "Colored" Paper Samples

Color	As Received				After Pulping			
	TAPPI Brightness	L*	a*	b*	TAPPI Brightness	L*	a*	b*
Beige *	37.23	84.04	3.80	29.97	37.24	82.69	4.90	27.60
Blue *	72.81	79.94	-11.58	-13.70	72.37	80.42	-11.17	-12.50
Canary	32.97	93.55	-14.44	50.78	33.70	91.44	-12.82	46.28
Cherry	26.14	61.63	45.55	6.05	28.53	63.07	41.87	4.78
Goldenrod *	17.58	84.63	3.99	60.96	22.62	84.33	5.86	50.83
Green *	46.69	81.47	-24.64	14.34	45.59	80.48	-23.80	13.72
Lilac *	55.09	71.10	5.19	-13.30	53.20	70.91	5.21	-11.72
Nile Green	44.44	76.85	-19.17	8.97	44.65	76.69	-18.20	8.32
Pink *	40.74	73.13	34.30	5.31	42.02	73.65	32.88	4.74
Salmon *	26.38	77.62	28.47	32.97	26.47	76.17	28.51	30.32

* Designated as MacBeth Standard on the Paper sheets

Table II: Brightness and Color Data of Decolorized Paper Samples

Color	NaOCl				ClO$_2$			
	TAPPI Brightness	L*	a*	b*	TAPPI Brightness	L*	a*	b*
Beige	82.61	95.73	-2.12	5.83	81.68	95.43	-1.41	5.95
Blue	88.78	96.38	-0.81	2.17	84.33	95.32	0.47	3.61
Canary	78.29	95.58	-2.77	8.93	80.30	95.67	-2.35	7.42
Cherry	79.62	94.22	1.35	5.41	77.41	93.32	1.39	5.47
Goldenrod	63.18	94.71	-5.87	20.59	78.66	95.33	-2.13	8.03
Green	79.98	95.42	-2.52	7.32	78.32	92.49	-4.58	3.48
Lilac	87.34	95.58	0.18	1.78	84.27	94.96	-0.20	2.99
Nile Green	76.99	95.75	-3.09	10.39	82.23	94.71	-1.05	4.22
Pink	86.64	95.48	0.69	2.16	84.16	95.30	-1.04	3.72
Salmon	82.38	94.63	2.00	3.84	78.36	93.56	3.66	4.98

Table III: Color Removal Index for Lab Process Steps

	Wash Color Removal (from Water Pulping)	NaOCl Color Removal after Wash	NaOCl Color Removal including Wash	ClO$_2$ Color Removal after Wash	ClO$_2$ Color Removal including Wash
Beige	7.02	94.77	95.14	94.63	95.01
Blue	8.26	97.22	97.45	94.71	95.15
Canary	15.88	95.51	96.22	96.67	97.20
Cherry	12.39	97.95	98.2	97.56	97.87
Goldenrod	27.84	83.01	87.74	96.83	97.71
Green	1.77	92.88	93.00	92.12	92.26
Lilac	2.71	97.75	97.81	96.6	96.69
Nile Green	4.07	85.64	86.22	95.03	95.23
Pink	6.68	98.58	98.67	97.94	98.08
Salmon	4.10	97.93	98.02	96.54	96.68
Average	9.07	94.12	94.85	95.86	96.19
Std Dev	7.91	5.49	4.49	1.74	1.80

**Table IV: Chlorate Ion Based Chlorine Dioxide Processes --
Generalized Effluent Comments and Equipment Lists**

Basic Raw Material	Reducing Agent	Generator Effluent [12-14]	Typical Major Equipment [12, 15, 16]
$NaClO_3$	SO_2	Spent Sulfuric Acid with Sodium Salts	Sulfuric Acid Storage, Sodium Chlorate Storage, SO_2 Storage and Handling, Purge Air System, Generator, Secondary Generator, Stripper, ClO_2 Absorption Tower, ClO_2 Solution Storage.
	NaCl	Spent Sulfuric Acid with Sodium Salts or Sodium Sesquisulfate or sodium sulfate saltcake depending on process specifics, NaOCl by-product	Sulfur Acid Storage, Sodium Chlorate Storage, Generator/Crystallizer, Reboiler, Dump Tank, Saltcake Filter and Vacuum Unit, Indirect Cooler, ClO_2 Absorption Tower, ClO_2 Solution Storage, Steam Ejector/Condenser, Steam Ejector and Condenser, Cl_2 Absorption Tower, Tailgas Scrubbing Unit.
	HCl	Low level Effluent. Generator is integrated with a Chlorate Production Facility and HCl Burner	Extensive Equipment Because of Integration to Chlorate
	CH_3OH	Sodium Sesquisulfate or sodium sulfate saltcake depending on process specifics	Sulfuric Acid Storage, Sodium Chlorate Storage, Methanol Storage, Generator/Crystallizer, Reboiler, Dump Tank, Saltcake Filter and Vacuum Unit, Indirect Cooler, ClO_2 Absorption Tower, ClO_2 Solution Storage, Vent Scrubber.
	H_2O_2	Sodium sulfate saltcake	Sulfuric Acid Storage, Sodium Chlorate Storage, Hydrogen Peroxide Storage, Generator/Crystallizer, Reboiler, Saltcake Filter and Vacuum Unit, Indirect Cooler, ClO_2 Absorption Tower, ClO_2 Solution Storage, Vent Scrubber.
$HClO_3$	H_2O (catalytic)	Minimal effluent. Periodic Solid Catalyst and acid change-out	Chloric Acid Storage, Generator, Heater, Catalyst Service Unit, Demister, ClO_2 Vacuum/Absorber/Scrubber, Heat Exchanger.

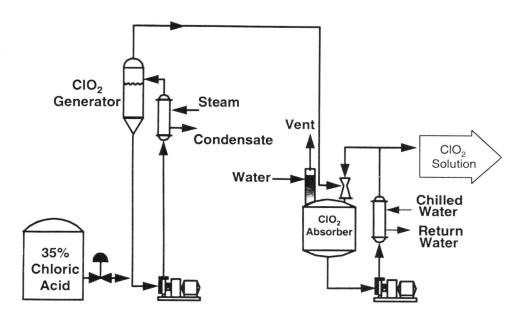

Figure 1 **O1® ClO₂ Solution System Process Diagram**

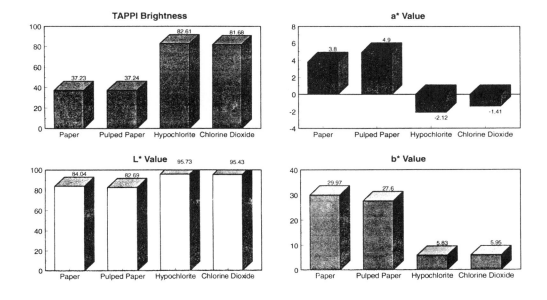

Figure 2 **Chart 1:Decolorization of Beige Paper**

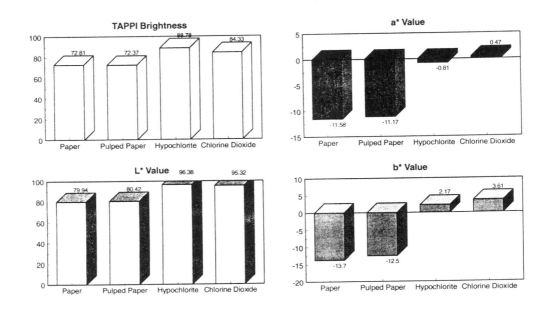

Figure 3 **Chart 2: Decolorization of Blue Paper**

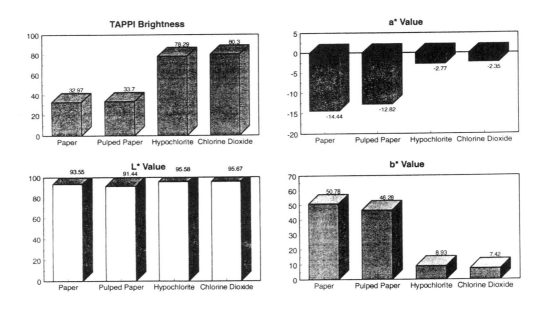

Figure 4 **Chart 3: Decolorization of Canary Paper**

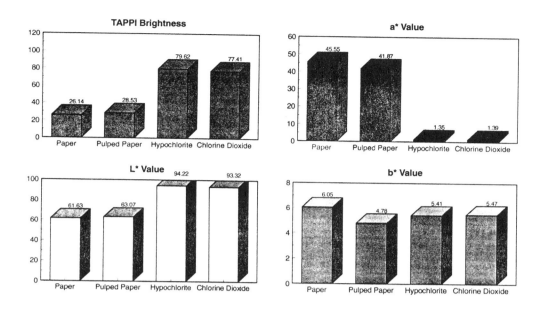

Figure 5 **Chart 4: Decolorization of Cherry Paper**

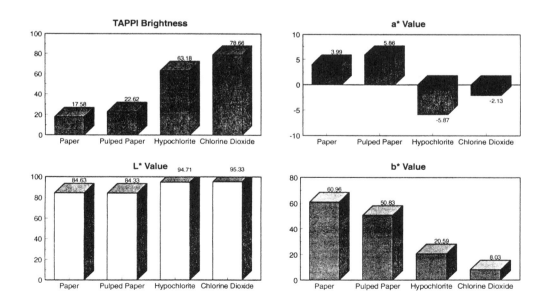

Figure 6 **Chart 5: Decolorization of Goldenrod Paper**

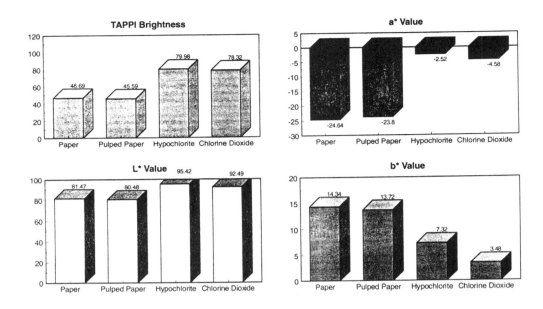

Figure 7 **Chart 6: Decolorization of Green Paper**

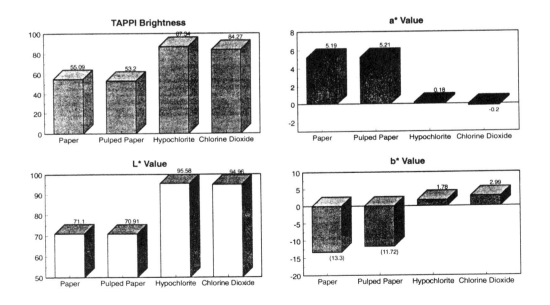

Figure 8 **Chart 7: Decolorization of Lilac Paper**

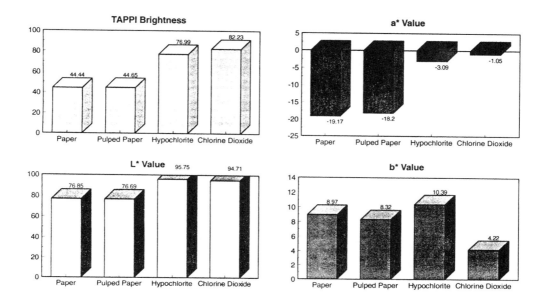

Figure 9 **Chart 8: Decolorization of Nile Green Paper**

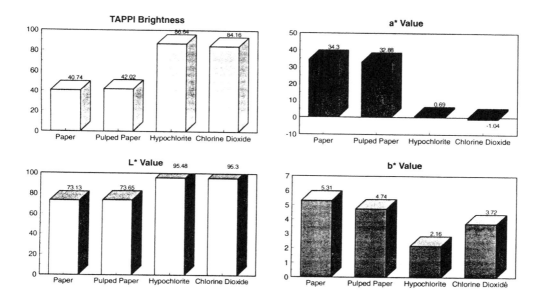

Figure 10 **Chart 9: Decolorization of Pink Paper**

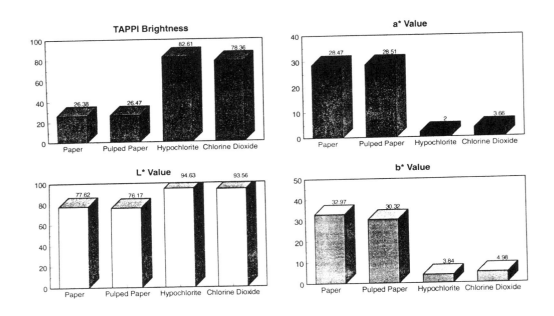

Figure 11 **Chart 10: Decolorization of Salmon Paper**

Hydrodynamic Analysis of Paper Forming

Cyrus K. Aidun and Agnes Kovacs

Institute of Paper Science and Technology, Atlanta, GA 30318

This study focuses on the secondary flows in headboxes as we have reported [25] that secondary flows result in nonuniform fiber orientation and mass formation. We can currently adjust the insert tubes at the tube bank to minimize the cross-flow at the slice and to eliminate the problems associated with these nonuniformities.

Two kinds of secondary flows are distinguished. The first kind is due to the geometric effects and the kinematics. The second kind is generated by the turbulent motion of the fluid. The first kind of secondary motion can occur in laminar as well as turbulent flows. The secondary flow of the second kind (as classified by Prandtl [1]) is caused by the anisotropy of the turbulent flow. Therefore, when secondary flows are important, as in headbox hydrodynamics, the anisotropy of normal Reynolds stresses has to be considered in the analysis. Mean Reynolds stresses can be obtained through direct numerical simulation (DNS) of the evolution of the instantaneous velocity field. However, DNS is not feasible in industrial problems. The standard linear $K - \varepsilon$ model cannot predict secondary flows of the second kind. A non-linear $K - \varepsilon$ method is examined and found capable to account for the anisotropy of the normal Reynolds stresses. This method can correctly predict the inequality of secondary normal Reynolds stresses, however, it introduces further constants in comparison with the linear (standard) $K - \varepsilon$ method.

The present research will also be extended to turbulent flows of the free surface jet past the headbox slice. This part of our work is to investigate the structure of turbulence near the free surface and the effect of free surface on secondary flows. The nonlinear $K - \varepsilon$ method is proposed for the simulation of free surface turbulent flows.

1. INTRODUCTION

A headbox is a converging channel which is used to form a rectangular free-surface jet of water with uniformly dispersed fibers. In order to achieve good paper formation, the fiber flocculation in the jet exiting the headbox must be avoided and the fibers have to be evenly distributed in the cross-machine direction (CD). The present study investigates the characteristics of turbulent flow in low consistency headboxes applied in the pulp and paper industry to educe mechanisms to optimize the flow configuration for most uniform fiber orientation and mass formation. The results from this study apply to low consistency (concentration) fiber suspensions where the effect of the fibers on the secondary flow is insignificant.

In general, the average fiber angle in a strip of paper varies considerably from one side to the other side of the paper machine. Several problems in the board and paper industry are attributed to this nonuniformity in the average fiber orientation. These range from twist/warp problems in the board grades to diagonal curl and cockling (I.M. Hutten (2)) in printing paper.

It is well known that if at a section of the headbox, the liquid jet is not aligned with the forming wire, this would result in nonuniform fiber orientation. There are a number of trivial external reasons for the misalignment of the jet with the wire. These are misalignment of the slice with the wire, nonuniform slice profile, imbalance in the pressure profile at the header (distributor), insert tube plugging, and nonuniform flow into the headbox from the header.

However, it is reported that even if all of these external issues are removed, the fiber orientation will still remain nonuniform with maximum average angles near the sides of the machine.

In this study, we remove all of the obvious external effects and show that the cause of this nonuniformity in fiber orientation is the secondary flows that are generated inside the headbox due to hydrodynamic effects. Secondary flows in a headbox are relatively weak three-dimensional flow patterns that superimpose on the basic or primary two-dimensional flow. These secondary patterns have small velocity components in the cross-machine direction. Although the magnitude of the cross-machine velocity component is relatively small compared to the streamwise velocity, its effect on fiber orientation is significant. Cross flows originating inside the headbox result in nonuniform shear on the wire in the cross-machine direction. Considering that the shear stress on the wire is the main factor determining fiber orientation, the secondary flows inside the headbox have profound influence on the average fiber angle causing nonuniform fiber orientation in the cross-machine direction.

We have identified two kinds of secondary flows in the headbox. The first kind is generated by the geometry and the tubes of a headbox. Examples of secondary flow induced by boundary layers at side walls are present in various hydrodynamic systems (see Aidun, et al. (3) and references). The second kind of cross flow is due to the anisotropy in turbulent Reynolds stresses and this will be discussed further below.

Let us consider a straight rectangular channel where the simple geometry of the channel leads to a fluid flow problem in which the physics of the formation of secondary flows of the second kind can be isolated (see e.g. Prandtl (1), Liggett (4)) from other cross flow generating effects. In this geometric configuration the secondary mean flows are solely generated by the structure of turbulent fluid motion. The relatively weak secondary flow is in a plane normal to the streamwise axis of the channel. Its magnitude is about 1-3% of the main flow. This flow configuration also gives the opportunity to develop and test turbulent closure models from the point of view of the correct/accurate simulation of secondary currents (see e.g. Demuren & Rodi (5), Speziale (6)).

Recently, Huser & Biringer (7) and Gavrilakis (8) have presented direct numerical simulations (DNS) of low-Reynolds number turbulent flows in straight channels. These simulations provide the database from which the turbulent velocity and pressure correlations can be calculated. The computed instantaneous velocity field near the channel wall captures the bursting events also observed in experiments (see e.g. Gessner & Jones (9), Melling & Whitelaw (10), Wei & Willmarth (11)). Mean flow streamwise velocity streamlines and secondary velocity distributions have been obtained by averaging the flow field in the streamwise direction, and in time. Huser & Biringer (7) point out that the ejection structures produced during bursting events create streamwise vortices. Near the corners, the reduced mean shear prohibits the occurrence of ejections while there are strong ejections along the walls away from the corners. This distribution of ejections is the major contributor to the anisotropy of the normal Reynolds stresses, and it generates the mean secondary circulations carrying streamwise momentum from the core of the channel toward the corners. They also observed that there is a nonlinear interaction between simultaneous ejections produced along perpendicular walls near a corner. This interaction results in the redistribution of turbulent intensities there.

To simulate flow problems of technological interest with DNS is beyond the scope of the presently available computers. For example, to achieve sufficient spatial resolution for the turbulent channel flow Gavrilakis (8) had to employ 16.1 million grid nodes and more than 60 days on a CRAY-2 for one run. Therefore, one has to rely on a turbulence model that can correctly account for the anisotropies in more realistic computational time (on the order of hours of CPU time). Speziale (6) evaluates different turbulent closure models and suggests the application of the two-equation nonlinear $K - \varepsilon$ method for engineering calculations. The advantage of this method compared to the linear (standard) $K - \varepsilon$ method is that it more accurately predicts the turbulent channel flows, and consequently, the turbulent secondary flows. Its derivation is based on an asymptotic expansion subject to the constraints of dimensional and tensorial invariance and realizability, as detailed by Speziale (12). This model obtains the turbulent

kinetic energy K and dissipation rate ε from a modeled version of their transport equations (see Speziale (12) and Hanjalic & Launder (13)) which are of the same form as the ones used in the linear $K - \varepsilon$ method. The closure formulation for the Reynolds stress tensor τ^t takes a simple nonlinear representation introducing new terms quadratic in the mean velocity gradients. This formulation is similar to the constitutive equation of dilute polymers and contains two more constants in comparison with the linear model. Speziale (12) concludes that future research is needed to obtain a more detailed picture of the turbulence structure in rectangular channels predicted by the nonlinear model.

The non-linear $K - \varepsilon$ method has been recently applied by Colombini (14) in the linear stability analysis of the formation of longitudinal ridges. In straight infinitely wide channel, the free surface turbulent flow over a deformable/erodible bed is unstable with respect to transverse disturbances with a wavelength of the order of the flow depth. The nonlinear $K - \varepsilon$ model has proven to be successful in modeling the turbulence-driven cellular secondary motions which are directed to amplify the bed perturbations. The interaction of the flow and the erodible bed thus leads to the formation of longitudinal ridges even in the absence of side walls. Secondary currents in straight channel free surface flows of different aspect ratio are experimentally studied by Nezu et.al (15). They address the initiation and maintenance mechanisms of cellular secondary currents in straight wide channel with flat solid bed and conclude that secondary currents appear only near the side walls. Also, if the ratio of width to depth (B/h) is greater than 4, cellular secondary flows are not produced in the central region of the channel. The numerical simulations of Naot & Rodi (16) are in agreement with the findings of Nezu et al. (15). The present work will systematically evaluate the effect of aspect ratio both in confined and free surface flows.

Analysis of the secondary flows and their effects on fiber orientation is considered in this paper. In the following sections, the governing equations (section 2) and the difficulties in obtaining a numerical solution (section 3) are outlined. These are then followed by applications to headbox hydrodynamics focusing on the secondary flows of the first and second kind in sections 4 and 5, respectively. The study concludes with a brief summary of present results and directions for future work (section 6).

2. GOVERNING FLUID FLOW EQUATIONS

The flow of an incompressible and homogenous viscous fluid is governed by the momentum conservation and continuity equations which are

$$\rho(\frac{\partial u}{\partial t} + u \bullet \nabla u) = -\nabla p + \rho g + \nabla \bullet \tau \tag{1a}$$

$$\nabla \bullet u = 0 \tag{1b}$$

where, $u = u_i = (u, v, w)$ denotes the instantaneous fluid velocity vector, p is the pressure, g is the gravitational acceleration or body force per unit mass, ρ is the density and τ represents the fluid stress tensor. For a Newtonian fluid with constant viscosity, the last term in the momentum conservation equation is given by

$$\nabla \bullet \tau = \mu \nabla^2 u \tag{2}$$

where, $\mu(= \nu \cdot \rho)$ is the dynamic viscosity of the fluid.

In a turbulent flow the velocity and pressure field can be decomposed into ensemble mean and fluctuating parts, respectively

$$u = \bar{u} + u'$$
$$p = \bar{p} + p' \tag{3}$$

where, the overbar denotes the ensemble mean and the prime denotes the fluctuating components. Figure 1 shows the mean and fluctuating velocity components in time for steady and unsteady flows, respectively. After substituting (3) into (1) and averaging (1) in time the governing equation of a turbulent flow can be written as follows:

$$\rho(\frac{\partial \bar{u}}{\partial t} + \bar{u} \bullet \nabla \bar{u}) = -\nabla \bar{p} + \rho g + \nabla \bullet \tau \tag{4a}$$
$$\nabla \bullet \bar{u} = 0 \tag{4b}$$

In (4a) the stress tensor τ includes both the viscous and turbulent Reynolds stress tensors, such that

$$\nabla \bullet \tau = \mu \nabla^2 \bar{u} + \nabla \bullet \tau^t \tag{5}$$

where the components of the Reynolds stress tensor (see e.g. Hinze (17)) τ^t are given by

$$\tau^t{}_{ij} = -\rho \overline{u'_i u'_j} \tag{6}$$

The Reynolds stress tensor τ^t introduces additional unknowns for a turbulent flow problem governed by (4). To describe the mean velocity and pressure fields a closure formulation is needed which relates the components of the Reynolds stress tensor to the mean flow velocity or velocity gradients. Without a closure formulation, theoretically the Navier-Stokes equations (i.e. (1) combined with (2)) can be solved (via DNS) to obtain the instantaneous velocity and pressure fields. However, this task demands a very fine space discretization which is still not a practical approach for many industrial problems.

3. NUMERICAL METHOD

To calculate secondary flows of the first kind (in section 4), several different models can be applied for closure of the averaged momentum equation (4a). The most important among these are the standard/linear $K - \varepsilon$ model, the anisotropic $K - \varepsilon$ model and the RNG $K - \varepsilon$ formulation.

The numerical method to obtain the second kind of secondary currents in confined and free surface flows should consider the anisotropy of the turbulent flow field. The most promising method for these calculations is the nonlinear $K - \varepsilon$ model as explained in section 5 & by Speziale (12).

A numerical solution of the governing equations is based on a space and time discretization of these transient partial differential equations. Due to nonlinearity and complex interdependence of the variables the solution is always an iterative procedure. Computationally the calculation of secondary flows of the second kind is much more difficult than simulation of secondary flows of the first kind. In our opinion the reason for this difficulty is embedded in the calculation of the pressure field and in the way the boundary conditions at the wall are prescribed. Our experience with the time-splitting method of McKibben & Aidun (18 and 19) suggests the following problems.

For turbulent flows, the logarithmic law of the wall is widely used in the prescription of a velocity boundary condition at walls. The law of the wall gives a boundary condition not at the wall but at a point outside the viscous sublayer where the logarithmic law of the wall prevails. The velocity at the sublayer is given by

$$\vec{U}_w = U_\tau \frac{1}{\kappa} \ell n(E \frac{yU_\tau}{\nu}) \frac{\vec{\tau}_b}{|\vec{\tau}_b|} \tag{7}$$

where, $\vec{\tau}_b$ is the wall shear stress, $U_\tau (= \sqrt{|\vec{\tau}_b|/\rho})$ is the resultant friction velocity, y is the distance from the wall, κ is the von Karman constant and E is the roughness parameter. For a developing turbulent flow in a straight duct, the resultant velocity $\vec{U}_w$ is tangential to the wall and has a streamwise, as well as, a transverse component. The velocity boundary condition given by (7) changes along the wall according to the flow conditions near the wall. Without a normal component (or with a zero normal component), it is obvious that this velocity boundary condition does not satisfy continuity on the boundary of the computational domain. In this case, such a solution method has to be chosen which does not require a divergence free velocity boundary condition. Otherwise, the problem formulation is ill-posed (see also Gresho (20)).

In some numerical methods, the calculation of the pressure field is based on the solution of a pressure Poisson equation. Application of a central difference scheme for the space discretization of the pressure Poisson equation leads to an ill-conditioned coefficient matrix (see also Huser and Biringer (22)). In case of a high Re number developing turbulent channel flow, the streamwise pressure gradient is small i.e. dp/dx is proportional to 1/Re, and the cross-flow pressure gradients are even smaller. Among these conditions, the iterative solution of the discretized pressure Poisson equation is not always convergent.

The finite element method available in a fluid dynamics analysis package (FIDAP, Engelman et al., (22)) is used to solve the standard (linear) $K - \varepsilon$ model to obtain the secondary flows of the first kind presented in this paper for confined flow in a headbox. The turbulence modeling enhancements in FIDAP 7.5 include the nonlinear $K - \varepsilon$ model and the RNG $K - \varepsilon$ formulation. We are currently investigating the capability of these models and numerical solutions to simulate secondary flows of the second kind.

4. HEADBOX SECONDARY FLOWS DUE TO SIDE WALLS

In this section we focus on the secondary flow of the first kind which is the main cause of nonuniform fiber orientation in CD. A full scale headbox is considered in this work. The specifications of the headbox (see also Figures 2 and 3) are listed below:

TABLE 1. Headbox parameters and flow conditions

Parameters	Dimensional	Dimensionless
Headbox width	300 Inches	20
Inlet height	15 Inches	1
Total flow rate	45,000 gal/min	
Slice opening, B	1.5 Inches	0.1
Average jet velocity	2,400 ft/min	10
No vanes		
No side ejection		

Since the governing equations are solved in nondimensional form, the results are also presented in the same nondimensional units. The length scale is the size of the box inlet and the velocity scale is the inlet velocity of the fluid into the box. Table 2 can be used to convert the dimensionless numbers in the figures to dimensional quantities for the case of 45,000 gallons/minute total flow rate through the headbox and a 1.5 inch slice opening. In this case, the average forming jet speed will be 2,400 feet/minute and the machine speed can be slightly higher or lower depending on the rush/drag mode of operation.

Since the boundary conditions and the geometry considered in this study is symmetric with respect to the Z-MD plane of the headbox, we present the results for half of the box. The result for the full box is simply a mirror image projection for the other half of the box.

TABLE 2. Conversion factors for nondimensional to dimensional units

To convert dimensionless variable	to dimension	for the case of 45,000 gal/min and 1.5" slice, multiply by
length	m (ft)	0.381 (1.25)
velocity	m/s (ft/min)	1.22 (240)
pressure	N/m^2 (psi)	1488 (0.216)

Uniform Inflow

First, the case with uniform pressure at the inlet to the box is considered. The resulting pressure contour lines in the symmetry plane are presented in Figure 4. The contour plots show that, as expected, pressure decreases as the fluid is accelerated through the box. The pressure contour lines become denser near the outflow indicating sharper decrease in pressure (larger pressure gradient) due to the rapid velocity increase toward the channel exit, as illustrated in the velocity vector plot in Figure 5. These plots only show a cross-section of the headbox. To learn more about the global features of the flow, it is necessary to examine the pressure variations in CD.

To investigate the pressure distribution in the headbox, the pressure contour plots on the inner surface are provided in Figure 6a. This figure presents a three-dimensional view of pressure on the boundaries of the headbox. Figure 6b shows the pressure contours (isobars) in a horizontal plane located in the middle of the slice. Although, the boundary conditions are uniform in CD, the isobars demonstrate that the variation in the pressure field is three-dimensional. That is the pressure changes in both the cross-machine as well as the machine direction.

For quantitative information, the magnitude of the pressure variation at various levels of the slice, presented in Figure 6c, can be compared to the plot of the machine direction (MD) pressure drop, shown in Figure 6d. The pressure variation in CD is primarily due to the retardation of velocity near the sidewall. Since our objective is to study the generation and features of cross flows - because of their effects on fiber orientation - it is important to examine the influence of CD pressure variation on the flow. In other words, does the CD pressure gradient generate finite cross-flow?

To address this question, it is necessary to examine the y-component (or cross-machine, CD, component) of velocity, v, inside the headbox. The contour plots of v, shown in Figure 7, clearly indicate a local minimum near the sidewall. The value of this local minimum is relatively small compared to the positive value of the cross-flow velocity. This can also be seen by Figure 7a which illustrates the distribution of the y-component of velocity in the slice. The relative magnitude of the cross flow velocity components is the critical factor in generation of nonuniform fiber orientation.

Figures 8 and 9 show the MD and CD components of velocity along a line in the middle of the slice, respectively. It is clear from these figures that in addition to the local minimum near the sidewall, there is also a positive cross-flow which reaches a maximum at about 3.3 ft (1 m) from the sidewall of the headbox. Comparing the x- and y-components of velocity, it can be shown that the maximum cross-flow is about 1% of the x-component of velocity. The cross-flow is generated due to the converging section of the headbox in the x-z plane bounded by the vertical sidewalls. The boundary layer at the vertical sidewall retards the flow in the streamwise direction and thus, by mass conservation, the flow is forced to move in the CD.

These results emphasize that even when a perfect pressure and flow rate distribution exist in the tube bank, the flow inside the headbox will be three-dimensional because of the secondary flows. Furthermore, the results show the location of the maximum cross-flow.

The formation and flocculation is partly controlled by turbulent flow characteristics. The computed turbulent flow characteristics inside the headbox are plotted in Figure 10. Figure 10c, b, and a present three-dimensional views of the turbulent kinetic energy, K, dissipation, ε, and turbulent viscosity, μ_t, in the headbox, respectively. These figures show an almost uniform turbulent intensity in the headbox. The only regions with large variations in turbulent kinetic energy, dissipation, and viscosity are near the solid walls of the converging channel. Here, as expected, there are large velocity gradients resulting in a more intensive turbulent energy production and dissipation.

The Influence of Nonuniform Inflow on Cross-Flow at the Slice

The effect of nonuniform influx at the inlet to the headbox on the cross-flow at the slice is examined by dividing the inlet to three sections as shown in Figure 11. Figure 12 presents the cross-flow at the slice when the flux in section B is $\pm 10\%$ of the flux in region A. The results show that the flux into the headbox has significant effect on the cross-flow at the slice. This result is consistent with the physical explanation of the nonuniform CD velocity by the retardation of the flow due to the sidewall.

These results demonstrate that by computationally optimizing the influx, we are able to substantially reduce CD flow and fiber disorientation.

5. SECONDARY FLOWS DUE TO TURBULENCE ANISOTROPY

Origin of Secondary Flows of the Second Kind

To understand the formation of secondary currents in straight rectangular channels the governing equations are transformed into a vorticity-stream function formulation. This demonstrates the condition for the existence of a vorticity vector in the axial (main) flow direction. The geometry of a rectangular channel is illustrated in Figure 13.

Taking the x-direction to be the axial streamwise flow direction and assuming that the steady flow does not change in this direction, the following set of equations is obtained:

$$\rho(\bar{v}\frac{\partial \bar{u}}{\partial y} + \bar{w}\frac{\partial \bar{u}}{\partial z}) = -\frac{\partial \bar{p}}{\partial x} + \rho g_x + \mu \nabla^2 \bar{u} +$$

$$\frac{\partial \tau^t_{zx}}{\partial z} + \frac{\partial \tau^t_{yx}}{\partial y} \tag{8a}$$

$$\rho(\bar{v}\frac{\partial \omega_x}{\partial y} + \bar{w}\frac{\partial \omega_x}{\partial z}) = \mu \nabla^2 \omega_x + \frac{\partial^2(\tau^t_{yy} - \tau^t_{zz})}{\partial y \partial z}$$

$$+\frac{\partial^2 \tau^t_{zy}}{\partial z^2} - \frac{\partial^2 \tau^t_{zy}}{\partial y^2} \tag{8b}$$

$$\nabla^2 \psi = \omega_x \tag{8c}$$

$$\bar{v} = \frac{\partial \psi}{\partial z}$$

$$\bar{w} = -\frac{\partial \psi}{\partial y} \tag{8d}$$

The derivation of equation (8) can be found in e.g. Speziale (24). In (7) ω_x is the axial vorticity, and ψ denotes the stream function.

On the right hand side of the vorticity equation (8b) the terms formed from the Reynolds stress components represent the source term for vorticity production. If the difference of the normal Reynolds stresses is equal to zero, i.e. $\tau'_{yy} = \tau'_{zz}$, then vorticity is not generated resulting in $\omega_x = \psi = \bar{v} = \bar{w} = 0$, in other words no secondary flow can exist in the duct. However, this would be a contradiction with the experimental observations (see e.g. Perkins (24)). In order to numerically model this flow phenomena the turbulent closure model has to be capable of predicting the anisotropy of turbulent normal stresses.

Figure 14 presents the instantaneous velocity field; $u = u_i = (u, v, w)$ in a straight duct, calculated via DNS by Huser & Biringer (7). Figure 14a shows the streamlines of the main flow and Figure 14b illustrates the instantaneous secondary flow vectors. Averaging the instantaneous streamlines of the main flow (i.e. u) and the secondary velocity vector field (i.e. v and w) in time and along the duct axis the mean flow quantities are obtained. These are displayed in Figure 15. Figure 15a shows the mean (i.e. $\bar{u}$) streamwise flow. Due to the secondary flow circulations directed from the center of the duct toward the corners, these streamlines bulge along the corner bisectors. The mean secondary velocity field (i.e. $\bar{v}, \bar{w}$) causing this bulging is presented in Figure 15b..

Numerical Modeling with the Nonlinear $K - \varepsilon$ Method

In closing equations (4) and (5) the nonlinear $K - \varepsilon$ method provides a formulation which is expected to simulate secondary flow currents. This formulation is based on the solution of two more transport equations which are identical with those of the standard (linear) $K - \varepsilon$ model.

The version of these equations in the present study is taken from Speziale (12). The transport of turbulent kinetic energy K and dissipation rate ε is described by

$$\frac{dK}{dt} = \frac{1}{\rho}\tau^t_{ij}\frac{\partial \bar{u}_i}{\partial x_j} +$$

$$C_1\frac{\partial}{\partial x_i}\{\frac{K}{\rho^2\varepsilon}(\tau^t_{jm}\frac{\partial \tau^t_{ij}}{\partial x_m} - \rho\tau^t_{ij}\frac{\partial K}{\partial x_j})\} - \varepsilon \qquad (9)$$

and

$$\frac{d\varepsilon}{dt} = -\frac{C_2}{\rho}\frac{\partial}{\partial x_i}(\frac{K}{\varepsilon}\tau^t_{ij}\frac{\partial \varepsilon}{\partial x_j}) + C_3\frac{\varepsilon}{\rho K}\tau^t_{ij}\frac{\partial \bar{u}_i}{\partial x_j}$$

$$-C_4\frac{\varepsilon^2}{K} \qquad (10)$$

respectively. $C_1, \ldots, C_4$ are dimensionless constants.

In the lowest order nonlinear $K - \varepsilon$ model the shear stress is calculated (see Speziale (12)) from

$$\tau^t_{ij} = -\frac{2}{3}\rho K\delta_{ij} + \rho K^{\frac{1}{2}}\ell\bar{D}_{ij} +$$

$$C_D\rho\ell^2(\bar{D}_{im}\bar{D}_{mj} - \frac{1}{3}\bar{D}_{mn}\bar{D}_{mn}\delta_{ij}) + \qquad (11a)$$

$$C_E\rho\ell^2(\tilde{D}_{ij} - \frac{1}{3}\tilde{D}_{mm}\delta_{ij})$$

where

$$\ell = C\frac{K^{\frac{3}{2}}}{\varepsilon} \quad , \quad \bar{D}_{ij} = \frac{1}{2}(\frac{\partial \bar{u}_i}{\partial x_j} + \frac{\partial \bar{u}_j}{\partial x_i}) \qquad (11b,c)$$

and $\tilde{D}_{ij} = \frac{\partial \bar{D}_{ij}}{\partial t} + \bar{u}\bullet\nabla\bar{D}_{ij} - \frac{\partial \bar{u}_i}{\partial x_k}\bar{D}_{kj} - \frac{\partial \bar{u}_j}{\partial x_k}\bar{D}_{ki}$ (11d)

In equation (11) further constants (i.e. C_D, C_E) are introduced in comparison to the linear $K - \varepsilon$ method. These parameters have to be calibrated with the help of experimental (or DNS) results.

Considering only the first two terms on the right hand side of (11a) the shear stress formulation of the linear $K - \varepsilon$ method is obtained. With this in mind it can be noted that the linear $K - \varepsilon$ model predicts that

$$\tau^t_{zz} = \tau^t_{yy} = \tau^t_{xx} = -\frac{2}{3}\rho K \qquad (12)$$

for equation (8b), consequently vorticity is not generated by the linear formulation.

In contrast to the linear model the nonlinear method yields

$$\tau^t_{zz} \cong -\frac{2}{3}\rho K + \frac{1}{4}C_D\rho\ell^2(\frac{\partial \bar{u}}{\partial z})^2 \qquad (13a)$$

$$\tau^t_{yy} \cong -\frac{2}{3}\rho K + \frac{1}{4}C_D\rho\ell^2(\frac{\partial \bar{u}}{\partial y})^2 \qquad (13b)$$

as explained by Speziale (12). Equation (13) satisfies the necessary condition for the development of secondary flows (i.e. $\tau^t_{yy} \neq \tau^t_{zz}$). This justifies the choice of the nonlinear $K - \varepsilon$ method for the study of secondary flows of the second kind.

The simultaneous solution of (9) to (11) with (4) provides the turbulent mean velocity and pressure fields. Figure 16 displays the secondary flow streamlines calculated by a simplified form of the nonlinear $K - \varepsilon$ method (see Speziale (12)).

6.   SUMMARY

In principle, secondary flow in a hydrodynamic system is defined as a weak stream with a more complex flow pattern which is superimposed on a more simple base or primary flow pattern. In a headbox, the base flow is the two-dimensional flow pattern with zero velocity component in the cross-machine direction. The secondary flows are relatively weak three-dimensional flow patterns that are superimposed on the primary flow. The result is a three-dimensional flow pattern. The secondary flows that are important in this study are of two kinds. The first kind is the secondary flow induced by the curvature in streamlines in the developing flow inside the headbox and the transverse velocity that is required to satisfy the continuity condition. The second kind of secondary flow that is very important in headbox hydrodynamics is caused by the anisotropic turbulent flow.

We have identified two types of secondary flow inside the converging section of the headbox. These secondary flows each result in nonuniform cross-flows in the headbox and at the slice. The secondary flow of the first kind is due to the flow retardation at the side walls. It generates cross flows at the slice resulting in a section of the forming jet to be misaligned with the wire. The nonuniform shear due to this misalignment results in a nonuniform fiber orientation. The effects of the secondary flows of the second kind are not well established yet. We believe that the cross streams due to the turbulent anisotropy results in more local nonuniformities in CD as well as Z, streamwise, direction. This results in nonuniform fiber orientation in the Z direction.

We can currently adjust the insert tubes at the tube bank to minimize the cross-flow at the slice and to eliminate the problems associated with nonuniform fiber orientation. We have used this approach to evaluate the hydrodynamics of a commercial headbox with the objective of optimizing the influx to achieve a more uniform fiber orientation. The optimized influx profile was obtained computationally. The location of the insert tubes were adjusted to achieve the same influx profile obtained computationally. During a shutdown period, the insert tubes at the tube bank were adjusted accordingly with notable improvement in the fiber orientation even at low rush/drag ratios.

The only means of obtaining the secondary flows of the second kind are by direct numerical solution of the full Navier-Stokes equations. This is very time consuming and it is not practical for engineering applications. We are extending this work to apply a nonlinear $K - \varepsilon$ model for computation of the secondary flows of the second kind in irregular geometries.

REFERENCES

1. Prandtl, L., in English: *NACA Tech. Memo.* 435, 62 (1926).

2. Hutten, I. M., "Paper Machine Evaluation by Fiber Orientation Profile Analysis", *Proceedings of the Nonwovens Conference*, (1993).

3. Aidun, C. K., Triantafillopoulos, N. G., and Benson, J. D., "Global Stability of a Lid-Driven Cavity with Throughflow: Flow Visualization Studies", *Phys. Fluid A*, 3: 2081 (1991).

4. Liggett, J. A., *Fluid Mechanics*, Second edition, McGraw-Hill, Inc., New York, 1994, p. 256.

5. Demuren, A. O., and Rodi, W., "Calculation of Turbulence-Driven Secondary Motion in Non-Circular Ducts", *J.Fluid Mech.*, 140: 189 (1984).

6. Speziale, C. G., "Analytical Methods for the Development of Reynolds-Stress Closures in Turbulence", *Annu.Rev.Fluid Mech.*, 23: 107 (1991).

7. Huser, A., and Biringer, S., "Direct Numerical Simulation of Turbulent Flow in a Square Duct", *J.Fluid Mech.*, 257: 65 (1993).

8. Gavrilakis, S., "Numerical Simulation of Low-Reynolds-Number Turbulent Flow Through a Straight Square Duct", *J.Fluid Mech.*, 244: 101 (1992).

9. Gessner, B. F., and Jones, J. B., "On Some Aspects of Fully Developed Turbulent Flow in Rectangular Channels", *J.Fluid Mech.*, 23: 689 (1965).

10. Melling, A., and Whitelaw, J. H., "Turbulent Flow in a Rectangular Duct", *J.Fluid Mech.*, 78: 289 (1976).

11. Wei, T., and Willmarth, W. W., "Reynolds-Number Effects on the Structure of a Turbulent Channel Flow", *J.Fluid Mech.*, 204: 57 (1989).

12. Speziale, C. G., "On nonlinear K-l and $K - \varepsilon$ Models of Turbulence", *J.Fluid Mech.*, 178: 459 (1987).

13. Hanjalic, K., and Launder, B. E., "A Reynolds Stress Model of Turbulence and its Application to Thin Shear Flows", *J.Fluid Mech.*, 52: 609 (1972).

14. Colombini, M., "Turbulence -Driven Secondary Flows and Formation of Sand Ridges", *J.Fluid Mech.*, 254: 701 (1993).

15. Nezu, I., Nakagawa, H., and Tominaga, A., "Secondary Currents in Straight Channel Flow and the Relation to Its Aspect Ratio", *Turbulent Shear Flows IV.*, Springer-Verlag, New York, 1985, pp. 246-260.

16. Naot, D., and Rodi, W., "Calculation of Secondary Currents in Channel Flow", *ASCE,* 108 (HY8): 948 (1982).

17. Hinze, J. O., *Turbulence*, McGraw-Hill, Inc., New York, 1975

18. McKibben, J. F., and Aidun, C. K., "Extension of the Volume-of-Fluid Method for Analysis of Free-surface Viscous Flow in an Ideal Gas", to appear in *Int.J. Num. Methods in Fluids*, (1995)

19. McKibben, J. F., and Aidun, C. K., "Computational Analysis of Free Surface Flows", *Tappi J.*, (1994).

20. Gresho, P. M., "On the Theory of Semi-implicit Projection Methods for Viscous Incompressible Flow and its Implementation via a Finite Element Method that also Introduces a Nearly Consistent Mass Matrix. Part 1: Theory", *J.Fluid Mech.*, 11: 587 (1990)

21. Huser, A., and Biringer, S., "Calculation of Two-Dimensional Shear-Driven Cavity Flows at High Reynolds Number", *Int.J. Num. Methods in Fluids*, 14: 1087 (1992).

22. Engelman, M. S., "FIDAP: fluid dynamics analysis package", *Fluid Dynamics International, Inc.*, 7.5 (1995).

23. Speziale, C. G., "The Dissipation Rate Correlation and Turbulent Secondary Flows in Noncircular Ducts", *Transactions of the ASME*, 108: 118 (1986).

24. Perkins, H. J., "The Formation of Streamwise Vorticity in Turbulent Flow", *J.Fluid Mech.*, 44: 721 (1970).

25. Aidun, C. K., Kovacs A., "Hydrodynamics of the Forming Section: The Origin of Nonuniform Fiber Orientation", *Proceedings of the 1994 TAPPI Engineering Conference*, (1994).

ACKNOWLEDGMENTS

This study has been supported by the National Science Foundation's Young Investigator Award (CKA) under grant CTS-9258667 and by industrial matching contributions. The computations are conducted, in part, using the Cornell National Supercomputer Facility, which is funded, in part, by the National Science Foundation, New York State, and IBM Corporation. We appreciate the assistance provided by Barbara Ericson in computer system administration and graphics.

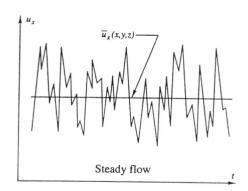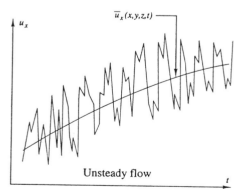

Figure 1. Fluctuating and mean velocity flow components in steady and unsteady flows (from Liggett (4)).

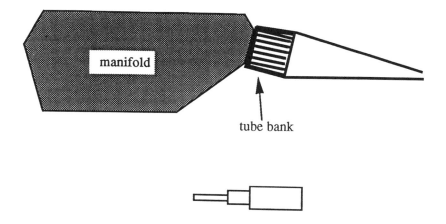

Figure 2. Schematic of the headbox and an individual tube.

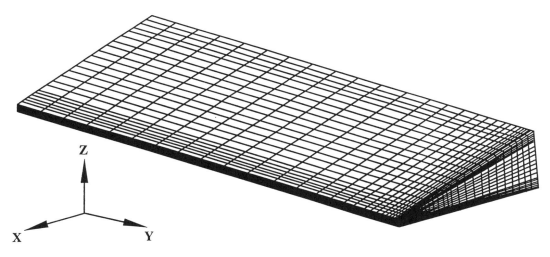

Figure 3. The geometry and the computational grid system for the headbox.

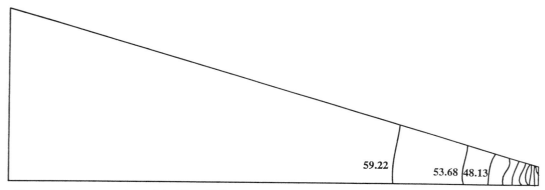

Figure 4. Pressure contour plot at the middle cross–section/symmetry plane.

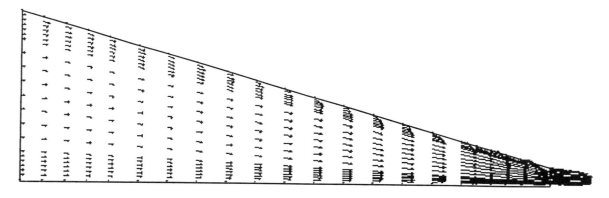

Figure 5. Velocity vector plot at the middle cross–section/symmetry plane.

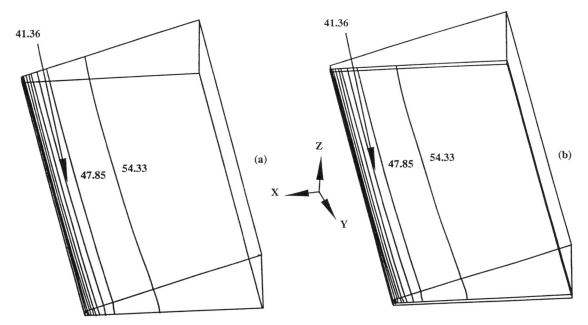

Figure 6. (a) Pressure contour plot on the boundaries of the headbox, (b) Top view of the pressure contour plot at the horizontal plane intersecting the middle of the slice.

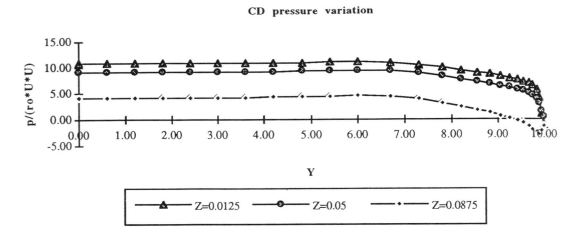

Figure 6(c). CD pressure variation in the headbox, at the slice.

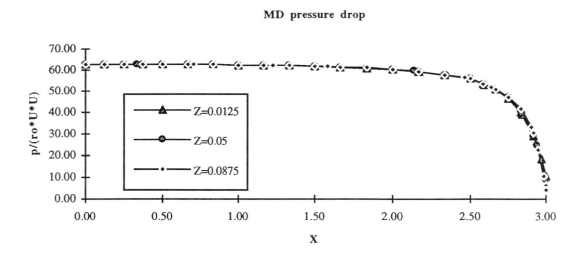

Figure 6(d). MD pressure drop along the axis of symmetry.

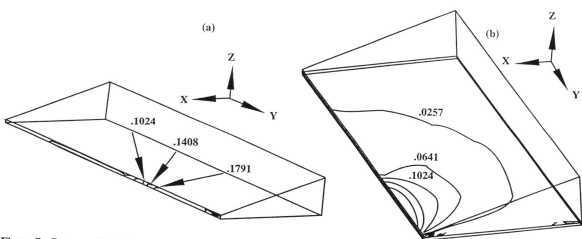

Figure 7. Contour plot of the y–component of fluid velocity in cross–machine direction inside the headbox.
(a) at the slice, and
(b) top–view of the horizontal plane intersecting the middle of the slice.

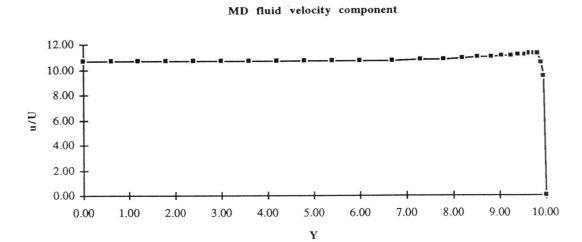

Figure 8. The x-component (MD) of fluid velocity, u, at the middle of the slice.

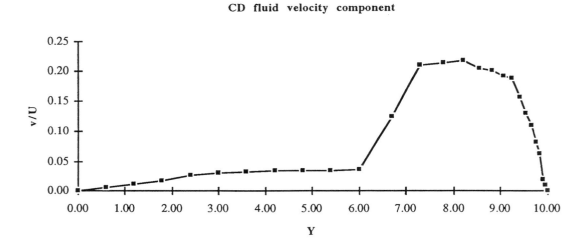

Figure 9. The y-component (CD) of fluid velocity, v, at the middle of the slice.

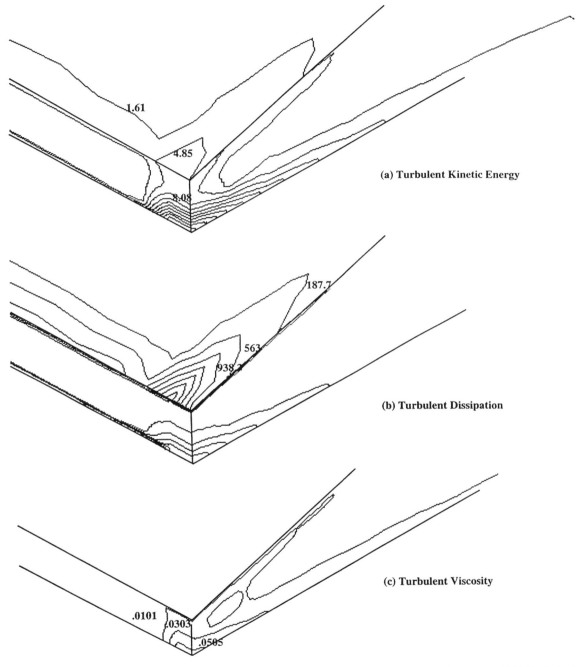

1.61

4.85

8.08

(a) Turbulent Kinetic Energy

187.7

563

938

(b) Turbulent Dissipation

(c) Turbulent Viscosity

.0101

.0303

.0505

Figure 10. Three–dimensional view of (a) Turbulent kinetic energy, (b) Turbulent dissapation rate, and (c) Turbulent (eddy) viscosity.

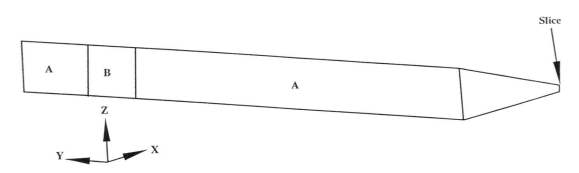

Figure 11. Schematic of regions showing variation in influx profile.

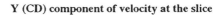

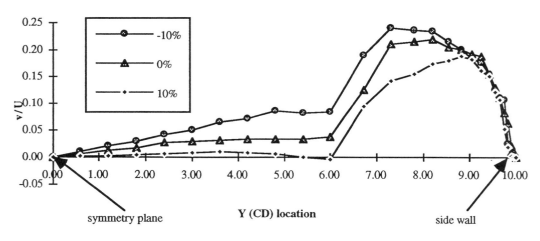

Figure 12. Variation of the cross-machine direction velocity profile across the headbox.

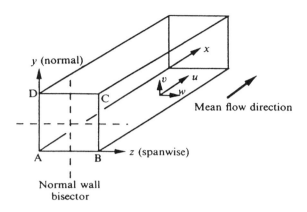

Figure 13. Geometry of a straight rectangular duct (from Gavrilakis (8)).

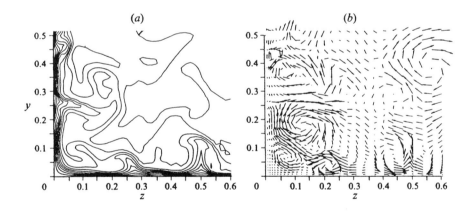

Figure 14. Instantaneous velocity field in the lower left corner of a straight duct.
(a) Main flow.
(b) Secondary velocity field (from Huser & Biringer (7)).

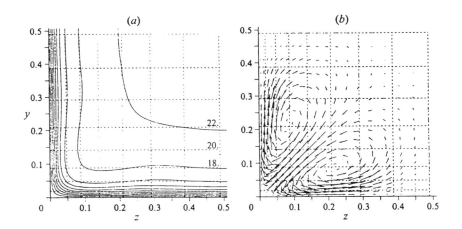

Figure 15. Ensemble mean velocity field in the lower left corner of a straight duct.
(a) Mean main flow.
(b) Mean secondary velocity field (from Huser & Biringer (7)).

Figure 16. Mean secondary flow streamlines (from Speziale (12)).

A New Concept of Basis Weight Profiling for Paper Machine Headboxes

J.A. Shands, C.L. Sanford, and T.D. Rogers

Beloit Corporation, Beloit, WI

The primary function of a paper machine headbox is to distribute the pulp suspension uniformly across the width of the machine. Cross machine basis weight uniformity is critical for paper properties as well as for paper machine and converting runnability. Conventional means for controlling cross machine basis weight profiles is slice lip bending. A flexible beam attached to the end of the headbox nozzle is adjusted locally to either increase or decrease the slice opening. This will not only affect the basis weight at the point of adjustment but also can redirect flow creating undesirable fiber orientation effects in the sheet. Further, due to both cross flows and to the stiffness of the beam, the zone that a single adjustment affects is often quite wide.

An alternate approach to controlling cross machine uniformity is to adjust local flow consistency. If the consistency is adjusted locally without affecting slice flow rate, basis weight can be adjusted while maintaining desired uniform jet exiting conditions. In this paper, a consistency profiling scheme is presented that allows high resolution profiling and a decoupling of basis weight from fiber orientation control schemes. Development laboratory trials and initial field experiences are discussed.

CONVENTIONAL BASIS WEIGHT PROFILING

Conventionally, cross machine basis weight profiles are controlled through adjustment of headbox slice opening. As shown in Figure 1, a typical arrangement would be to have a thin flexible beam attached on the end of the headbox nozzle. This beam is bent up or down locally through a series of mechanical actuators spaced across the machine for local adjustment of slice opening.

Cross machine basis weight control by slice lip bending is a complex task. Adjustment of a single actuator will affect not only the slice opening at that actuator, but also at neighboring actuators. Further, basis weight response at neighboring zones is affected by cross flow generation (Figure 2). A typical dry weight response to the movement of a single actuator is shown in Figure 3. A positive response region is followed by areas of negative response. Total response width is a function of grade and varies from a width of several actuators for newsprint, to 10 to 14 actuators width (1.5 to 2 meters) on sack kraft, and to even greater widths on higher slice opening grades [1,2]. Basis weight control by slice bending is difficult due to these strong cross-couplings and complex response characteristics. An additional implication is that significant adjustments are often required at grade changes, resulting in lost production time on grade.

Historically, the desire for improved basis weight profiles has led to systems with narrower and narrower actuator spacings. The earliest systems in the 1970s had slice lip adjustors on 300 mm centers; a short time later, 150 mm became the standard. This later dropped to 100 mm, and now 75 mm centers are used on critical paper grades. However, due to physical constraints imposed by actuator size, complex system response, and cost, mechanical actuators spaced at less than 75 mm have not yet been employed, even though paper quality requirements are becoming more stringent.

Perhaps, the greatest disadvantage of slice bending systems is the generation of cross flows. Cross flows will lead to misalignment in the main fiber orientation angle in the finished sheet. Fiber misalignment will adversely affect twist warp in linerboard, diagonal curl in copy paper grades, and stack lean in forms bond. For otherwise well-designed headbox and approach flow systems, one of the larger factors leading to cross machine fiber misalignment is shrinkage in the dryer section. Slice lips are typically adjusted to reduce slice opening at the edges to compensate for shrinkage effects. This creates inflows which will lead to an "S" shaped cross machine fiber orientation profile as shown in Figure 4.

CONSISTENCY PROFILING CONCEPT

Basis weight is not only a function of slice opening but also of flow consistency. An alternate approach to cross machine basis weight control is to keep the slice opening constant and adjust basis weight by locally increasing or decreasing flow consistency. In this approach, the slice opening can be kept uniform across the machine, which will decouple basis weight control from fiber orientation effects. Further, basis weight response has the potential to be less complex with less cross coupling and narrower response widths, is mechanically simpler, and allows closer spacing for higher resolution control.

The concept is quite old [3,4]. Renewed interest in this technique has been driven mostly by developments in fiber orientation measurement. With the ability to monitor fiber misalignment, paper mills are now controlling the process to minimize fiber misalignment. A need has arisen to decouple basis weight control from fiber orientation effects. Additionally, what has been missing up to now has been an injection system to produce consistency variations on a fine and controlled scale.

Requirements for a successful dilution injection scheme include that (1) the local flow rate is not changed so that cross flows are not created, and that (2) the flow is sufficiently stable after the injection point to avoid excessive spreading of the "dilution" effect.

Several potential injection schemes are illustrated in Figure 5. These show injection tubes located either in the headbox nozzle, tube bank, or in the approach flow to the tube bank. These tubes would then be located across the width of the machine. Each of these schemes faces various disadvantages. A disadvantage common to all is illustrated in Figure 6. The issue is of maintaining constant volumetric flow rate. If the injection is at too low an angle to the main flow, "pumping" or an increase in flow rate may occur. At too large an angle, increases in dilution flow rate might reduce the throughput. For any given angle, outlet flow rate is likely to be dependent on the dilution flow rate. Any change in flow rate across the width of the machine is undesirable as it will lead to cross flows and fiber misalignment in the sheet. A streaky sheet may result.

An injection scheme that offers the potential to decouple dilution flow rate from total volumetric flow rate is shown in Figures 7 and 8. Here, dilution flow is injected at the tube bank inlet face perpendicular into the cross header flow and then turns into the adjacent manifold tube. The total flow rate in any tube should be constant if the resistance offered by the manifold tubes is sufficiently large. Any change in dilution flow rate will be offset by a corresponding change in flow from the header.

INJECTION DEVELOPMENT TRIALS

Laboratory trials were conducted to verify this injection concept (Figures 7 and 8) and to establish operating parameters. A schematic of the experimental arrangement is shown in Figure 9. A linear tapered header with manifold tubes was set-up on a recirculating flow loop. The header and manifold tubes were dimensioned and flow rates were run to simulate operating conditions typical for a central section of a commercial headbox.

The inlet to the header test section was 170 mm by 176 mm. The outlet dimensions were 127 mm by 176 mm. Test section length was 263 mm. Manifold tube arrangement and dimensions are shown in Figure 10. Injection port locations and diameters were varied. Measurements reported in this paper are for a port, the same internal diameter as the manifold tubes (12 mm), located midway between adjacent manifold tubes. The manifold tubes were left open to the atmosphere for consistency sampling and flow rate measurements. A pressurized dye tank was connected to the injection line to allow visualization of the injection flow in the header.

In Figures 11-13, the effect of injecting fresh water into a 0.55% consistency 50/50 hardwood/softwood suspension flow is shown. Consistencies of the flow in the manifold tubes immediately upstream and downstream of the injection tube are graphed. Mean tube flow was 69 lpm. Injection flow rate was 11, 23, and 34 lpm (Figures 11 to 13, respectively). The various sets of data points in each graph represent different header velocities, ranging from 2.2 to 4.5 mps. It can be seen that the consistency in the tube immediately downstream of the injection tube is lowered by an amount proportional to the amount of injected flow. For most cases, the consistency in the tubes further downstream is not affected. These results illustrate that significant consistency changes in a single tube can be achieved independent of flow conditions in other manifold tubes. That the consistency reduction is proportional to the injected flow rate suggests that flow rate in the manifold tube is also not being changed.

In Figures 14 and 15, the impact of injection flow rate on tube flow rate is examined for a series of runs conducted with fresh water. The ratio of individual tube flow rate to average flow rate of all tubes is plotted in Figure 14 as a function of injection flow rate for tubes upstream and downstream of the injection port. Flow rate upstream of the tubes is not affected by injection flow. For the tube immediately downstream of the injection port, tube flow rate increases by less than 1% for flow rates less than 30 lpm (40% of tube flow rate). At greater than 30 lpm, tube flow rate decreases by up to 9%. For the tubes further downstream, a similar effect is noticed, but to a lesser effect on flow rate.

In Figure 15, the effect of injection rate on tube flow ratio is examined in further detail for the tube immediately downstream of the injection port. Here, tube flow ratio is plotted as a function of injection velocity non-dimensionalized by header velocity (for three different header velocity conditions). For all conditions when the injection velocity is less than the header velocity, the manifold tube flow remains virtually unchanged (<1% variation).

Dye injection has shown that at low flow rates, all of the injected flow is swept into the immediate downstream tube. As the injection flow rate is increased, the jet reaches higher into header flow. At the condition where the injection velocity is just greater than the header velocity, the majority of the injection jet still flows into the tube immediately downstream, but some of the flow is intermittently swept further downstream. As injection rates are increased further, the injection jet will reach higher into the header, with more flow being swept downstream.

The above results demonstrate that this injection technique meets the requirement of being able to adjust consistency levels to a significant degree without changing tube flow rate. For effective process control, injection velocity should be maintained at less than header velocity. A second requirement for successful consistency profiling scheme is that the flow be sufficiently stable after the injection point to avoid excessive spreading of the control zones. A new design headbox that promotes flow stability was developed for this purpose and is discussed in [5].

INDUSTRIAL APPLICATION

Consistency profiling has been implemented on several commercial headboxes with the first of these starting up during the past year. A high resolution cross machine profile for a Fourdrinier machine producing LWC with consistency profiling is shown as Figure 16. The CD spread (2 sigma of the cross machine profile) is 0.16 lbs/3000 ft². The data is plotted per actuator spacing, which is nominally 40 mm. In Figure 17, the same profile is shown after the data has been averaged over 150 mm zones (the previous actuator spacing before the system change). The CD spread of the lower resolution profile is 0.10 lbs/3000 ft². In Figure 18, a comparison of results is shown for before and after the system change. CD basis

weight spreads have been reduced by more than 50%. Improvement in CD caliper profiles (Figure 19) and improved reel building has also resulted.

Use of consistency profiling has effectively decoupled basis weight from fiber orientation control. In Figure 20, results from a second headbox with consistency profiling are shown. A uniform basis weight profile is shown, but one where fiber orientation angle varied from -10 to +12 degrees. Edge flows at the headbox were adjusted to achieve fiber angles within -1 to + 2.5 degrees, as shown in Figure 21, with the basis weight profile still remaining uniform.

An additional benefit of consistency profiling is fast response. Due to the less complex cross coupling characteristics, basis weight profiles stabilize faster than for slice bending systems. In Figure 22, CD spread values for cross machine basis weight profiles are plotted as a function of time. It can be seen that profiles are reaching a stable state after about eight minutes from a start-up.

SUMMARY

Conventionally, cross machine basis weight profiles are controlled through adjustment of headbox slice opening. Slice lip bending is complex, has limited resolution control potential, contributes to lost production time at grade changes, and can adversely affect fiber orientation profiles. An alternative to cross machine basis weight control is to control consistency locally across the machine. A key requirement for successful consistency profiling is that consistency be able to be varied without affecting local flow rate, otherwise cross flows and fiber misalignment in the sheet will result. An injection scheme is examined that achieves this objective. Additionally, the use of consistency profiling permits higher resolution control, has narrower, less complex response characteristics, and faster system response. Initial industrial applications have demonstrated improved cross machine weight and caliper profiles, improved reel building, and the ability to decouple fiber orientation control from basis weight control.

REFERENCES

1) Karlsson, H., I. Lundqvist, and T. Ostman, "Principles and Potentials of CD-Basis Weight Control," EUCEPA Conference 238 (1982).

2) Hansson, A., L. Haglund, and I. Gladh, "Experiences with CD-Basis Weight Control, Case III - A Sack Kraft Machine at the Skoghall Mill," EUCEPA 252 (1982).

3) Witham, G.S., U.S. Patent #1,662,226, March 13, 1928.

4) Springuel, P.F., U.S. Patent #3,407,114, October 22, 1968.

5) Shands, J.A., and H.P. Frei, "A Novel Concept for Cross Generation Basis Weight Control - A Next Generation Headbox," EUCEPA Conference (1993).

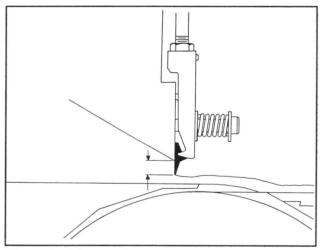

Figure 1. Slice bending system

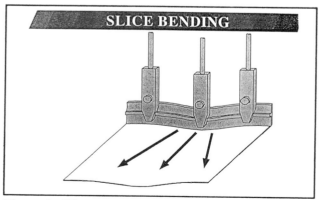

Figure 2. Slice bending controls basis weight at expense of creating cross flows and jet velocity differences.

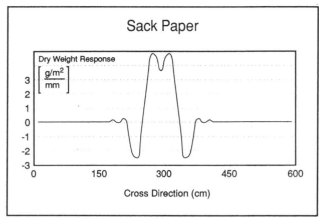

Figure 3. Dry weight response to a single actuator move for a slice bending system.

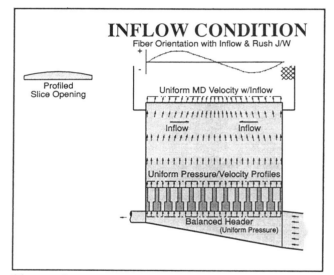

Figure 4. Reducing slice opening at the edges of machine will lead to inflow and fiber misalignment.

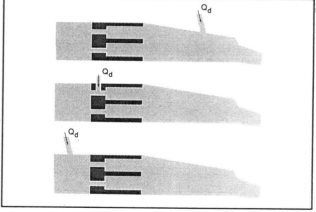

Figure 5. Potential consistency profiling injection schemes.

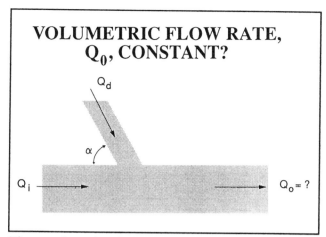

Figure 6. An injection scheme must meet the requirement that volumetric flow rate across the machine remain constant to avoid cross flows.

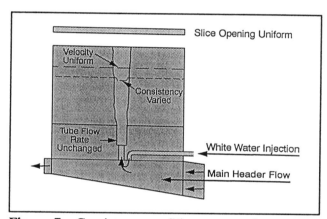

Figure 7. Consistency profiling concept for constant local flow rate.

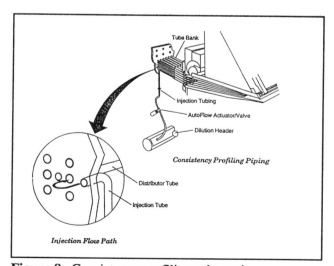

Figure 8. Consistency profiling schematic.

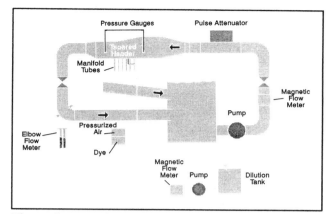

Figure 9. Experimental arrangement.

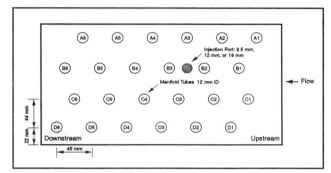

Figure 10. Manifold tube inlet face.

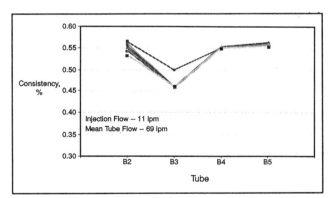

Figure 11. Effect of 11 lpm dilution flow on consistency.

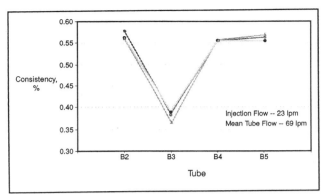

Figure 12.   Effect of 23 lpm dilution flow on consistency.

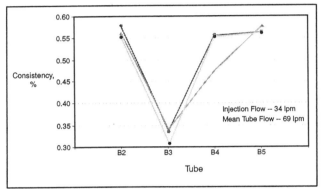

Figure 13.   Effect of 34 lpm dilution flow on consistency.

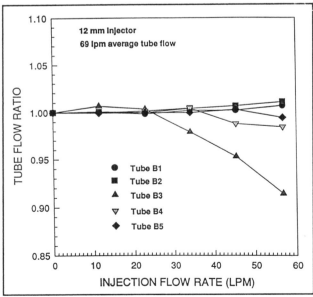

Figure 14. Effect of injection flow on individual tube flow rate.

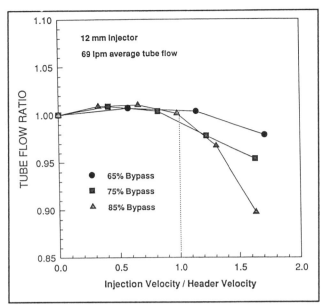

Figure 15. Effect of injection rate on tube B1 flow ratio.

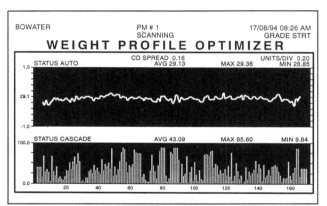

Figure 16.   Basis weight profile at 40 mm resolution with consistency profiling.

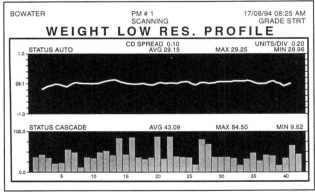

Figure 17.   Same basis weight profile at 150 mm resolution with consistency profiling.

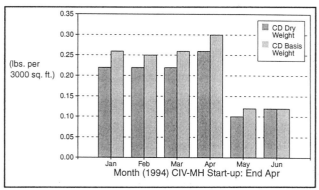

Figure 18. Effect of consistency profiling on CD weight profiles.

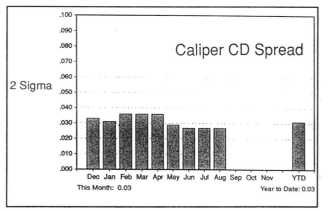

Figure 19. Effect of consistency profiling on caliper profiles (April start-up).

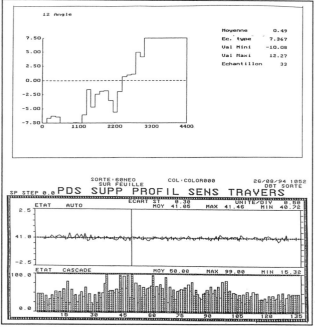

Figure 20. Fiber orientation and basis weight profiles with edge flow valves full open.

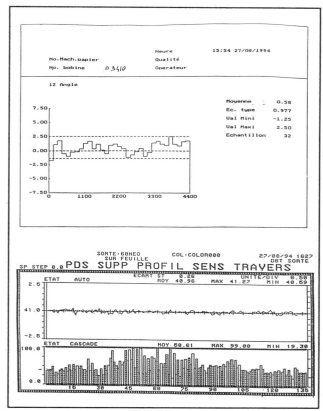

Figure 21. Fiber orientation and basis weight profiles with edge flow valves adjusted to achieve uniform fiber orientation.

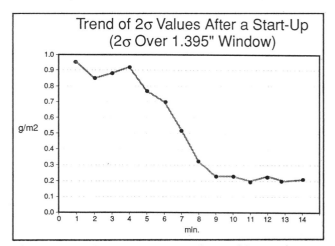

Figure 22. System response time with consistency profiling.

Impact of Three Dimensional Headbox Flows on Tissue Layer Purity

Joseph K. Baker, Paul D. Beuther, and Theodore E. Farrington, Jr.

The Kimberly-Clark Corporation, 2100 Winchester Road, Neenah, WI 54957

The role of three dimensional flows within tissue machine headboxes in determining layer purity is explored. Previous CFD work suggests the presence of swirling flows within certain headbox designs. Laser Induced Fluorescence is employed to verify the existence of both spanwise and streamwise structures within the wake of headbox dividers. Pilot plant studies explore the impact of headbox design and former geometry on layer purity. Clearly, all of these phenomena play some role in determining layer purity. The use of flexible headbox slice extensions is seen to improve layer purity. However the exact mechanism is unclear as these extensions impact several key phenomena simultaneously.

INTRODUCTION

Tissue products seek to meet consumer requirements by providing an optimum combination of sheet strength, thickness and stiffness. The business desire for low raw material costs causes a simultaneous demand for low density structures. Thus the development of superior tissue structures is largely the search for opportunities to expand the strength - thickness - stiffness envelope, while minimizing fiber requirements. More specifically, a common objective is to minimize bending stiffness while maximizing strength and thickness.

For homogenous plate-like structures strength (tensile stiffness), thickness and bending stiffness are related by the following:

1) $\quad (EI/EA) = (EWT) / (EWT^3/12) \propto T^2$

where:

E = Young's Modulus

I = Moment of Inertia
A = Plate Crosssectional Area
W = Plate Width
T = Plate Thickness
(EI/EA) = Bending Stiffness / Tensile Stiffness

One's ability to manipulate strength, stiffness and thickness are very limited for homogeneous structures due to the close coupling of the properties. This has led to the development of composite tissue structures in which these characteristics can be made more independent.

One common approach to decoupling these properties is to employ layered tissue technology. For illustration, a three layered tissue composite is illustrated in Figure 1. Now, using the transformed section method for bending stiffness, the equations describing tensile and bending stiffness are:

2) $\quad EA = E_2W(2T_2 + nT_1)$

Kimberly-Clark Corp., 2100 Winchester Road, Neenah, WI 54957-0999

3) $EI = (2/3)W\{[(T_2 + (1/2)T_1)^3 - (1/2T_1)^3] + n(1/2T_1)^3\}$

4) $(EI/EA) \propto \{[(T_2 + (1/2)T_1)^3 - (1/2T_1)^3] + n(1/2T_1)^3\} / (2T_2 + nT_1)$

where: $n = E_1/E_{2A}$

As an example of the impact of layered structures on the ability to further manipulate strength and stiffness, Figure 2 shows the ratio (EI/EA) over a range of n and T_1. Total thickness and tensile stiffness are held constant. The theoretical ratio (EI/EA) can be changed a factor of three by manipulating n and T_1 over quite practical ranges.

To realize the potential benefits of layered tissue structures the individual layers must be as pure and as uniform in thickness as possible. Headbox design and form roll geometry have both been seen to impact layer uniformity. Figure 3 shows a typical 3-layered tissue structure produced by a headbox of design illustrated in Figures 4-6 and Table 1 in conjunction with a twin wire former with suction form roll. The layers are dyed different colors and clearly show the lack of uniform coverage. Significantly, the scale of nonuniformity is quite large and on the order of the diffuser tube spacing in the headbox. This observation led to numerical, flowloop and pilot plant studies to determine possible causes of layer nonuniformity and indentify potential improvements.

Table 1 - Headbox Design Parameters

H(mm)	15.9	D(mm)	31.8
A(m)	.39	C-C(mm)	40.6
B(m)	.65	R-R(mm)	57.2
θ(degrees)	135		

NUMERICAL STUDIES OF HEADBOX FLOWS

Computational Fluid Dynamics (CFD) investigations of the internal flows of the headbox described above were presented at a previous AIChE conference[1]. Design 1 of that paper represents the headbox used in studies reported here. The most interesting result of that work was the formation of streamwise vortical flows within the headbox. Each flow channel within the headbox contains a series of pairs of counter-rotating swirling flows, one pair for each diffuser tube hole. Three aspects of this headboxes design contribute to the formation of such flows:

1. -   Sharp turn of the flow immediately upon entering the flow channel sets up Gottler type flow instability.

2 -   Relatively high land area of the diffuser tube bank further exacerbate pressure variations across headbox.

3 -   High convergence of headbox accentuates swirling flow.

While this CFD work clearly suggested the initiation of such streamwise vortical flows, use of the k-ε turbulence model rendered any information on persistence of these flows speculative at best.

PREVIOUS WORK ON MIXING LAYERS

Another possible source of streamwise vortical flows exists in headboxes of this design. Thin plastic sheets are often used for internal turbulence generation and external layer separation. This sets up a classic mixing layer situation which has been studied many time before[2-8]. The three dimensionality of such flows has been known for some time. The flow structure can be considered a combination of a two dimensional mixing layer plus the superposition of streamwise vortical flows triggered by some horizontal nonuniformity in the flow. In some cases the scale of these swirling flows has been directly linked with upstream grid conditions. Recent numerical simulations have modeled this phenomenon and experiments have demonstrated the ability to control the spacing of swirling flows by forcing the flow instability.

Thus there are at least two potential sources of 3-dimensional flows that could be related to the pattern of sheet nonuniformity observed.

THE FREE JET SURFACE

Previous studies[9] of paper machines have shown the dramatic effect upstream flow conditions can have on the surface of the jet after it has left the headbox. Thus one concludes the mechanism responsible for tissue layer uniformity is some combination of the following phenomena as shown in Figure 7:

1 -   Streamwise vortical flows are initiated at the headbox entrance due to geometrical factors described above.

2 -   Remnants of these swirling flows trigger or combine with three dimensional flows caused by the various dividers in the headbox.

3 -   Cross machine nonuniformities and swirling flows cause disturbance of the free jet surface and continued mixing of layers after the flow leaves the headbox.

FLOW LOOP EXPERIMENTS

Most mixing layer investigations have considered the mixing of two streams exhibiting some differences, typically different densities or velocities. To determine if such flows are likely to occur at typical headbox conditions a flow loop was set up[11]to simulate the mixing of two water streams at high speed. Figures 8a-8c depict the three orientations at which Laser Induced Florescence (LIF) was employed to identify possible coherent structures inthe flow. Experiments

were conducted at mean velocities of .9m/s, 1.5m/s and 3.0m/s. A variety of dividers was studies to assess the impact of divider thickness and stiffness. The same qualitative behavior was observed in all cases. Divider thickness had the greatest impact on turbulent wake properties.

Figures 9a-9c show typical LIF images taken according to the orientations shown in Figure 8. Both the streamwise and spanwise structures would negatively impact layer purity.

SUCTION FORM ROLL TISSUE TRIALS

To better understand the relative importance of the mechanisms operating to determine layer purity a series of high speed trials were conducted. The first trials were conducted with a suction form twin wire former. Process details are given in Table 2. The outer layers of the sheet were dyed a different color than the center layer. While all layers were approximately 50/50 hardwood/softwood blends, outer layer purity could be quantified by determining the % populus in the outer layer hardwood, which should ideally be pure eucalyptus. Three means were used to assess outer layer uniformity: visual ranking, simple image analysis and % populus in outer hardwood layer.

Table 2 - Suction Form Roll Trials

Sheet Dryer Basis Weight =   27 gsm
Layer Split:
Roll/Center/Wire = 25%/50%/25%
Furnish:
Outer layers = 50/50 Eucalyptus / NHWK (dyed blue)
Center Layer = 50/50 NHWK/ / NSWK (dyed orange)
Machine Speed =   16 meters/sec
Headbox Slice Opening = 2.0 cm

Several experiments were performed. First, a

designed experiment was conducted as shown in Figure 10. Independent variables were jet impingment, suction form roll vacuum level and suction form roll vacuum zone position relative to jet impingement point. Then, two alternative divider setups were explored as shown in Figures 11 and 12. All blunt recessed dividers (BRL) were employed in the first. In the second, lexan sheets were glued to the headbox top and bottom surfaces, forming a flexible extension of the headbox slice lips (EFSL).

Figures 13 and 14 show typical sheets that were obtained from BRL and EFSL respectively. Figure 3 showed a typical sheet from the standard (STD) headbox setup. One can see visually that in terms of uniformity of coverage EFSL > STD > BRL.

Visual inspection of the designed experiment points led to their ranking in several groups with lower numbers representing better layer coverage. These results are given in Figure 15 versus gray level histograms which were also used to quantify layer purity.

The graph shows poor performance with only recessed blunt dividers, improved purity with increasing jet impingement and superior coverage with EFSL. Fiber analysis (weight percent) results are shown in Figure 16. Most significant is the substantial difference between the roll and fabric side layer purity.

SOLID FORM ROLL TRIALS

A second set of high speed trials was performed to better define the effect of the extended flexible slice lips which showed interesting results above. These were conducted with a solid form roll and same headbox as before. Three headbox geometries were investigated with and without EFSL. First was the standard configuration (STD) from Figure 5. The other designs are shown in Figures 17. Jet-to-wire curves were run for each cases and fiber analysis performed. Conditions for these trials are given in Table 3. Results (number percent fiber analysis) are given in Figures 18 and 19. In each case the addition of EFSL's improved layer purity as measured in this study.

Table 3 - Solid Form Roll Trials

Sheet Dryer Basis Weight =   16 gsm
Layer Split:
Roll/Center/Wire = 25%/50%/25%
Roll Side layer = 50/50 Eucalyptus / NHWK (dyed blue)
Other Layers = 50/50 NHWK/ NSWK (dyed orange)
Machine Speed =   16 meters/sec
Headbox Slice Opening = 1.6 cm

CONCLUSIONS

Three dimensional flows within tissue machine headboxes can have a significant effect on layer purity.

Potential mechanisms responsible for such flows include the formation of swirling flows at the diffuser tube bank, three dimensional wakes formed at divider tips and instability of the free jet surface.

Both spanwise and streamwise structures exist in the headbox divider tip wake. Properties of this wake are impacted most significantly by divider thickness.

Layer purity is sensitive to former geometry, with some level of jet impingement being generally beneficial.

The use of extended flexible slice lips can improve layer purity although the exact mechanism is not clear.

LITERATURE <u>CITED</u>

1.   Farrington, T. E., A Numerical Investigation of Three Tissue Machine Headboxes, Proceedings of the 1991 AIChE Annual Meeting -San Francisco, 1992.

2.   Brown, L. B. and Roshko, A. On the Effects of Large Structure in Turbulent Mixing Layers, Journal of Fluid Mechanics, V64, 775-816, 1974.

3.   Bernal, L. P. and Roshko, A. Streamwise Vortex Structure in Plane Mixing Layers, Journal of Fluid Mechanics, V170,499-525, 1986.

4.   Lasheras, J. C., Cho, J. S. and Maxworthy, T., On the Origin and Evolution of Streamwise Vortical Structures in a Plane Shear Layer, Journal of Fluid Mechanics, V172,231-258, 1986.

5.   Grinstein, F. F., Oran, E. S. and Boris, J. P., Numerical Simulations of Asymmetric Mixing in Planar Shear Layers, Journal of Fluid Mechanics, V165, 201-220, 1986.

6.   Ashurst, W. T. and Meiburg, E., Three-dimensional Shear Layers via Vortex Dynamics, Journal of Fluid Mechanics, V189,87-116, 1988.

7.   Lasheras, J. C. and Choi, H., Three Dimensional Instability of a Planar Free Shear Layer: an Experimental Study of the Formation and Evolution of Streamwise Vortices. Journal of Fluid Mechanics, V189, 53-86, 1988.

8.   Meiburg, E. and Lasheras, J. C., Experimental and Numerical Analysis of the Formation and Evolution of Streamwise Vortices in the Plane Wake Behind a Flat Plate, 6th Symposium on Turbulent Shear Flows, paper 16-1, 1987.

9.   Hauptmann, E., Vyse, R. and Mardon, J., The Wake Effect as Applied to Modern Hydraulic Headboxes, Part 1, Pulp and Paper Canada, V91:9, T357-T364, 1990.

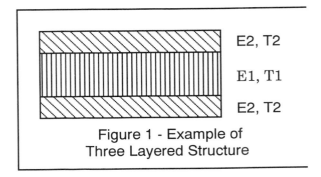

Figure 1 - Example of
Three Layered Structure

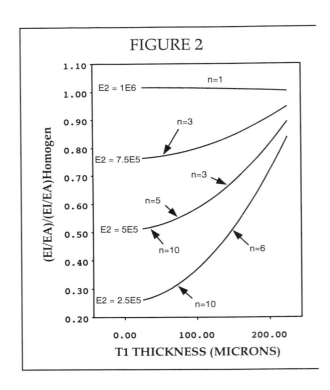

FIGURE 2

Figure 3 - Typical 3- Layer Headbox Performance

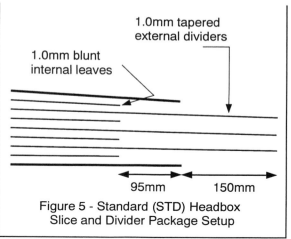

Figure 5 - Standard (STD) Headbox Slice and Divider Package Setup

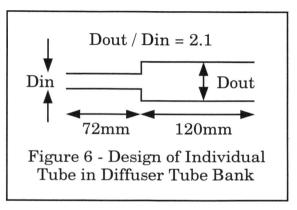

Figure 6 - Design of Individual Tube in Diffuser Tube Bank

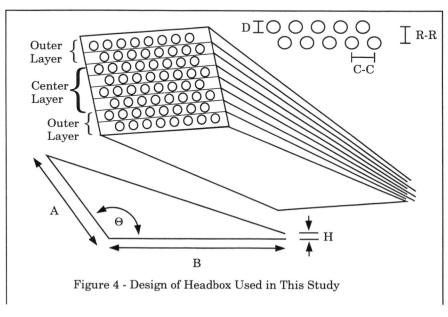

Figure 4 - Design of Headbox Used in This Study

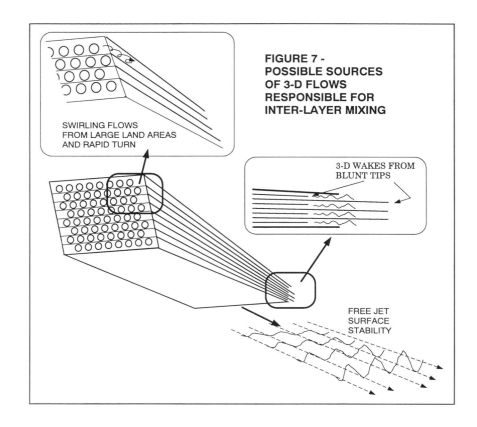

FIGURE 7 -
POSSIBLE SOURCES
OF 3-D FLOWS
RESPONSIBLE FOR
INTER-LAYER MIXING

SWIRLING FLOWS
FROM LARGE LAND AREAS
AND RAPID TURN

3-D WAKES FROM
BLUNT TIPS

FREE JET
SURFACE
STABILITY

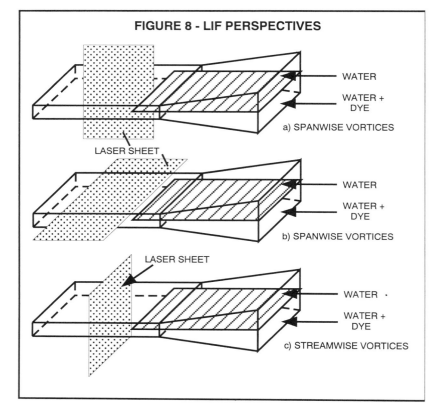

FIGURE 8 - LIF PERSPECTIVES

WATER

WATER +
DYE

a) SPANWISE VORTICES

LASER SHEET

WATER

WATER +
DYE

b) SPANWISE VORTICES

LASER SHEET

WATER

WATER +
DYE

c) STREAMWISE VORTICES

FIGURE 9a
MIXING
LAYER

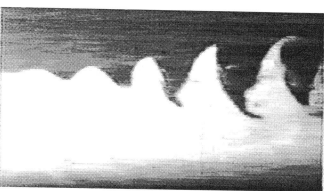

FIGURE 9b
SPANWISE
FLOW VIEWED
FROM TOP

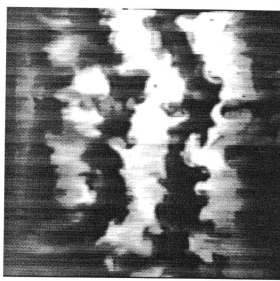

FIGURE 9c
STREAMWISE
FLOW
COMING
OUT OF PAGE

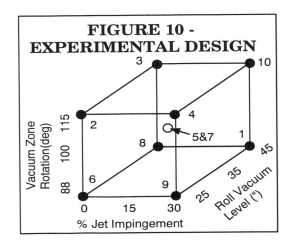

FIGURE 10 - EXPERIMENTAL DESIGN

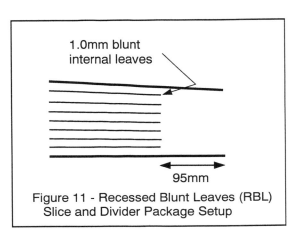

Figure 11 - Recessed Blunt Leaves (RBL) Slice and Divider Package Setup

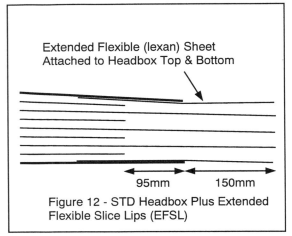

Figure 12 - STD Headbox Plus Extended Flexible Slice Lips (EFSL)

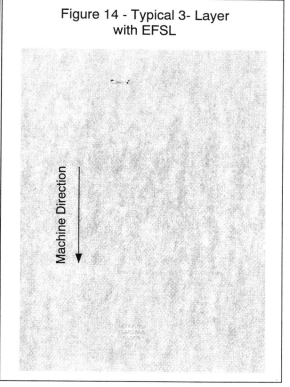

Figure 13 - Typical 3- Layer
Blunt Recessed Leaves

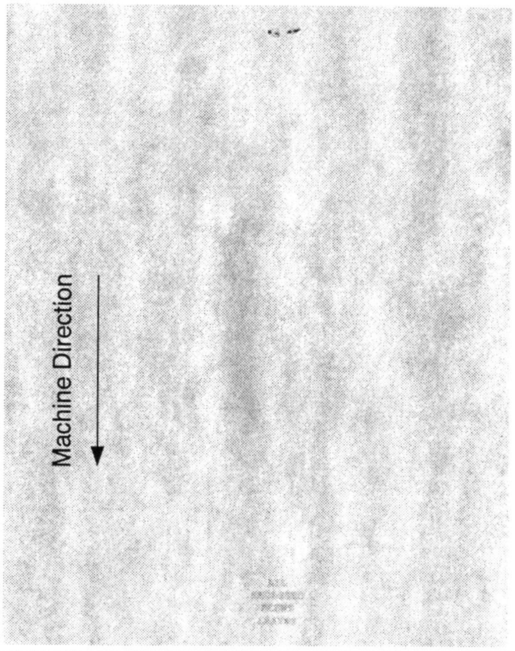

Machine Direction

Figure 14 - Typical 3- Layer
with EFSL

Machine Direction

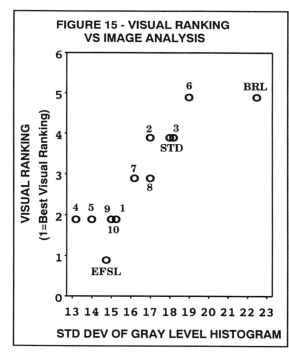

FIGURE 15 - VISUAL RANKING
VS IMAGE ANALYSIS

VISUAL RANKING
(1=Best Visual Ranking)
0
1
2
3
4
5
6
4
5
9
1
10
EFSL
7
8
2
3
STD
6
BRL
13 14 15 16 17 18 19 20 21 22 23
STD DEV OF GRAY LEVEL HISTOGRAM

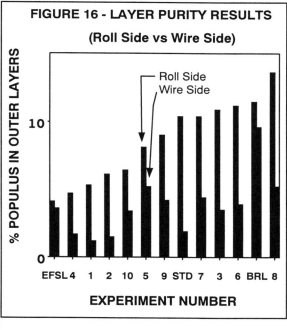

FIGURE 16 - LAYER PURITY RESULTS
(Roll Side vs Wire Side)

% POPULUS IN OUTER LAYERS
0
10
Roll Side
Wire Side
EFSL 4 1 2 10 5 9 STD 7 3 6 BRL 8
EXPERIMENT NUMBER

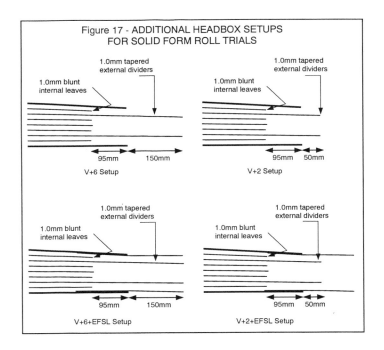

Figure 17 - ADDITIONAL HEADBOX SETUPS FOR SOLID FORM ROLL TRIALS

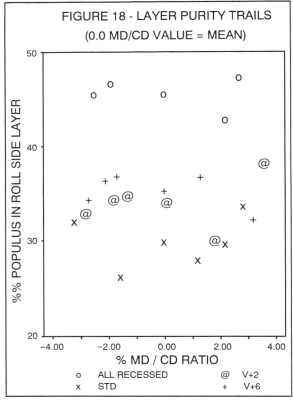

FIGURE 18 - LAYER PURITY TRAILS
(0.0 MD/CD VALUE = MEAN)

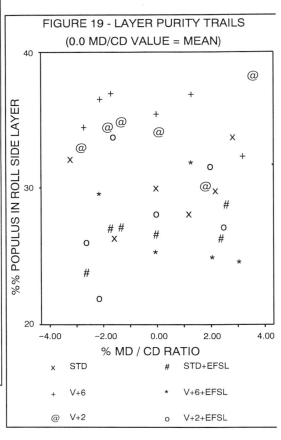

FIGURE 19 - LAYER PURITY TRAILS
(0.0 MD/CD VALUE = MEAN)

Pyrolysis and Combustion
Kinetics of Pine Bark

Wei-Yin Chen

Department of Chemical Engineering, Anderson Hall, University of Mississippi, University, MS 38677

Bark has been considered a viable renewable energy resource. This paper focuses on our experimental and modeling efforts on the bark combustion kinetics.

Combustion and pyrolysis experiments have been conducted by lowering a sample-containing basket into a preheated, 2.5" fluidized sand bed. This fluidized bed provides both rapid heating and quenching to the samples. Fluidized sand bed provides a very effective heat transfer medium between the gas (air or nitrogen) and the sand. Rapid quenching has been accomplished by raising the basket into a water-cooled, reversed-nitrogen flow section. The basket is made of a 40 mesh stainless steel screen. Combustion and pyrolysis of 10 mm diameter bark particles have been performed in the temperature ranges 500 to 800 °C, and 750 to 850 °C, respectively. The gas velocity has been in the range of 5.4 to 10.8 cm/s. Weight loss of bark after the experiments has been used as an index of conversion in the kinetic study.

The combustion/pyrolysis model contains three dynamic equations: bark pyrolysis, char combustion, and heat transfer to bark particles. It has been assumed that the volatiles disengagement from char is governed by temperature-dependent desorption in an exponential form. By fitting the model to the experimental data, the seven parameters in the model have been recovered. These parameters include the four Arrhenius parameters for pyrolysis and combustion, total volatile at infinite temperature and temperature sensitivity in the volatile desorption equation, and heat of pyrolysis. Good agreement with the experimental data for pyrolysis and combustion demonstrates that the present model is capable of depicting the bark weight remaining in the bed at any time during combustion or pyrolysis. In addition, the kinetic parameters for the pyrolysis and heat of pyrolysis are in good accord with those in the literature.

Wood is one of the most abundant renewable resources. Among its associations with various kinds of industries, wood supplies approximately 3 percent of the U.S. energy consumption (Schreuder and Tillman, 1980). Bark represents about 10-15% of the weight of the trunk cut in the forest. The composition of bark is superficially similar to that of the corresponding wood, i.e., cellulose (40%-45%), lignin (15-30%) and hemicellulose (20-35%) (Gray and Parham, 1982). The content of carbohydrates in bark is generally lower, and the amount of lignin or other polyphenolic substances is somewhat higher.

Wood combustion phenomena has been extensively reviewed (e.g., Tillman *et al.*, 1981). Recent technological development is reflected in an article by Barsin *et al.* (1988), and a report published by the Electric Power Research Institute (Johnston *et al.*, 1993). Fundamental understanding of wood pyrolysis has also grown substantially in the last two decades. Shafizadeh (1982) reviewed the wood pyrolysis and combustion kinetics based on weight loss profiles. About the same time, Hajaligol *et al.* (1982) reported the kinetics of the individual product species for rapid pyrolysis of cellulose. Boroson *et al.* (1989) observed that heterogeneous cracking of wood pyrolysis tars takes place over flesh wood char surface. Pyrolysis kinetics of different lignocellulosic materials have been investigated by Bilbao *et al.* (1989, 1990). Heat and mass transfer limitations are inevitable during burning of large particles, and have been the target of a number of modeling efforts (e.g., Kanury, 1972; Maa and Bailie, 1973; Chan *et al.*, 1985; Ragland *et al.*, 1988; Bilbao *et al.*, 1993).

Due to its lower physical strength and less uniform structure than interior wood, and its generally highly colored look, bark is viewed more as a nuisance than an asset and is usually burned along with wood waste as a fuel, particularly by sawmills and pulp mills. Bark has the heating value of 8,000 to 10,000 Btu/lb, which is higher than that of wood (Wegner, 1991). The objective of this paper is to experimentally acquire information about the bark kinetics during pyrolysis and combustion conditions. A kinetic model is also developed for the comparison.

EXPERIMENTAL

Since weight loss is used as a measure of bark conversion in the present study, the design of experiments has some salient features of a thermal balance. Figure 1 illustrates the experimental apparatus for both pyrolysis and combustion. The center piece of the reactor is a cylindrical sample basket of dimension 1 in × 2 in length, which is made of 40 mesh stainless steel screen. The reactor vessel is an alumina tube with inside diameter of 2.5 in, which is heated to the desired temperature by a

Thermcraft furnace model 23-18-1ZH with dimensions 3 in × 18 in long. The reactor is equipped with a distributor made of a 40 mesh screen located at about 6 in from the bottom end of the furnace. The 30 mesh fluidized sand bed placed above the distributor provides heat to the gas stream during the operation.

Samples of pine bark, cut into 10mm spheres, were dried at 105°C for 24 hours before the experiment. Nitrogen and air were used as the fluidizing gas during pyrolysis and combustion, respectively. For the pyrolysis experiments, the system was flushed with nitrogen for 30 minutes. To begin a run, the sample basket containing a single particle of bark is lowering into the preheated fluidized sand bed. After a predetermined period of time, the basket was raised to a water-jacketed, reversed-nitrogen flow section for rapid quenching. Sample weight before and after the experiment were recorded. The ultimate analysis of the bark sample is shown in Table 1.

Experiments were conducted at sand temperatures 750°C, 800°C, and 850°C for pyrolysis; and 500°C, 600°C, 700°C, and 800°C for combustion. To achieve these temperatures, the furnace was set 90°C higher than the desired sand temperature. Since the sample basket was immersed in the sand during the experiment, sand temperature was considered the reaction temperature in the subsequent interpretations. Gas flowrate was set at 15,000 ml/min. This flowrate was chosen after an initial set of combustion experiments was completed and the highest rate of weight loss was obtained. Specifically, it was three times higher than the theoretical air required for complete combustion of bark during that time.

KINETIC MODEL

The bark combustion model under consideration contains three major components: bark pyrolysis, char combustion, and heat transfer.

During pyrolysis, the organic portion of the bark converts to volatiles and solid char, i.e.,

$$Bark + heat \Rightarrow Volatiles + Char \qquad (1)$$
$$(V) \qquad (1-V)$$

Here, the fraction of weight loss, V, is used as an

index of bark conversion. The volatile compounds include the gaseous species and tarry species disengaged from the char. Similar to a number of coal pyrolysis studies (e.g., Howard, 1981), bark pyrolysis is treated as a first order reaction in the following form

$$\frac{dV}{dt} = k_1(V_\infty - V) \qquad (2)$$

where V_∞ is the final volatile yield as time approaches infinity. The pyrolysis rate constant k_1 is assumed to follow the Arrhenius law

$$k_1 = k_{10}e^{-\frac{E_1}{RT_p}} \qquad (3)$$

where T_p is particle temperature, and E_1 is the pyrolysis activation energy.

Similar to coal pyrolysis (Howard, 1988), we observed temperature dependence of V_∞ during regression. Niksa (1988) proposed that phase equilibrium determines partitioning of tar in the gas and condensed phase, and the final volatile yield in the gas phase, V_∞, depends on temperature as follows:

$$V_\infty(T_p) = V_{10}e^{-\frac{E_3}{T_p}} \qquad (4)$$

where V_{10} and E_3 are adjustable parameters.

In the presence of oxygen, oxidation of the organics in the char contributes to additional weight loss

$$Char + O_2 \Rightarrow CO_2 + H_2O \qquad (5)$$
$$(W)$$

Assuming char combustion is first order with respect to oxygen concentration and the weight of char, we obtain

$$\frac{dW}{dt} = -k_1(V_\infty - V) - k_2'W(O_2) \qquad (6)$$

Since oxygen was continuously fed into the combustor at a rate four times that required for burning the volatile carbon, oxygen concentration is assumed to be constant during the combustion. Thus, we can combine k_2' and the oxygen concentration as a new constant k_2 and Eq. 6 becomes

$$\frac{dW}{dt} = -k_1(V_\infty - V) - k_2 W \qquad (7)$$

Assuming that the combustion rate constant, k_2, follows the Arrhenius law,

$$k_2 = k_{20}e^{-\frac{E_2}{RT_p}} \qquad (8)$$

Mass transfer limitations, such as oxygen diffusion into the char, are usually involved in combustion of particles of 1 cm in diameter, thus the rate measured based on Eqs. 7 and 8 should be considered effective or global reaction rate (Carberry, 1976).

Combustion of volatiles generated in bark pyrolysis will also take place outside bark particles at the same time,

$$\textit{Volatiles} + O_2 \rightarrow H_2O + CO_2 \qquad (9)$$

However, since this reaction does not contribute to the weight loss and it is not included in the present model.

Weight loss measurements indicate that devolatilization of bark particles takes place almost instantaneously at 800°C. However, at 500°C, devolatilization does not start until at about 20 s. These observations imply that heat transfer is a limiting factor in the range of our investigation, and an equation governing the temperature variation of the particle is required. Based on the published value of thermal conductivity of cellulosic materials, 0.12 W.m^{-1}.K^{-1} (Reed, 1983), the estimated Nusselt number of heat transfer for a bark particle gives values in the range 0.8 to 1.8. Since this is not a large number, we assume that the temperature is uniform inside a bark particle during pyrolysis and combustion. It should be mentioned that there is evidently a radial temperature profile and diffusion limitations of volatiles inside the wood particles with diameter 56 mm (Bilbao *et al.*, 1993). Energy balance yields

$$\rho_p V_p C_p \frac{dT_p}{dt} = Ah(T - T_p) + \varepsilon A \sigma (T_w^4 - T_p^4)$$
$$+ \Delta H_p r_p W_{p0} + \Delta H_c r_c W_{p0} \qquad (10)$$

Equation 10 states that temperature rise of a bark particle is governed by convective heat transfer, radiative heat transfer, heat of pyrolysis, and heat of combustion. We assume that the heat of volatiles combustion is carried away by gas, and is not included in this equation. Our calculation reveals that convection contributes to less than 20% of radiative heat transfer (APPENDIX A). Furthermore, experiments indicate that char combustion is much slower than pyrolysis, and char combustion does not contribute significant weight loss and temperature rise during the heat-up period. Thus, the first and the fourth terms on the right hand side of Eq. 10 are eliminated in the regression process, i.e.,

$$\rho_p V_p C_p \frac{dT_p}{dt} = \varepsilon A \sigma (T_w^4 - T_p^4) + \Delta H_p r_p W_{p0} \qquad (11)$$

Again, due to the fact that significant char combustion does not take place during the heat-up period, the bark particle external surface area, A, in Eq. 11 is assumed to be a constant during the combustion process. The published value for heat capacity of bark, C_p, is 0.327 cal/g.°C (Reed, 1983), and the nominal density of bark particle, ρ_p, was experimentally determined, 0.42 kg/dm^3.

The model discussed above has three dynamic equations, Eqs. 2, 7, and 11. Equations 3, 4, and 8 are also required for the integration of the three dynamic equations. The seven parameters, k_{10}, E_1, k_{20}, E_2, V_{10}, E_3, and ΔH_p are recovered from regression through comparison of the model with the data obtained from pyrolysis and combustion experiments. The optimization has been achieved by resorting to BCONF/DBCONF, a subroutine in the International Mathematical and Statistical Library which minimizes a multi-variable function subject to bounds on the variables using a quasi-Newton method and a finite-difference gradient. The integration of the large sets of differential equations has been carried out on a Cray X-MP2/216 supercomputer with LSODE, a software package based on Gear's method for solving stiff differential equations (Hindmarsh, 1982).

RESULTS AND DISCUSSION

The optimization procedure resulted in the following values of the seven system parameters:

$k_{10} = 1,557 \ s^{-1}$ $E_1 = 37,333 \ J/mol$
$k_{20} = 0.295 \ s^{-1}$ $E_2 = 22,028 \ J/mol$
$V_{10} = 0.862$ $E_3 = 228 \ K$
$\Delta H_p = 434 \ J/g$ of dry bark

The value of final volatile yield, V_{10}, is in good accord with the reported volatile matter for cedar bark, 0.869, moisture and ash free basis (Tillman et al., 1981). The heat of pyrolysis, ΔH_p, is somewhat higher than that reported for cellulose, 274 J/g (Bilbao et al., 1993), and that for cottonwood, 268 J/g (Pan, 1993). This discrepancy may be caused by the high heating rate, or the assumptions used in the present study. It has been demonstrated that high temperatures favor decomposition to volatiles, which require heat, while low temperatures favor char formation, which release heat (Shafizadeh and DeGroot, 1976). Bilbao et al. and Pan obtained their values through DSC analysis with a heating rate below 20 °C/min, and the heating rate in the present study is above 400 °C/min. The activation energy of bark pyrolysis is consistent with those found by other researchers: 24,208 J/mol between 290 and 400 °C (Bilbao et al., 1993) and 52,900 J/mol above 325°C for pine wood (Bilbao et al., 1991).

Figures 2 and 3 present the comparisons of pyrolysis data and predicted results at the reactor wall temperatures 750°C and 850°C, respectively. The experimental data are in good accord with the predictions of the model. The predicted temperature profiles of bark particle during heating are also included in these Figures. Slower rise in temperature between 170 to 230 °C indicates endothermic reaction of pyrolysis in this temperature range, which is somewhat narrower than that reported by Wegner, 100 to 450 °C (1991).

Figure 4 presents the comparison of combustion and pyrolysis at 800°C. Note that char combustion does not contribute significant weight loss in the first 20 s, while pyrolysis is essentially complete during this time. This observation is consistent with the assumption that heat of combustion of char does not play an important role during the heat-up period.

Figures 5, 6, and 7 demonstrate the weight loss profiles during combustion at 700°C, 600°C and 500°C reactor wall temperature. The data generally conform well with the model predictions. However, at 500°C, the pyrolysis is slower in the experiment than predicted by the model. This illustrates the limitations of the present phenomenological model. Bark is a complex material and its decomposition products contain numerous compounds, while the present model uses weight loss as an index of reaction conversion. The assumptions associated with heat transfer can also cause discrepancies. Furthermore, from thermodynamic principles and collision theory, both the frequency factor and the activation energy can be functions of temperature (Zellner, 1984).

Fragmentation of bark particles and volatiles ignition during combustion may be important to the future developments of phenomenological model. We observed fragmentation of bark particles at temperatures 600°C and above. Each bark particle breaks into 2 to 6 pieces along its geological planes after 15 to 25 seconds in the furnace, and higher temperatures cause more vigorous fragmentation. Fragmentation results in increase in larger surface areas and therefore reduced transfer limitations. Furnace temperature also affects ignition of volatiles. At 800°C and 700°C, flame starts at about 2 s after the bark particle is lowered into the furnace. At 600°C, flame was observed at about 5 s. At 500°C, ignition was delayed to 19 s.

CONCLUSIONS

Bark from pine has been investigated in both pyrolysis and combustion environments. The experimental data are in good accord with a kinetic model which includes three dynamic equations: bark pyrolysis, char combustion, and heat transfer to the bark particle. Three of the seven parameters, final volatile yield, heat of pyrolysis, and activation energy of bark pyrolysis, are in good agreement with published values for similar species. These results suggest that the model is capable of depicting the weight loss profiles in a furnace with a temperature in the range 500 to 850 °C.

Experiments also reveal that volatiles evolution and char combustion take place during two different periods of time during the thermal process. Furthermore, fragmentation of bark particles was also observed at temperatures above 600°C.

ACKNOWLEDGMENT

This research was supported by the Mississippi Chemical Corporation (MCC). The author is grateful to Dr. David W. Arnold and Mr. Gerald L. Tucker of MCC, who provided valuable advices during the course of this research.

NOMENCLATURE

A	external surface area of bark particle, m^2.
C_p	heat capacity of bark, $J.g^{-1}.K^{-1}$.
E_1	activation energy of bark pyrolysis, $J.mol^{-1}$.
E_2	activation energy of char combustion, $J.mol^{-1}$.
E_3	evaporation sensitivity of condensed tar to temperature.
h	convective heat transfer coefficient between bark particle and air, $g.s^{-3}.K^{-1}$.
ΔH_c, ΔH_p	heat of char combustion and bark pyrolysis, $J.g^{-1}$.
k_1, k_2	rate constant of bark pyrolysis and combustion, s^{-1}.
k_{10}, k_{20}	frequency factor of bark pyrolysis and combustion, s^{-1}.
r_c, r_p	rate of weight losses during combustion and pyrolysis normalized to the original weight, $g.g^{-1}.s^{-1}$.
T	temperature of gas, K.
T_w, T_p	temperature of furnace wall and bark particle, K.
V	volatile yield of bark normalized to its original weight, $g.g^{-1}$.
V_∞	total volatile yield of bark as time approaches infinite normalized to its original weight, $g.g^{-1}$.
V_{10}	final volatile yield of bark as time and temperature approaches infinite, %.
V_p	volume of bark particle, cm^3.
W	char weight normalized to its original weight, $g.g^{-1}$.
W_{po}	initial weight of bark particle, g.

Greek Symbols

ρ_p	bark density, g/cm^3.
σ	Stefan-Boltzmann constant, $J.s^{-1}.m^{-2}.K^{-4}$.
ε	emissivity, or absorptivity.
μ	viscosity, $g.cm^{-1}.s^{-1}$.
ν	kinematic viscosity, $cm^2.s^{-1}$.

LITERATURE CITED

Barsin, J.A., J. Pottera, and G. Stewart, "Conversion of A Recovery Boiler to Bark Burning," Tappi Journal, **71**, 107-113 (1988).

Bilbao, R., A. Millera, and J. Arauzo, "Thermal Decomposition of Lignocellulosic Materials: Influence of the Chemical Composition," Thermochimica, **143**, 149-159 (1989).

Bilbao, R., A. Millera, and J. Arauzo, "Kinetics of Weight Loss by Thermal Decomposition of Different Lignocellulosic Materials: Relation between the Results Obtained from Isothermal and Dynamic Experiments," Thermochimica, **165**, 103-112 (1990).

Bilbao, R., M.B. Murillo, and A. Millera, "Thermal Decomposition of Lignocellulosic Materials: Comparison of the Results Obtained in Different Experimental Systems," Thermochimica Acta, **190**, 163-173 (1991).

Bilbao, R., A. Millera, and M.B. Murillo, "Temperature Profiles and Weight Loss in the Thermal Decomposition of Large Spherical Wood Particles," Ind. Eng. Chem. Res., **32**(9), 1811-1817 (1993).

Bird, R.B., W.E. Stewart, and E.N. Lightfoot, "Transport Phenomena," John Wiley & Sons, New York, P.409, 1960.

Boroson, M.L., J.B. Howard, J.P. Longwell, and W.A. Peters, "Heterogeneous Cracking of Wood Pyrolysis Tars over Fresh Wood Char Surfaces," Energy & Fuels, **3**, 735-740 (1989).

Carberry, J.J., "Chemical and Catalytic Reaction Engineering," McGraw-Hill, New York, p.205, 1976.

Chan, W.C.R., M. Kelbon, and B. Krieger, "Modeling and Experimental Verification of Physical and Chemical Processes during Pyrolysis of a Large Biomass Particle," Fuel, **64**, 1505-1513 (1985).

Gray, R.L., and R.A. Parham, "A Good Look at Wood's Structure," Chemtech, **4**, 232-238 (1982).

Hajaligol, M.R., J.B. Howard, J.P. Longwell, and W.A. Peter, "Product Compositions and Kinetics for Rapid Pyrolysis of Cellulose," Ind. Eng. Chem. Proc. Des. Dev., **21**, 457-465 (1982).

Hindmarsh, A.C., "ODEPACK, A Systematized Collection of ODE Solvers," Report UCRL-88007, Lawrence Livermore National Laboratory, August (1982).

Howard, J.B., "Fundamentals of Coal Pyrolysis and

Hydropyrolysis" in "Chemistry of Coal Utilization," second supplementary volume, edited by Elliott, M. A.,, Wiley Interscience, New York, pp.688-785, 1981.

Johnston, S.A., J.G. Cleland, R.S. Truesdale, T.C. Clark, W.D. Stancil, L.D. Ostlie, and B. Weigel, "Whole Tree Energy[TM] Design - Volume 1: Engineering and Economic Evaluation," Final Report submitted to the Electric Power Research Institute, Report TR-101564 under Project 2612-15, Palo Alto, CA, December, 1993.

Kanury, A.M. "Rate of Burning Wood: A Simple Thermal Model," Combustion Science and Technology, **5**, 135-146 (1972).

Maa, P.S., and R.C. Bailie, "Influence of Particle Sizes and Environmental Conditions on High Temperature Pyrolysis of Cellulosic Material - I. Theoretical," Combustion Science and Technology, **7**, 257-269 (1973).

Niksa, S., "Rapid Coal Devolatilization as an Equilibrium Flash Distillation," AIChE J., **34**, 790-802 (1988).

Pan, W.P., Western Kentucky University, Personal Communication, September 29, 1993.

Ragland, K.W., J.C. Boerger, and A.J. Baker, "A Model of Chunkwood Combustion," Forest Products Journal, **38**(2), 27-32 (1988).

Reed, R.J., North American Combustion Handbook, second edition, North American Mfg. Co, Cleveland, Ohio, 1983.

Schreuder, G.F., and D.A. Tillman, "Wood Fuels Consumption Methodology and 1978 Results," in "Progress in Biomass Conversion," Vol. 2, K.V. Sarkanen and D.A. Tillman eds., pp.60-88, Academic Press, New York, 1980.

Shafizadeh, F., "Introduction to Pyrolysis of Biomass," Journal of Analytical and Applied Pyrolysis, **3**, 283-305, 1982.

Shafizadeh, F., and W.F. Degrade, "Thermal Analysis of Forest Fuels," in "Fuels and Energy from Renewable Resources," D.A. Tillman et al. ed., pp.93-114, 1977.

Tillman, D.A., A.J. Rossi, and W.D. Kitto, "Wood Combustion - Principles, Processes, and Economics," Academic Press, New York, 1981.

Wegner, T.H., "Wood" in "Encyclopedia of Polymer Science and Technology, edited by J. I. Kroschwitz, second edition, John Wiley & Sons, New York, **17**, pp. 843-887, 1991.

Zellner, R., "Bimolecular Reaction Rate Coefficients," in "Combustion Chemistry," W.C. Gardiner ed., Springer-Verlag, New York, pp.129-134, 1984.

APPENDIX A. Comparison of Radiative and Convective Heat Transfer

For bark particle in a tubular reactor, the heat transfer coefficient can be estimated through the Frossling correlation (Bird et al., 1960)

$$\frac{h_m D}{k_f} = 2.0 + 0.6 (\frac{D v_\infty \rho_f}{\mu_f})^{1/2} Pr^{1/3}$$

where h_m is convective heat-transfer coefficient, D is the particle diameter, 10 mm, v_∞ is the fluid velocity, 10 cm/s at 600°C in the experiment, and Pr is the Prandtl number at the film temperature, i.e.,

$$Pr = \frac{C_p \mu}{k_f} \qquad at \ T_f = (T_p + T_\infty)/2$$

In the expression above T_∞ and T_p are the temperatures of fluid and bark particles, respectively.

By definitions, the convective heat transfer can be estimated from heat transfer coefficient

$$H_c = A h_m (T_\infty - T_p)$$

and the radiative heat transfer can be estimated by

$$H_r = \varepsilon \sigma A (T_w^4 - T_p^4)$$

where ε is absorptivity, assumed to be 1 for the bark particle, σ is the Stefan-Boltzanman constant, 1.355×10^{-12} cal s^{-1} cm^{-2} K^{-4}, and T_w is tube wall temperature. Assuming the fluid has the same temperature as the reactor wall, then the ratio of convective to radiative heat transfer equals

$$R = \frac{H_c}{H_r} = \frac{h_m}{\sigma (T_w^2 + T_p^2)(T_w + T_p)}$$

This equation indicates that radiative heat transfer is more important than convective heat transfer at higher temperature. Our results of calculation for the selected wall/particle temperatures are shown in Table 2 below. In this table, the kinematic viscosity is the ratio of viscosity to the fluid density, i.e.,

$$v = \mu_f / \rho_f$$

These results suggest that the convective heat transfer is below 24% of the radiative heat transfer.

TABLE 1. Bark Compositions (Report by Huffman Laboratory)

dry-loss, %	4.92
ash, %	4.08
carbon, %	51.20
hydrogen, %	5.66
oxygen, %	40.67
nitrogen, %	0.21
sulphur, %	0.02
chlorine, %	<0.10
bromine, %	<0.10
iodine, %	<0.10
fluorine, %	<0.01
arsenic, ppm	<1.00
cadmium, ppm	<0.10
chromium, ppm	100.00
copper, ppm	25.00
lead, ppm	<1.00
mercury, ppm	0.37
nickel, ppm	41.00
beryllium, ppm	0.05

The sample was ground prior to analysis. Moisture was determined by loss on drying in air at 105°C to a constant weight and is on an as received basis. All other results are on a dried sample basis by weight.

TABLE 2. Relative Importance of Radiative and Convective Heat Transfer

T_w (°C)	T_p (°C)	T_f (°C)	Pr	$v \times 10^6$ (m^2/s)	$k_f \times 10^2$ (w/m.K)	h_m (w/m^2.K)	R
800	25	412.5	0.678	63.09	5.206	18.84	0.19
800	800	800	0.713	134.8	7.17	22.69	0.08
500	25	261.5	0.677	40.61	4.625	10.24	0.24
500	500	500	0.687	79.38	5.74	19.88	0.18

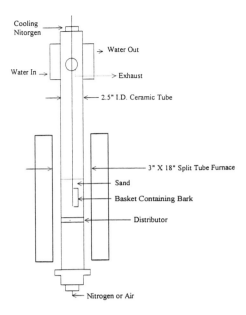

Figure 1. Experimental apparatus

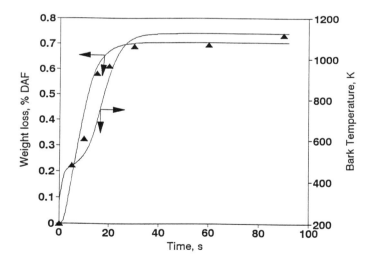

Figure 2. Experimentally observed and model predicted weight loss of bark during pyrolysis
at 850°C wall temperature. Predicted bark particle temperature is also shown.

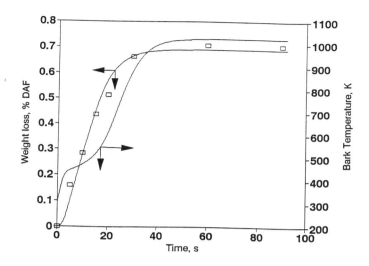

Figure 3. Experimentally observed and model predicted weight loss of bark during pyrolysis at 750°C wall temperature. Predicted bark particle temperature is also shown.

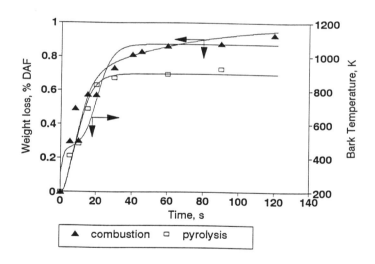

Figure 4. Experimentally observed and model predicted weight loss of bark during pyrolysis and combustion at 8000°C wall temperature. Predicted bark particle temperature is also shown.

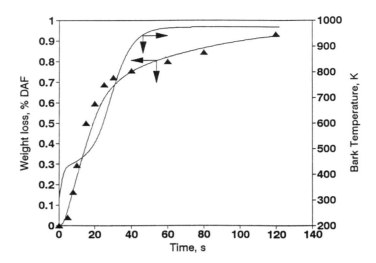

Figure 5. Experimentally observed and model predicted weight loss of bark during combustion at 700°C wall temperature. Predicted bark particle temperature is also shown.

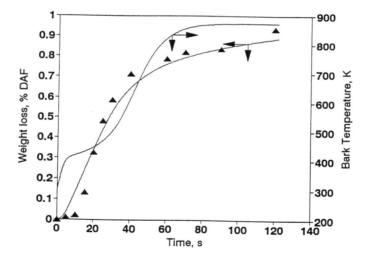

Figure 6. Experimentally observed and model predicted weight loss of bark during combustion at 600°C wall temperature. Predicted bark particle temperature is also shown.

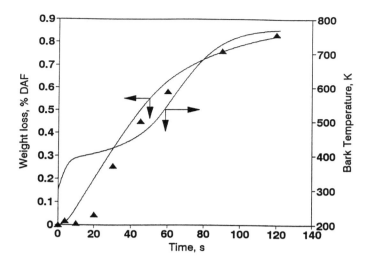

Figure 7. Experimentally observed and model predicted weight loss of bark during combustion at 500°C wall temperature. Predicted bark particle temperature is also shown.

Effects of Pulping Conditions and Black Liquor Composition on the Heat of Combustion of Slash Pine Black Liquor

A.A. Zaman and A.L. Fricke

Department of Chemical Engineering, University of Florida, Gainesville, FL 32611

Kraft pulping of slash pine was conducted in a large (0.11 m³) pilot scale digester at a variety of conditions. The conditions used constitute a rotatable composite designed experiment in four variables–effective alkali, sulfidity, time at temperature and temperature used to produce pulps with Kappa numbers ranging from 18 - 120. In all cases, the time to temperature was approximately 1,200 seconds and the white liquor was adjusted to a causticizing efficiency of 85% and a reduction of 93% with Na_2CO_3 and Na_2SO_4. Heats of combustion of all of these liquors have been determined for 100% solids concentrations. The effects of pulping conditions and liquor solids composition have been analyzed statistically and quantitative models developed for heats of combustion as a function of pulping conditions and black liquor composition. These results are presented and their utility are discussed.

Black liquor, a by-product of chemical pulping, is a biomass fuel that is burned in a recovery furnace to recover energy, as well as the cooking chemicals. It is an aqueous solution of the spent inorganic cooking chemicals and organic components dissolved during the kraft pulping process. After concentrating in multiple effect evaporators and high solids concentrators, black liquor is sprayed into the recovery furnace, dried and burned. The cooking chemicals are recovered as a molten mixture of Na_2CO_3 and Na_2S [1].

The heat of combustion of black liquor solids is normally reported on the basis of combustion products being in a completely oxidized state as CO_2, liquid H_2O, and carbonate solids at a stated temperature, usually 298.2 K (25°C). Sulfur can be measured or treated as gaseous SO_2, but may also be reported as liquid H_2SO_4 or as solid Na_2SO_4. The heat of combustion is often called the higher heating value. Knowledge of the heat of combustion of black liquor is important for design and efficient operation of kraft recovery furnaces.

The heat of combustion of black liquor solids results almost entirely from the combustion of organics in the black liquor solids and is a function of pulping conditions and wood species used [1,4]. Also, it varies from liquor-to-liquor due to differences in the composition of the liquors. Results of a number of investigations have been reported [1-8]. In general, the combustion products were considered to be carbon dioxide, liquid water, sodium carbonate, and sodium sulfate in these studies.

McDonald [4] showed that the heating value for liquors from a number of kraft mills varied linearly with solids content with a scatter of about ±13% at about 65% solids. This scatter can be reduced to about ±4% at 65% solids, if the heating value is treated as a linear function of total organic solids or total organic carbon in the solids.

In attempting to develop enthalpy balances for kraft pulping, Gessner [14] considered lignin, polysaccharides, and volatile and non-volatile organics to be the major contributors to heating value. He assumed these to be additive and assigned average chemical structures to each group. He corrected the heating value to account for the effects of CO_2 produced during pulping and for the presence of Na_2SO_4 and Na_2CO_3 in the pulping liquor. The actual calculations were applied only to pulping spruce at a 45-46% yield.

Annergren et al. [5] performed a limited, but well defined, study to develop a method for accounting for the effects of species and pulping conditions on the heating value of black liquor. Experimental pulping was conducted on three species at two to four conditions, and heating values and composition of the liquor were determined. Using heats of combustion of model compounds, they calculated theoretical heating values for each liquor from the liquor composition. Theoretical heating values were always higher than the experimental values, but the results clearly demonstrated that the organics are the dominant contributors to heating value.

Green and Grace [3] proposed a method for estimating heating value of black liquor that would account for pulping conditions, species, white liquor variations, and the state of sulfur oxidation. The primary purpose was to provide a method to estimate the total heating value of black liquor from pulping conditions. They indicated that heating value varies with pulp yield and Kappa number, and that one source of error is neglect of the contribution of the heating value of sulfur compounds.

No results have been reported for a systematic study of the variation of heating value and solids composition for pulping one species over wide ranges of even a limited number of pulping variables. In this study, the heats of combustion and major liquor solids constituents were determined for a series of characterized liquors made from kraft pulping of slash pine from statistically designed pulping experiments in four variables. Statistically based models for the heat of combustion have been determined for these results, and corrections for differences in "dead load" inorganics and soap are discussed.

SAMPLE PREPARATION

Black liquors used in this work were obtained by cooking slash pine in a 0.11 m^3 pilot scale digester with liquor circulation. The pulping variables were effective alkali, sulfidity, cooking temperature, and time at cooking temperature. Time to temperature was held constant at 1,200 seconds (20 minutes) ± 30 seconds. Debarked and screened chips from a commercial mill source were used. The liquor-to-wood ratio was constant at 4/1, and synthetic white liquors with Na_2CO_3 and Na_2SO_4 added equivalent to a causticizing efficiency of 85% and a sulfur reduction of 93% were used. The final drained liquor and two displacement washing volumes were collected and combined to provide the black liquor sample for a cook. Liquor samples from two identical cooks were combined to provide the sample for testing. The pulp was thoroughly washed and samples beaten. Yield and Kappa number of the pulp were determined. The pulping conditions used, along with the yield and Kappa number of the pulp and heat of combustion of the black liquor solids are summarized in Table 1. Full details for the procedures are given elsewhere [8-9].

Analyses performed can be divided into six categories: 1) inorganic anions (sulfide, sulfite, thiosulfate, sulfate, carbonate and chloride); 2) inorganic cations (Na, K, Ca, Mg); 3) low carbon number organic acids; 4) lignin; 5) lignin molecular weight, and 6) TAPPI tests (Kappa number, yield, sulfated ash). The analyses that have been performed and the methods used are described elsewhere [8-9].

Elemental analysis to determine the carbon, hydrogen, sulfur, and oxygen contents in the black liquor solids have not been performed.

The black liquor sample was concentrated to 28-30% solids in a 0.093 m^2 (1 ft^2) wiped film evaporator operated at about 45.6 kPa (0.45 atm). After settling at about 333 K (60°C), the liquor was skimmed thoroughly to minimize soap. At these conditions, soap solubility is a minimum and is equal to 2.6 - 2.9 kg/1,000 kg of liquor solids, or less than 0.29 wt% of the solids [15]. The skimmed liquor was then concentrated to about 45% solids in a second pass, drained in plastic containers, sealed under nitrogen, and stored at 277 K (4°C) until used.

Liquor samples at concentrations up to 83% solids were prepared by concentration in a small scale evaporator at reduced pressure (about 24 kPa or 0.237 atm) to minimize decomposition reactions [8-9]. Liquor samples at 100% solids were prepared by freeze drying samples containing about 20-30% solids [8-9]. These samples were stored in sealed containers under dry conditions. Transfer and weighings were made in a dry box, since the liquor solids are highly hygroscopic.

MEASUREMENT OF HEAT OF COMBUSTION

A Parr automatic adiabatic combustion calorimeter equipped with several bombs was used in this study. The apparatus was calibrated with duplicate samples of 1.0 gram benzoic acid pellets. Heat of combustion of 100% black liquor solids (pressed into a pellet with a pellet press) was determined to accuracies of ± 0.18% or better by performing triplicate tests. Heats of combustion of several black liquors at 55-76% solids concentration were determined to accuracies of ± 0.4% or better by performing triplicate tests. The poorer accuracy at this range of solids is due to the fact that it is difficult, apparently, to obtain complete combustion at concentrations lower than 100% solids. Heats of combustion for 100% black liquor solids determined for 25 experimental slash pine liquors are given in the last column of Table 1. The heats of combustion vary considerably with the pulping conditions (11.82 to 16.55 MJ/kg solids) used.

Heats of combustion of selected liquors were measured at other solids concentrations. Typical results are shown in Figure 1. As can be seen, the heat of combustion for a liquor is a linear function of solids concentration with very little variation in slope. Therefore, the heats of combustion determined at 100% solids can be used to predict heats of combustion at other solids concentrations.

EMPIRICAL MODELLING BY RESPONSE SURFACE METHODS

Response surface methodology as described by Box [11] was used to perform the empirical study between the heat of combustion as the measured response to the input variables of pulping. In order to develop plots of the response surface and contours, the following general multiple regression linear model, which consists of the main effects, interactions and quadratic terms, was employed [12]:

$$Y = \beta_o + \sum_{i=1}^{4}\beta_i X_i + \sum_{i<j}^{4}\beta_{ij}X_i X_j + \sum_{i<j<k}^{4}\beta_{ijk}X_i X_j X_k$$

$$+ \sum_{i<j<k<l}^{4}\beta_{ijkl}X_i X_j X_k X_l + \sum_{i=1}^{4}\beta_{ii}X_i^2 \quad (1)$$

where Y is the estimate for the dependent variable (ΔH_c) and X_i's are independent variables (EA; S; T; and t) known for each experimental run. The constants β_o; β_i; β_{ij}; β_{ijk}; β_{ijkl} and β_{ii} are the regression parameters.

Before employing equation 1 for surface response and contour analysis, the RSREG procedure (least-square regression) in SAS (Statistical Analysis Systems) which fits a quadratic response-surface model and which is useful in searching for factor values that optimize a response [13], was employed to generate quadratic effects, perform a lack of fit test, find the solution for critical values of the surface and find the eigenvalues of the associated quadratic form. The quadratic response surface model is:

$$Y = \beta_o + \sum_{i=1}^{4}\beta_i X_i + \sum_{i<j}^{4}\beta_{ij}X_i X_j + \sum_{i=1}^{4}\beta_{ii}X_i^2 \quad (2)$$

The results of applying the RSREG routine [13] contained in the SAS program indicates that R^2 for equation 1 is 0.9. The analysis also indicates that the response of heat of combustion to pulping conditions is highly non-linear. Because of the high degree of non-linearity, the results were reanalyzed using equation 1.

Different selection procedures—coefficient of determination R^2 criterion with Mallow's Cp criterion and STEPWISE procedure with forward selection, backward elimination and maximum R^2 strategy—discussed in many references [i.e., 11, 12] were used to determine the set of independent variables for Equation 3 that would yield the best fit without bias. In all cases, the best fit without bias was obtained

with twelve parameters. The twelve parameter predictive model for heats of combustion as a function of cooking variables is:

$$
\begin{aligned}
\Delta H_c = \ &11481.0 + 968.84*S - 4469.96*EA \\
&- 2224.13*t - 2.56*S*T + 173.92*EA*t \\
&+ 8.53*EA*T + 0.0316*S*EA*T \\
&- 0.00083*S*T*t - 0.399*EA*t*T \\
&+ 16.51*EA*EA + 5.14*T*t \qquad (3)
\end{aligned}
$$

where ΔH_c is heat of combustion (Btu/lbm); EA = % effective alkali; S = % sulfidity; t = cooking time (min); and T = cooking temperature (K).

The regression procedure in SAS was used for residual analysis. Figure 3 is a plot of residuals (%) of this model with respect to predicted values of ΔH_c. The residuals are scattered around zero and the model can be used to predict values of heat of combustion of the slash pine black liquors from knowledge of the pulping conditions to within ±1% for all except three liquors.

Equation 3 can be used to construct response surfaces so that the effects of pulping conditions on heat of combustion can be examined visually two-at-a-time. Three examples of such surface responses are shown in Figures 4-6. For consistency, the values of the pulping variables at the center of the experimental pulping design were used.

Figure 4 represents the heat of combustion response surface as a function of effective alkali and sulfidity at a constant cooking temperature of 444.4 K (171.2°C) and a constant cooking time of 60 minutes. The response is highly non-linear and is a saddle with respect to sulfidity and effective alkali.

Figure 5 represents the effects of cooking time and temperature on heat of combustion at a constant EA of 14.5% and S of 27.5%. The heat of combustion response is a saddle with respect to cooking temperature and cooking time. At a fixed level of cooking time, heat of combustion decreases, reaches a minimum and then increases with further increase in the level of cooking temperature. At any level of cooking temperature, ΔH_c increases with cooking time, reaches a maximum and decreases slightly.

Figure 6 is the response surface plot for heat of combustion with respect to effective alkali and cooking time at a constant cooking temperature of 444.4 K and sulfidity of 27.5%. The surface is a falling-rising ridge with respect to effective alkali at lower cooking times and a falling ridge at higher levels of cooking time. At low levels of EA (< 14.5%), ΔH_c is an increasing function of cooking time. At higher levels of EA, ΔH_c increases with increasing cooking time, reaches a maximum and then decreases.

This analysis applies strictly only to the liquors derived from pulping slash pine under the conditions given. Adjustments for soap content and different dead loads for application for mill liquors can be made. Carbonate, sulfate, and chloride salt dead loads can be adjusted for by assuming these to be inert and passing through to the black liquor, determining the difference in the mill dead load and the dead load used in the study, and adjusting the liquor solids accordingly with the additional dead load considered as an inert diluent. Similarly, the soap content in excess of the 0.26 - 0.29 wt% of solids equilibrium solubility at 28-30% solids and 333 K (60°C) could be determined. The average heat of combustion of soap is reported to be 37.2 to 41.8 MJ/kg (16,000 - 18,000 Btu/lb) with an average of 39.5 MJ/kg (17,000 Btu/lb) [15]. Assuming the heats of combustion of black liquor solids and soap are additive, one could then adjust the heat of combustion. For example, suppose that the mill liquor contained 5 wt% solids more dead load chemicals and 2 wt% near soap solids for a condition for which heat of combustion for the liquor is predicted to be 14.64 MJ/kg (6,300 Btu/lb). The excess soap represents 1.1 wt% of the solids and the remaining 98.9 wt% solids contain an additional 5 wt% inerts. The adjusted heat of combustion would be:

$$\Delta H_{adjusted} = (14.64)(0.939) + 0.011(39.5)$$

$$= 13.75 + 0.435 = 14.19 \text{ MJ/kg}$$

This is a -5% adjustment for dead load difference and a +3% adjustment for soap level difference in this example.

MODEL FOR HEAT OF COMBUSTION AS A FUNCTION OF BLACK LIQUOR COMPOSITION

The concentrations of major constituents of the black liquor composition were determined for each liquor. The constituents that varied substantially and were found to have significant effects on heat of combustion were lignin concentration, L gm/gm; other organics, O gm/gm; sodium concentration, SO gm/gm; and other inorganics, I gm/gm. Although unevenly spaced, these were used as inputs and the same statistical methods were used to determine the

equation for the best fit, which is also a 12 parameter model that is:

$$\begin{aligned}
\Delta H_c = {} & 198816.38 - 519916.72*L \\
& - 1328770.5*O + 128333.63*I \\
& - 1301897.82*SO + 3686978.36*L*O \\
& + 3493534.21*L*SO - 1168303.15*O*I \\
& + 9119447.1*O*SO \\
& - 25082980.42*L*O*SO \\
& - 1926415.97*L*I*SO \\
& + 17681617.5*L*O*I*SO \quad (4)
\end{aligned}$$

where ΔH_c is in Btu/lbm. Although statistically this model is not quite as good as the empirical model developed to relate heat of combustion to pulping conditions, it is adequate for surface response exploration. These results and the results of the earlier statistically derived empirical model relating heat of combustion to pulping conditions were used to suggest non-linear correction possibilities.

NON-LINEAR REGRESSION MODELS

Since organics dissolved from the wood are responsible for most of the heat of combustion, it seemed that it might be possible to develop a very simple relation between heat of combustion and pulp yield for these liquors. The best relation developed was:

$$\Delta H_c = 0.36 \; Y^{3.35} \exp(-0.066Y) \quad (5)$$

where ΔH_c = heat of combustion at 100% solids, $\dfrac{\text{Btu}}{\text{lbm}}$; Y = pulp yield (%, oven dry wood). Figure 7 is a plot of $\log\left(\Delta H_c / Y^{3.35}\right)$ as a function of the pulp yield. The correlation is reasonable. This applies only to the experimental liquors used and it would be extremely difficult to adjust for variations in dead load or soap content, for example. A relation of this form could find use in correlating mill data for single species pulping under fairly constant conditions of dead load, soap removal, and sulfur oxidation.

Non-linear models for relating heat of combustion to pulping conditions and liquor solids composition were also developed that are much simpler. These are:

a.   Model for ΔH_c as a function of the cooking variables:

$$\Delta H_c = 0.49 \ EA^{-0.13} \ S^{0.075} \ T^{1.57} \ t^{-0.011} \qquad (6)$$

with $R^2 = 0.99^+$.

b.   Model for ΔH_c as a function of black liquor solids composition:

$$\Delta H_c = 11947.45 \ L^{0.63} \ I^{-0.06} \ O^{0.024} \ SO^{0.096} \qquad (7)$$

with $R^2 = 0.99$. These results indicate that cooking temperature has a more significant effect on heat of combustion than the other pulping variables. Also, as could be expected, heat of combustion is more affected by lignin concentration than other components. A good non-linear correlation using H-factor to combine the effects of time and temperature could not be found.

These models apply strictly only to the slash pine liquors used. However, values calculated from these equations could be adjusted for variations in dead load and soap concentration, as done earlier. Also, these correlation forms could very likely be used for other liquor systems for which as few as eight or nine data are available.

CONCLUSIONS

Results of this work show that heat of combustion for 100% solids should be measured experimentally on freeze dried solids to insure that the experimentally measured heat of combustion is not affected by chemical changes that might occur during drying. The range of heat of combustion of 100% solids for a liquor derived from pulping a slash pine at different conditions with a constant dead load and minimum soap content was found to be (11.82 to 16.55 MJ/kg).

The heat of combustion is very non-linear with respect to the pulping conditions used and with respect to the levels of solids constituents investigated. Accurate empirical models have been developed for heat of combustion of slash pine liquors, and results can be adjusted for variations in dead load and soap content, assuming dead load is inert and soap is additive. Simpler non-linear product models have also been developed. A non-linear form relating heat of combustion to pulp yield only is reasonably accurate and could be useful in approximate correlation of limited data for other systems. Surprisingly, the heat of combustion can be correlated to the four liquor solids composition variables better by a non-linear product model than by an additive model. The non-linear model forms developed are the best of many that were tested. These models involve only five constants. Therefore, if the forms developed should be applicable to other liquor systems, it would be possible to develop relations with a small amount of data, possibly as few as eight or nine data.

ACKNOWLEDGMENTS

The authors are grateful for the financial support provided by a number of industrial firms and the U.S. Department of Energy under grant no. DE-FG02-85CE40740. We are also grateful for the assistance of Mrs. Barbara Speck, Mr. A. Preston, and others for experimental assistance.

LITERATURE CITED

1.   Grace, T.M. et al., "Recovery Boiler Modeling: An Improved Char Burning Model Including Sulfate Reduction and Carbon Removal," Sixteenth National Industrial Energy Technology Conference Proceedings, pp. 199-208, April, 1994.

2.   Hupa, M., Solin, P. and Hyöty, P., 1985 International Chemical Recovery Conference Proceedings, TAPPI Press, Atlanta, p. 335.

3.   Green, R.P. and Grace, T.M., TAPPI, Vol. 67, No. 6, June, 1984.

4.   McDonald, K.L., TAPPI, Vol. 60, No. 12, (December 1977).

5.   Annergren, G.E., Haglund, A. and Rydholm, S.A., "On the Composition and Fuel Value of Black Liquor," Svensk Pappertidning drg., No. 15, (August 15, 1986).

6.   Frederick, W.J., Noopila, T. and Hupa, M., TAPPI, pp. 163-170, (December 1991).

7.   Grace, T.M., Cameron, J.H. and Clay, D.T., TAPPI, pp. 108-113, (October 1986).

8.   Fricke, A.L., "A Comprehensive Program to Develop Correlations for the Physical Properties of Kraft Black Liquor," Interim Report No. 2, December (1990).

9.   Fricke, A.L., "Physical Properties of Kraft Black Liquor:" Summary Report—Phase I and II, DOE Report Nos. AC02-82CE40606 and FG02-85CE40740, (1987).

10. Stoy, M., Zaman, A.A. and Fricke, A.L., "Vapor-Liquid Equilibrium for Black Liquors," International Chemical Recovery Conference Proceedings, Book 2, p. 495 (1992).

11. Box, G., Hunter, W. and Hunter, J., Statistics for Experimenters, John Wiley and Sons, Inc., New York (1978).

12. Ott, L., An Introduction to Statistical Methods and Data Analysis, PWS-Kent Publishing Company, Boston, 1988.

13. SAS User's Guide: Statistics, Version 5 Edition, SAS Institute Inc., Box 8000, Cary, North Carolina 27511-8000, 1985.

14. Gessner, A.W., Chem. Eng. Prog., Vol. 61, No. 2, (February 1965).

15. Drew, J. and Propst, M., Tall Oil, Pulp Chemicals Association, New York, 1983.

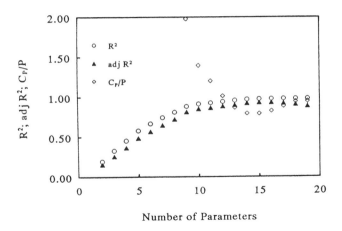

Figure 2. R^2, Adjusted R^2, and C_P/P for Heats of Combustion Versus Pulping Conditions.

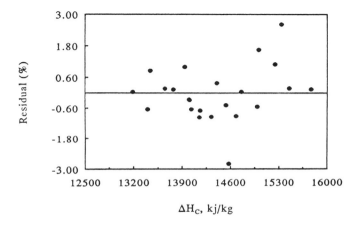

Figure 3. Residuals as a Function of Predicted Values From Equation 4.

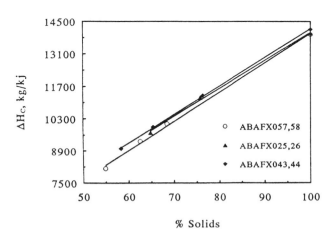

Figure 1. Heats of Combustion as a Function of Solids Content for Different Black Liquors.

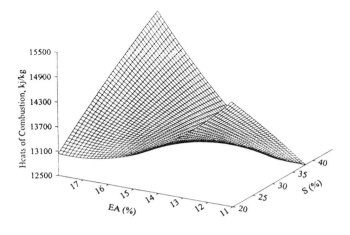

Figure 4. Three D Plots for Heats of Combustion as a Function of Sulfidity and Effective Alkali at t=60 min and T=444.4 K.

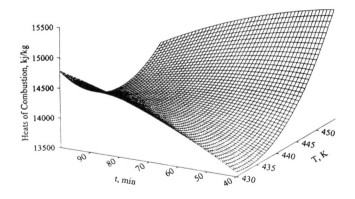

Figure 5. Three D Plots for Heats of Combustion as a
Function of Cooking Temperature and Cooking
Time at EA=14.5% and S=27.5%.

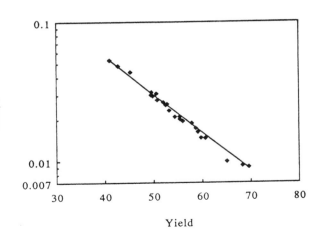

Figure 7. Heats of Combustion at 100% Solids as a
Function of the Pulp Yield.

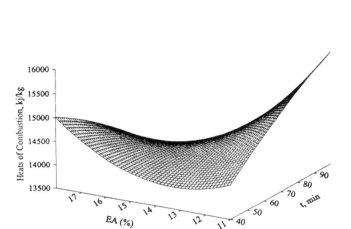

Figure 6. Three D Plots for Heats of Combustion as a
Function of Cooking Time and Effective Alkali
at S=27.5% and T=444.4 K.

Table 1   Pulping Conditions, Kappa Numbers, Pulp Yield and Heats of Combustion of Slash Pine Black Liquors

Cook #	t, min	T, °C	EA, %	S, %	K #	Y, %	ΔH_c at 100% Solids kJ/kg
ABAFX011,12	40.0	165.6	13.0	20.0	107	69.6	13450
ABAFX013,14	80.0	176.7	13.0	20.0	40.2	50.6	15780
ABAFX015,16	80.0	165.6	16.0	20.0	61.1	54.4	13660
ABAFX017,18	40.0	176.7	16.0	20.0	34.8	49.9	14410
ABAFX019,20	80.0	165.6	13.0	35.0	90.4	56.0	14020
ABAFX021,22	40.0	176.7	13.0	35.0	53.8	55.4	14540
ABAFX025,26	80.0	176.7	16.0	35.0	18.5	42.7	14010
ABAFX027,28	80.0	165.6	13.0	20.0	77.5	59.1	14040
ABAFX029,30	40.0	176.7	13.0	20.0	74.1	58.7	14590
ABAFX031,32	40.0	165.6	16.0	20.0	88.1	59.7	13200
ABAFX033,34	80.0	176.7	16.0	20.0	26.5	41.0	13410
ABAFX035,36	40.0	165.6	13.0	35.0	77.0	60.6	13780
ABAFX037,38	80.0	176.7	13.0	35.0	43.3	49.5	14310
ABAFX039,40	80.0	165.6	16.0	35.0	48.3	52.8	15250
ABAFX041,42	40.0	176.7	16.0	35.0	35.9	49.6	15140
ABAFX043,44	60.0	171.1	14.5	27.5	51.1	53.2	16550
ABAFX051,52	60.0	182.2	14.5	27.5	24.8	45.2	15340
ABAFX053,54	60.0	171.1	11.5	27.5	83.3	57.9	15110
ABAFX055,56	60.0	171.1	17.5	27.5	29.4	50.8	14330
ABAFX057,58	60.0	171.1	14.5	12.5	81.3	55.4	13950
ABAFX059,60	60.0	171.1	14.5	42.5	42.2	52.5	14770
ABAFX069,70	60.0	160.0	14.5	27.5	92.9	65.1	11820
ABAFX073	100.0	171.1	14.5	27.5	35.2	---	14160
ABAFX075,76	20.0	171.1	14.5	27.5	108	68.3	12950

t, cooking time; T, cooking temperature; EA, effective alkali; S, sulfidity; K #, Kappa number; Y, ΔH_c, heat of combustion

Kraft Black Liquor Rheological Behavior With Respect to Solids Concentration, Temperature, and Shear Rate

A.A. Zaman and A.L. Fricke
Department of Chemical Engineering, University of Florida, Gainesville, FL 32611

Kraft black liquor is a complex fluid consisting of heterogeneous polymers, organic and inorganic salts, caustic, and water. Its rheological behavior is equally complex. The character of the fluid changes from a Newtonian to a non-Newtonian to a viscoelastic fluid as the non-volatile component (solids) concentration is increased. Methods have been developed to measure rheological properties in all three regions and to correlate these using models based on theories developed for polymeric fluids. The three flow regimes occur because the liquor undergoes several second order thermodynamic transitions as it is concentrated. This appears to be universal behavior. The models developed and their relationship to the transition is explained. The practical implications of this for application of Tomlinson combustion technology at high solids and for process control of liquor concentration and combustion processes are discussed.

Black liquor produced in kraft pulping is subjected to a series of operations to recover the cooking chemicals, and to generate part of the energy required for pulping and papermaking processes. The recovery unit plays a very important role in the economics of a pulping mill because of the recovery and recycling of the cooking chemicals and production of energy from the combustion of the organic compounds of black liquor.

In a typical recovery unit, black liquor with a solids concentration of 12-18% solids is fed to multiple effect evaporators and high solids concentrators to remove the water and concentrate the liquor to above 65% solids. The concentrated liquor is then fed by spray nozzles into a Tomlinson recovery furnace where the organic compounds are burned to produce energy and the inorganic constituents are collected as a smelt at the bottom of the furnace. The inorganics are regenerated as white liquor by dissolving and causticizing the smelt, which is recycled back to the pulping process. Usually, 95-97% of the cooking chemicals are recovered and more than 40% of the energy required for the pulping and papermaking processes is produced [1]. There is a continuous trend towards firing black liquor at higher solids concentration (with a suggested upper limit of above 80% solids) because of the energy savings and an increase in the safety of the operations associated with an increase in the furnace capacity, reduced energy losses used for evaporating water in the furnace, and reduced sulfur emissions in the furnace.

The rheological properties of black liquor significantly affect a number of important parameters in the recovery process. They affect heat transfer and evaporation rate in evaporators, droplet size and distribution in the furnace, loads and constraints in the transport of black liquor, flow patterns, stability of combustion and SO_x emissions.

In this study we present results on the rheological properties of slash pine kraft black liquors for concentrations up to 80% solids and temperatures up to 140°C. The flow behavior of black liquors have been characterized by means of the shear viscosity in steady shear flow and by means of dynamic viscosity and storage modulus in oscillatory shear flow at different temperatures and solids concentrations. As was shown in our earlier works [2-7], black liquor can be treated as a polymer solution; therefore, in this work, the concept of reduced variables methods developed for polymers was employed to obtain reduced correlations for rheological properties of black liquor as a function of temperature, solids concentration, shear rate and frequency. These kinds of correlations will provide a useful tool for process engineers and operators in selecting proper processing conditions, and will lead eventually to developing techniques for viscosity control. Furthermore, these correlations can be used to estimate the rheological properties of black liquor at processing conditions over a wide range of temperatures and solids concentrations. Prior to this work, quantitative evaluation of the reduced variables method has been frustrated by lack of accurate and reliable data on rheological properties of well characterized black liquors.

MATERIALS AND METHODS

The black liquors used in this work are from a four variable-two level factorial or rotatable composite statistically designed experiment for pulping slash pine that was conducted in a pilot scale digester operated with liquor circulation [8,9]. The four cooking variables were effective alkali, sulfidity, temperature, and time at temperature. Chip size, reduction, causticizing efficiency and time-to-temperature were held as constant as possible. The experiments were conducted so as to include all potential commercial conditions without exhaustion of chemicals; pulping Kappa numbers varied from about 18 to 120.

The liquor was drained from the digester, the pulp washed in place with the first portion of the wash added to the liquor and then this combined liquor was concentrated in two steps in a wiped film evaporator operated at about 0.45 atm. In the first step, the liquor was concentrated to about 30% and skimmed. It was then concentrated in the second step to 45-50% solids. The concentrated liquors were stored in sealed containers at about 4°C.

For rheological studies, the liquors were concentrated up to about 80-83% solids in a small laboratory evaporator [10] operated at 0.2-0.4 atm. The concentrated liquors were drained into plastic bottles, sealed, cooled, and stored at 4°C for use.

Since the rheological properties of black liquor vary over an extremely wide range depending upon temperature, solids concentration, solids composition and shear rate, different kinds of rheological instruments were employed to characterize the liquors. At concentrations lower than 50% solids and temperatures up to 100°C, kinematic viscosities of the liquors were determined by using glass capillary viscometers in which the solution flows through the capillary under its own head. At concentrations above 50% solids, a Haake RV-12 viscometer with normal open cup (for 40°C ≤ T ≤ 90°C and % solids ≤ 65) and a custom built pressure cell coaxial cylinder viscometer (for T ≥ 100°C and % solids < 75) were used to study the shear flow properties of concentrated black liquors for shear rates up to 1,000 s^{-1}. An Instron capillary rheometer (Model 3211) was used for highly concentrated black liquors (≥ 65%) at temperatures up to 120°C and shear rates up to 10,000 s^{-1}. A Rheometrics RMS-800 Mechanical Spectrometer (with a solution chamber) with a parallel plate set up was used to determine the lower limiting viscosities (zero shear rate viscosity) at temperatures below 85°C.

The linear viscoelastic characteristics of black liquors were determined in small amplitude oscillatory shear experiments performed with a Rheometrics Mechanical Spectrometer (RMS-800) using a parallel-plate geometry with plates of different diameters, depending upon the operating temperature and solids concentration of the samples. The mathematical analyses and full details of the experimental procedures for the instruments used in this work can be found elsewhere [6,11,12].

VISCOSITY AT LOW SOLIDS CONCENTRATION

At low concentrations (≤ 50%), black liquor behaves as a Newtonian fluid [3,7,13] with lignin as a solute. Theories developed for dilute polymer solutions can be used [14,15] to define the relations between the viscosity, temperature, and the combined effects of temperature and solids concentration.

Typical kinematic viscosity results as a function of temperature for a black liquor are shown in Figure 1. The relationship between the kinematic viscosity and temperature can be defined by using absolute rate and free volume theories [7]. These resulting relations can be written as:

$$\mu = A_1 T^{0.5} \exp\left(\frac{B_1}{T}\right) \qquad (1)$$

and

$$\mu = A_2 T^{0.5} \exp\left(\frac{B_2 T_o}{T - T_o}\right) \qquad (2)$$

where

μ	=	kinematic viscosity
A_1 and A_2	=	solids dependent constants
B_1	=	solids and composition dependent constant related to activation energy for flow
B_2	=	solids and composition dependent constant related to free volume
T_o	=	absolute reference temperature where free volume becomes zero
T	=	absolute temperature

Both equations 1 and 2 fit the kinematic viscosity data of different black liquors with very high accuracy [7]; however, equation 2 could be arranged such that A_2 is universal for all liquors derived from a single species and B_2 can be written as a function of solids concentrations for a single liquor [7]. Theoretically, one should expect A_2 to depend only on the polymer concentration and T_0 to be the same for all liquors of the same type [7,16]. Data for slash pine black liquors with 25 different solids compositions have been correlated using equation 2. With T_0 set to a constant value (220 K), A_2 for slash pine liquors is given by:

$$A_2 = 2.75 \times 10^{-3} + 3.18 \times 10^{-4} S \qquad (3)$$

where:

$$S \quad = \quad \text{solids mass fraction}$$

B_2 then expresses the variation of free volume with solids concentration and solids composition. This was found to be [7]:

$$B_2 = b_1 + b_2 S + b_3 S^2 \qquad (4)$$

where b_1, b_2, and b_3 are solids composition dependent constants and S is the solids mass fraction.

Figure 2 is representative of kinematic viscosity as a function of solids concentration at different temperatures for a typical black liquor. At a fixed temperature, there is at least two orders of magnitude change in viscosity as the solids concentration is increased from 10% to 50%. At any temperature, the viscosity curves can be defined accurately by [16]:

$$\log_e \mu = a + bS + cS^2 \qquad (5)$$

where a, b, and c are constants (which are dependent on the temperature and composition) and S is the solids mass fraction.

If dilute solution theory is used [7], the effects of temperature and solids concentration can be combined into a single correlating variable and a reduced plot for the reduced kinematic viscosity of black liquors (with respect to water) can be obtained [7]. Figure 3 represents typical results for several black liquors. The differences in kinematic viscosity data for every liquor is due to the fact that the liquors are compositionally different. The reduced kinematic viscosity for every liquor can be described as:

$$\log_e(\mu_R) = \sum_{i=1}^{n} a_i \left(\frac{S}{T}\right)^i \qquad (6)$$

where:

$$\mu_R \quad = \quad \frac{\mu}{\mu_w} \quad = \quad \text{reduced kinematic viscosity with respect to water}$$

$$S \quad = \quad \text{solids mass fraction}$$

$$T \quad = \quad \text{absolute temperature}$$

$$a_i \quad = \quad \text{constants}$$

This correlation method has been found to be successful for all experimental and mill black liquors. Two constants that depend only on solids composition are sufficient to correlate the data successfully [7,16].

For slash pine liquors, it was observed that the first constant which represents the initial slopes of the reduced viscosity curves can be treated as a universal constant; therefore, there is only one constant for these liquors that depends upon solids composition. This constant was correlated to the pulping conditions and black liquor composition [17].

VISCOSITY AT HIGH SOLIDS CONCEN-TRATIONS

Viscosity at high solids concentrations is extremely important and has received specific attention in this study. In general, black liquors are non-Newtonian fluids at high solids concentrations [4,6,12]. They exhibit pseudoplastic (shear thinning) behavior. The exact level of viscosity at any given temperature, solids concentration and shear rate is dependent upon the solids composition that will vary from liquor to liquor.

Precise and accurate measurements over the entire range of interest were made using a variety of instruments mentioned earlier. Figures 4 and 5 represent viscosity data as a function of shear rate and temperature for a typical black liquor at 72% and 81% solids respectively. These data serve to illustrate the great effects of both temperature and solids concentration on both apparent viscosity and on flow behavior; as solids concentration increases or temperature decreases, the fluid becomes more non-Newtonian. Also, direct measurements at very low shear rates demonstrate that viscosity always approaches Newtonian behavior, the lower limiting viscosity, at low shear rates [4,5,6,12].

The flow behavior of black liquors at different temperatures and solids concentrations could be defined by using Power-Law, Cross and Carreau-Yasuda models [4,12]; however, the Cross and Carreau-Yasuda models can predict the shape of the viscosity-shear rate curves over the entire range of shear rate. The Cross equation is given by:

$$\frac{\eta - \eta_\infty}{\eta_o - \eta_\infty} = \frac{1}{\left(1 + (\lambda \dot{\gamma})^\alpha\right)} \quad (7)$$

where η_0 (Pa·s) is the zero shear rate viscosity, η_∞ (Pa·s) is the viscosity at infinite shear rate (in this work, it is assumed to be zero), λ (s) is a constant parameter, and α is a dimensionless constant, and $\dot{\gamma}$ (s^{-1}) is the shear rate. The Carreau-Yasuda model is given by:

$$\frac{\eta - \eta_\infty}{\eta_o - \eta_\infty} = \left[1 + (\lambda \dot{\gamma})^\alpha\right]^{\frac{(n-1)}{\alpha}} \quad (8)$$

here λ is a characteristic time for the fluid and $1/\lambda$ is equal to a critical shear rate at which η begins to decrease with shear rate. The Parameter, α, adjusts the breadth of the transition region between the zero shear rate viscosity and the Power-Law region and $(n-1)$ is the Power-Law slope.

The above mentioned models were used to fit the experimental data for different black liquors. Both Cross and Carreau-Yasuda models fit the experimental data with very good to high accuracy over the entire range of shear rate [4,12].

REDUCED CORRELATIONS FOR SHEAR VISCOSITY

The data for shear viscosity of concentrated polymer solutions and polymer melts can be normalized by superposition principles [14,15]. This is normally done by "temperature superposition." In this method, the viscosity data is first normalized and the normalized curves shifted along the shear rate axis to superimpose them. The logarithmic shifting distance required is a function of temperature. This method permits one to partition the effects of temperature so that only a single viscosity-shear rate curve need to be defined. For black liquors, we have the additional complication of solids concentration.

With any temperature shift, there is still a family of curves representing the effects of solids concentration. Therefore, some method of superposition that combines the effects of temperature and solids concentration was necessary. For polymer melts and concentrated polymer solutions, the following equation applies [15]:

$$\frac{\eta}{\eta_o} = f(a_T \dot{\gamma}) \quad (9)$$

where a_T is a shift factor given by:

$$a_T = \frac{\eta_o T_o \rho_o}{\eta_o^o T \rho} \quad (10)$$

where

η	=	shear viscosity, Pa·s
η_o	=	zero shear rate viscosity at T, Pa·s
η_o^o	=	zero shear rate viscosity at T_o, Pa·s
ρ	=	density at T, kg/m^3
ρ_o	=	density at T_o, kg/m^3
T	=	absolute temperature, K
T_o	=	absolute reference temperature, K over the temperature range studied, it may be assumed that $\rho \approx \rho_o$.

It is known that [15] the shift factor for polymer melts can be expressed as:

$$\log_e a_T = \frac{-C_1(T - T_o)}{(C_2 + T - T_o)} \quad (11)$$

where C_1 and C_2 are constants and To is an absolute reference temperature.

For polymers, T_0 is related to the glass transition temperature and usually lies about 50 degrees above it. Earlier studies [3,5,18] on phase transition behavior of different black liquors indicate that the glass transition temperature of black liquors is a function of solids concentration. If we use this relation to express the effect of solids concentration on T_0, all normalized viscosity data for a liquor can be superimposed [4,12]. For slash pine black liquors, we found that $1.3\ T_g \leq T_0 \leq 1.4\ T_g$, where T_g is the glass transition temperature. The shift factor for slash pine black liquor, can be defined as [4,12]:

$$\log_e a_T = \frac{-26.77(T - T_o)}{(104.16 + T - T_o)} \qquad (12)$$

Figure 6 is an example of the superimposed viscosity curves (master curve) for a typical black liquor. The resulting master viscosity curves can be modeled using the modified form of either Cross or Carreau-Yasuda models [4,12]. These can be written as:

a)   Cross Model

$$\frac{\eta}{\eta_o} = \frac{1}{\left(1 + (\lambda a_T \dot\gamma)^\alpha\right)} \qquad (13)$$

and

b)   Carreau-Yasuda Model

$$\frac{\eta}{\eta_o} = \left[1 + (\lambda a_T \dot\gamma)^\alpha\right]^{\frac{(n-1)}{\alpha}} \qquad (14)$$

The final result is a sound procedure for complete correlation of black liquor viscosity at high solids concentrations. Superposition requires that the effect of solids concentration on the glass transition be defined, requiring two constants. The resulting master curve can be correlated by a model requiring two constants (or three constants if the Carreau-Yasuda model is used). The zero shear rate viscosities can be defined with a model of three constants [5,6]. Thus three functions must be defined requiring a total of seven (or eight, if equation 13 is used) constants. Overall, the black liquor viscosity can then be predicted within about 25%. When one considers the range of variables (35% for solids concentration, over 100°C for temperature, and six orders of magnitude in shear rate) with the resulting range of response (seven orders of magnitude for viscosity), this is quite good. One should consider, however, that all seven constants are affected by solids composition. It does not appear that the glass transition temperature of black liquors

varies much with solids composition [5,18], but the others apparently do. Work is in progress to define the solids compositional effects on constants for the viscosity master curves for slash pine black liquors.

VISCOELASTIC PROPERTIES OF BLACK LIQUORS AT HIGH SOLIDS

The linear viscoelastic characteristics of several slash pine liquors with solids concentration ranging from 67% to 81% were investigated in small amplitude oscillatory shear flow for a temperature range from 40°C to 85°C [4,11]. Figures 7 and 8 are typical results for dynamic viscosity and storage modulus as a function of temperature and frequency for one of the liquors at 76% solids.

Both dynamic viscosity and storage modulus show changes with temperature, frequency, solids content, and they also vary from liquor-to-liquor. At lower temperatures and higher concentrations, dynamic viscosity falls monotonically with increasing frequency as shown in these figures. Also, it can be observed that, at sufficiently low frequencies, the dynamic viscosity (η') will approach a finite limiting value which is close to the zero shear rate viscosity. The storage modulus (G'), also shows changes with temperature, solids content, solids composition, and frequency. At high solids concentrations and low temperatures, the liquors show an indication of a plateau region at higher frequencies. The linear viscoelastic functions of black liquors at different temperatures and solids concentrations can be defined very well by Cross and Carreau-Yasuda models described earlier over the entire range of frequency.

The data for linear viscoelastic functions of black liquors were normalized by superposition principles for effects of temperature. The reduced functions can be written as [4,11,15,19]:

$$\frac{\eta'}{\eta_o} = f(a_T \omega) \qquad (15)$$

$$G' \frac{T_o}{T} = g(a_T \omega) \qquad (16)$$

where $(\eta')(Pa \cdot s)$ = dynamic viscosity, $G'\ (Pa)$ = storage modulus, and $\omega(rad/s)$ = frequency. However, the one-step procedure that was used successfully for shear viscosity of black liquors to superimpose data for the effects of solids concentration and temperature did not work for linear viscoelastic functions of black liquor. Therefore a two-step shifting procedure was followed to combine the effects of temperature and solids concentrations and obtain a reduced plot for dynamic viscosity of black liquors. In the first step a temperature shift factor as defined earlier (equation 10), with T_0 as an arbitrary reference temperature (313.16 K in this work), was employed to combine the effects of temperature and frequency and obtain a reduced plot for linear viscoelastic functions of black liquors at every solids concentration. The typical results are shown in Figures 9 and 10 for dynamic viscosity and storage modulus, respectively. The reduced plots for dynamic viscosity at every solids concentration could be described by Cross and Carreau-Yasuda models (using $a_T\omega$ instead of $\dot{\gamma}$). The reduced storage modulus at every solids content was defined as:

$$\log_e\left(G'\frac{T_0}{T}\right) = a + b\left(\log_e(a_T\omega)\right) + c\left(\log_e(a_T\omega)\right)^2 \quad (17)$$

where a, b, and c are constants.

In the second step, the reduced curves at different solids concentrations for dynamic viscosity were superimposed by defining a solids shift factor as:

$$a_s = \frac{\eta_o S^o}{\eta_o^o S} \quad (18)$$

where S = solids mass fraction, S^o = reference solids mass fraction, and η_o^o = zero shear rate viscosity at S^o.

Figure 11 is a plot of reduced dynamic viscosity (η'/η_o) as a function of reduced frequency $(a_T a_s \omega)$ for one of the liquors. The data for reduced storage modulus at different solids concentrations were treated in the same manner, but the reduced curves at different solids concentrations for storage modulus did not superimpose on a single curve.

The reduced correlations for linear viscoelastic functions of black liquor were used to estimate the elasticity of different black liquors $((G'/\omega)/\eta')$ for the nominal operating temperature in a recovery furnace (120°C). Comparison of viscoelasticity of black liquors with viscoelasticity of other fluids that have been reported [13,20] to have difficulties in jet breakup and droplet formation indicate that viscoelastic effects should not affect droplet formation at 80% solids, if the temperature is above 120°C. As the solids concentration is increased above 80%, the

temperature must be increased to keep the elastic forces at a low level.

Finally, in order to find an analogy between the viscometric functions and linear viscoelastic functions of black liquors, plots of shear viscosity versus shear rate were superimposed on the plots of complex viscosity (η^*) as a function of frequency. The typical plot is shown in Figure 12. This shows an excellent agreement between the shear viscosity and complex viscosity at low shear rates and frequencies. The shear viscosity and the magnitude of the complex viscosity agree within experimental error; therefore, the lower limiting viscosity of black liquors can be determined from small amplitude oscillatory shear experiments.

SUMMARY AND CONCLUSIONS

In this work, it is shown that black liquor at low solids content ($\leq 50\%$) behaves as a polymer solution and theories developed for dilute polymer solutions were employed to define the viscosity as a function of temperature and solids concentrations. The low solids viscosity data were correlated to the temperature by using either free volume theory and an average value for freezing point of the liquors or absolute rate theory. The model based on free volume theory was arranged such that the viscosity behavior of a liquor can be defined as a function of both temperature and solids concentrations. Also, by using the dilute solution theory, the effects of temperature and solids concentrations were combined into a single correlating variable (S/T) and the relative kinematic viscosity data were defined as a function of the temperature-concentration variable.

It was shown that at high solids (> 50%), black liquors can exhibit non-Newtonian behavior depending upon temperature, solids concentration, solids composition, and shear rate. The flow behavior of black liquors were described by Cross and Carreau-Yasuda models over the entire range of experimental shear rate. By choosing a suitable reference temperature, related to the glass transition temperature of black liquors, the shear viscosity data were normalized to obtain a reduced plot and reduced correlations for viscosity as a function of temperature, solids concentration and shear rate. A WLF type shift factor is presented that can be applied to reduce the shear viscosity data of other black liquors of the same species with T_0 as a parameter.

The linear viscoelastic properties of high solids black liquors were investigated in small amplitude oscillatory shear flow and the linear viscoelastic functions were described by Cross and Carreau-Yasuda models over the entire range of experimental frequency. Superposition principles were applied to obtain the reduced correlations for linear viscoelastic functions of black liquors as a function of temperature, solids content and frequency. The reduced correlations were used to estimate the elasticity of the liquors for the nominal operating temperature in a recovery furnace (120°C) and it was found that black liquors will not have problems in droplet formation at up to 80% solids and temperatures above 120°C. It was shown that there is an excellent agreement between the shear viscosity and the magnitude of the complex viscosity at low shear rates and frequencies; therefore, the zero shear rate viscosity of black liquors can be determined from small amplitude oscillatory shear experiments.

While the results described are for kraft black liquors derived from Slash Pine, the principles developed are generally applicable with few exceptions to other liquors. Results of studies of kraft mill liquors derived from hardwoods, western softwoods, and northern softwoods as well as results from experimental solvent pulping have been correlated by using the methods described. The methods permit complete description of the rheological behavior of a black liquor over the entire range of processing with respect to solids concentrations, temperature, and shear rate with much less experimental effort. Also, the nearly universal applicability of the correlation methods provide algorithms for potential viscosity control in mill operations that will prove to be valuable, if not essential, for furnace operation at up to 80-85% solids. Finally, for slash pine liquors (and for probably other southern softwood liquors), it has been shown that viscoelastic effects very likely will adversely affect droplet formations at solids concentrations above 80%.

ACKNOWLEDGMENTS

The authors are grateful for the financial support provided by the Office of Industrial Technologies of the U.S. Department of Energy in Grant No. DE-FG02-85ER40740 and by a large number of industrial firms.

NOTATION

A_1, A_2, B_1, B_2, C_1 and C_2	=	constants of equations 1, 2 and 11
a, b, c, b1, b_2 and b_3	=	constants of equations 4, 5 and 17
$a_1, a_2, a_3, \cdots$	=	constants of equation 6
a_T	=	shift factor
G'	=	storage modulus, Pa
n	=	Power-Law exponent
S	=	solids mass fraction
S^o	=	reference solids mass fraction
T	=	absolute temperature, K
T_g	=	glass transition temperature, K
T_o	=	absolute temperature where free volume equals zero in equation 2, reference temperature elsewhere
α	=	Cross and Carreau-Yasuda model parameter
$\dot{\gamma}$	=	shear rate, s^{-1}
η	=	shear viscosity, Pa·s
η_0	=	zero shear rate viscosity, Pa·s
η_∞	=	infinite shear rate viscosity, Pa·s
η_o^o	=	zero shear rate viscosity at T_o, Pa·s
η'	=	dynamic viscosity, Pa·s
λ	=	Cross and Carreau-Yasuda model parameter, S
μ	=	kinematic viscosity
μ_R	=	reduced kinematic viscosity with respect to water
ρ	=	density, kg/m^3
ρ_0	=	density at T_o, kg/m^3
ω	=	frequency, rad/s

LITERATURE CITED

1. Empie, H.J., Lien, S. and Samuels, D.B., Distribution of Mass Flows in Black Liquor Sprays," presented at AIChE 1994 Annual Meeting, Nov. 13-18, San Francisco, CA.

2. Fricke, A.L., "Physical Properties of Kraft Black Liquor:" Interim Report - Phase II, DOE Report on Contract No. DG AC02-82CE40606, University of Maine, Orono and University of Florida, Gainesville (1985).

3. Fricke, A.L., "Physical Properties of Kraft Black Liquor:" Summary Report - Phase I and II, DOE Report Nos. AC02-82CE50606 and FG02-85CE40740, University of Florida, Gainesville and University of Maine, Orono (1987).

4. Zaman, A.A., "An Investigation of the Rheological Properties of High Solids Kraft Black Liquors," PhD Dissertation, University of Florida, Gainesville (1993).

5. Zaman, A.A. and Fricke, A.L., Ind. Eng. Chem. Res., Vol. 33, No. 2, pp. 428-435 (1994).

6. Zaman, A.A. and Fricke, A.L., "Viscosity of Black Liquor Up to 130°C and 84% Solids," AIChE Forest Products Symposium Proceedings, pp. 59-77 (1991).

7. Zaman, A.A. and Fricke, A.L., "Correlations for Viscosity of Kraft Black Liquors at Low Solids Concentrations," AIChE, Vol. 40, No. 1 (1994).

8. Zaman, A.A., Dong, D.J. and Fricke, A.L., "Kraft Pulping of Slash Pine," AIChE Forest Products Symposium Proceedings, pp. 49-57 (1991).

9. Fricke, A.L., "A Comprehensive Program to Develop Correlations for Physical Properties of Kraft Black Liquors", Interim Report No. 2, University of Florida, Gainesville (1990).

10. Stoy, M., Zaman, A.A. and Fricke, A.L., "Vapor-Liquid Equilibria for Black Liquors," International Chemical Recovery Conference Proceedings (1992), Book 2, pp. 495-511.

11. Zaman, A.A. and Fricke, A.L., Ind. Eng. Chem. Res., Vol. 34, No. 1, pp. 382-391 (1995).

12. Zaman, A.A. and Fricke, A.L., "Shear Flow Properties of High Solids Softwood Kraft Black Liquors: Effects of Temperature, Solids Concentrations, Lignin Molecular Weight and Shear Rate," Chemical Engineering Communications, in press (1995).

13. Wight, M.O., "An Investigation of Black Liquor Rheology Versus Pulping Conditions," Ph.D. Dissertation, University of Maine at Orono (1985).

14. Aklonis, J.J. and MacKnight, W.J., Introduction to Polymer Viscoelasticity, Wiley, New York, NY, 1983.

15. Ferry, J.D., Viscoelastic Properties of Polymers, 3rd ed., John Wiley and Sons, Inc., New York, NY, 1980.

16. Zaman, A.A. and Fricke, A.L., Journal of Pulp and Paper Science, Vol. 21, No. 4, (April 1995).

17. Zaman, A.A. and Fricke, A.L., "Effects of Pulping Conditions and Black Liquor Composition on Viscosity of Softwood Kraft Black Liquor: Predictive Models with Statistical Approach," TAPPI, in press, (1995).

18. Massee, M.A., "Thermal Analyses of Kraft Black Liquor," M.S. Thesis, University of Maine, Orono (1984).

19. Co, A. and Wight, M.O., "Rheological Properties of Black Liquors," Black Liquor Recovery Boiler Symposium, Helsinki, Finland, (1982).

20. Goldin, M., Yerushalmi, J.R. and Shinnar, R., Journal of Fluid Mechanics, 38(4), pp. 689-711 (1969).

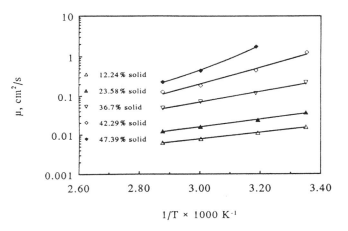

Figure 1. Kinematic Viscosity as a Function of Temperature for a Typical Kraft Black Liquor.

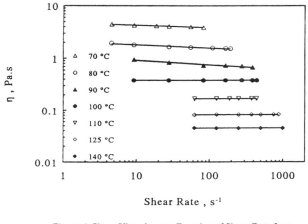

Figure 4. Shear Viscosity as a Function of Shear Rate for a Typical Kraft Black Liquor at 72% Solids.

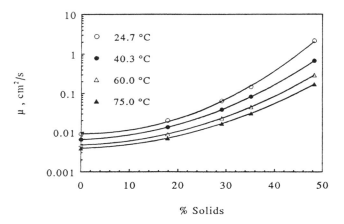

Figure 2. Kinematic Viscosity as a Function of Solids Concentration for a Typical Kraft Black Liquor.

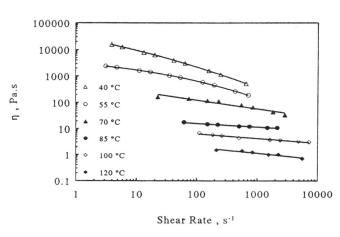

Figure 5. Shear Viscosity as a Function of Shear Rate for a Typical Kraft Black Liquor at 81% Solids.

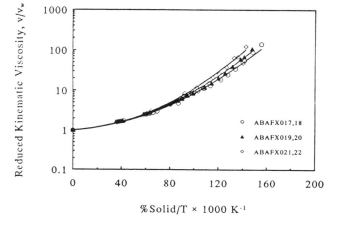

Figure 3. Reduced Kinematic Viscosity of Different Kraft Black Liquors.

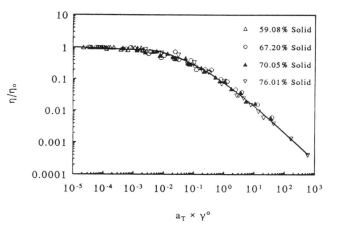

Figure 6. Reduced Plot for Shear Viscosity of a Typical Kraft Black Liquor.

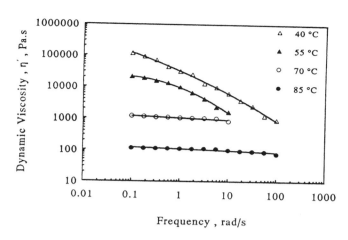

Figure 7. Dynamic Viscosity as a Function of Frequency for a Typical Kraft Black Liquor at 76.28% Solids.

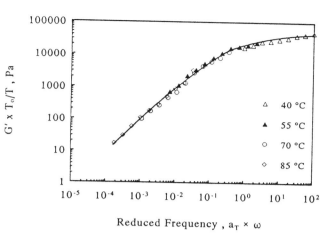

Figure 10. Reduced Plot for Storage Modulus of a Typical Kraft Black Liquor at 76.28% Solids.

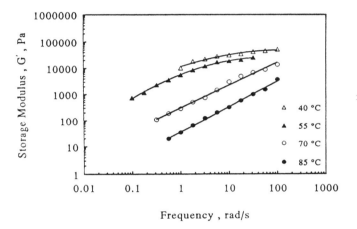

Figure 8. Storage Modulus as a Function of Frequency for a Typical Kraft Black Liquor at 76.28% Solids.

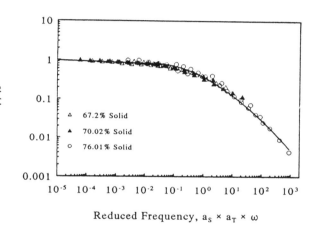

Figure 11. Reduced Plot for Dynamic Viscosity of a Typical Kraft Black Liquor at Different Temperatures and Solids Concentrations.

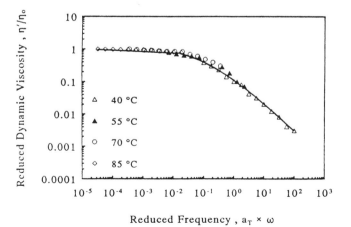

Figure 9. Reduced Plot for Dynamic Viscosity of a Typical Kraft Black Liquor at 76.28% Solids.

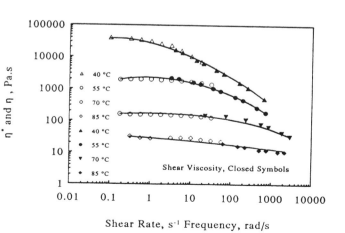

Figure 12. Complex and Shear Viscosity for a Typical Kraft Black Liquor at 81% Solids.

An Experimental/Modelling Study of Solid-Liquid Separation in a Screw Press

Tom H. Egenes[*] and Torbjørn Helle

Norwegian Institute of Technology, Department of Chemical Engineering,
N-7034 Trondheim, Norway

The scientific literature on screw press separation is reviewed. An experimental study proves that assumptions commonly applied to modelling in literature are not valid. Based on the findings, a conceptual understanding of the process is established, forming the base for an a priori *modelling of the process. Experimental verification of the model proves accurate.*

Introduction

Separation of solid-liquid mixes consitutes a very important unit process in many instances, like: 1) Fulfilling the requirements for subsequent process steps or 2) removing undesirable components from the solids fraction, ranging from dissolved material to particle contaminants (partial retention).

Screw presses are frequently used for solid-liquid separation of materials like oil seeds, sludges, papermaking pulps etc. Consisting basically of a threaded screw rotating in a stationary perforated screen cylinder, they are simple and reliable machines. Although in use for nearly a century, surprisingly few scientific analyses have been published on the mechanisms that control the deliquoring and transport processes in the machine.

As the screw shaft radius usually increases from the feed to the discharge end of the screw press, along with a gradual decreasing flight pitch, one may readily assumne the deliquoring process to be one of volumetric displacement; and this is indeed the apprehension commonly reflected in the literature on screw press S/L separation. However, as the material fed to the press may be a free flowing suspension, deliquoring by filtration will often take place. To achieve true volumetric displacement, the material must move linearly along the press axis at constant linear velocity. It has been amply proven that this indeed is not the case.

In this paper the available scant analytical literature on the screw press process will be reviewed. In an experimental study, significant limitations of the existing literature were revealed. Based on the experimantal findings a conceptual understanding of the process was established, and this form the base for the development of a deductive model of the screw press operation.

---

*Present address: Kvaerner Hymac,
P.O. Box 173, N-3401 Lier, Norway.

The Screw Press

A screw press generally consists of a rotating screw encapsulated in a stationary perforated screen cylinder. A wide variety of designs exist; having constant or gradually increasing screw shaft root diameter from the feed to the discharge end, constant or retracting screw pitch, being cylindrical or conical, horizontal or inclined. However, the by far most common screw presses are horizontal ones with increasing root diameter from the feed to the discharge end, having retracting flight pitch (Fig. 1). Noteworthy is a discharge back-pressure system at the discharge end which allows adjustment of the pressure in the *plug zone* -the zone between the discharge and the end of the flight.

The variety in screw press designs appear to reflect a lack of fundamental understanding of the mechanisms that control the process.

The operating parameters of the screw press, the feeding pressure, the applied back-pressure at the discharge of the press and the speed of rotation, may be varied at will, affecting the solids throughput rate, the final dryness of the material as well as the content of particulate material in the removed liquid, somewhat inaccurately termed filtrate.

Scientific Literature on Screw Press Separation

Scientific literature on the screw press separation process is scarce [8]. Most authors divide the process and hence the press into a zone of filtration followed by one of consolidation [14]. To simplify of the analysis, the channel formed by the screw thread and the cylinder is then unrolled and laid flat on top of a stationary plate, Fig. 2. A filter cake builds gradually up in the filtration zone which extends from the point of feeding to a Transition point T. The formed cake is then assumed to slide along the gradually narrowing unrolled channel with uniform, constant speed and gradually increasing fluid pressure. Consolidation effects are ignored in this part of the press. At T the channel is filled with filter cake and from then on further separation is considered to be one of consolidation. Even in the *consolidation zone*, the cake is assumed to slide along the channel at constant velocity. Hence, consolidation is assumed to take place corresponding to the reduction in cross-sectional area toward the point of discharge. Shirato et al. [14-17] modeled the screw press separation process along these lines, applying advanced models for predicting consolidation. Although neglecting filter cake compression arising from frictional forces, as well as possible nonuniform flow along the channel, Shirato et al. report a good fit between measured and modeled data for the dryness of the discharged material. Shirato

et al. did measure the pressure profile along the screw axis for use in their model, so their modelling was not deductive, *per se*.

Although the mentioned simplifications have proven useful in modelling attempts, they do not comply with observations reported in later work. Egenes and Helle [5-9] studied the movement pattern and drainage of the material along the screw press axis, when applied on papermaking pulp suspensions. They found, contrary to the assumption of Shirato and coworkers, that the filter cake formed during filtration does not slide along the channel on the septum. Instead, they found that the screw thread doctors the formed filter cake off the septum, allowing it to be collected in front of the screw flight. There the cake was found to be consolidated as a response to compression pressure arising from friction drag forces created while being pushed forward. In the wake of the flight, a cake free area was found to be continuously formed, allowing influx and rapid drainage of suspension. Hence, in each cross-sectional area of the first part of the machine, filtration and consolidation occur simultaneously. The rapid drainage in the wake of the flight proved to induce a forward flow of suspension, moving at a velocity much higher than the apparent forward velocity of the screw flight. Evidence for this phenomenon was brought about via mass balance calculations. The forward flow of suspension was theorized to induce a fluid pressure drop in the helical channel. Experiments proved the existence of such a fluid pressure drop.

The significance of Egenes and Helle's findings is obvious: The average filter cake thickness at a certain cross-section will be less if doctored off the septum than if sliding on the septum without being disrupted, as assumed by Shirato et al. (hence the filtration rate will be much higher when the cake is doctored off the septum rather than sliding along it).

Screw presses may have a significant diameter, up to some 1.5 m, and the variation in fluid pressure and thus the driving force for filtration around the periphery may vary greatly (e.g. from 5-20 kPa). In the modelling reported in the literature, this effect has altogether been ignored, cf. [6] and references herein.

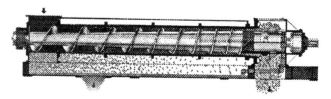

Figure 1 Thune screw press.

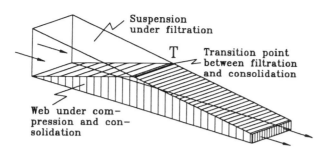

Figure 2 *The unrolled screw channel with initial filtration of the suspension and filter cake consolidation after the transition point T [14-17].*

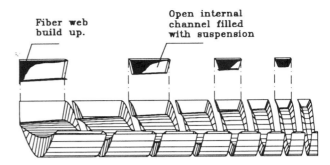

Figure 3 *Sketch of the channel formed by the screw thread and screw shaft. The scraping action causes a web accumulation in front of the flight, simultaneously exposing free barrel surface to suspension present in the open internal channel.*

An Attempt to Model the Screw Press Separation Process

The conceptual understanding of the process as described by Egenes and Helle [5-9] will be the basis for the analysis. Rather than unrolling the screw channel, a concept of direct integration over the geometry of the press will be applied. Models of the sub-processes of the dewatering process will be developed, being 1) models for drainage by filtration in the first part of the press, 2) pressure buildup arising from friction drag forces, 3) consolidation of the cake and 4) forward conveying of the material. The basic assumptions are that the two phases, slurry and cake, are not being remixed, and the slurry phase is assumed to flow freely in an internal channel behind the formed cake which is held firmly onto the septum by the fluid pressure. For the simplicity of the analysis, the fluid pressure loss in the internal channel of free flowing suspension is ignored.

The strategy of the modelling is applying operating data of the press (feed mass concentration and pressure, speed of rotation and discharge back pressure) along with geometrical data of the press and drainage/consolidation characteristics of the suspension to assess the output variables of the press, i.e., discharge mass concentration and solids throughput rate.

1) Slurry filtration on the inner side of a screen cylinder

The standard model for constant pressure filtration is based on a modified form of Darcy's law for flow through incompressible ideal porous beds; the pores or voids being evenly distributed in every layer of infinitesimal thickness of the filter cake. In the model it is assumed that the volumetric flow rate is balanced by a driving force divided by a resistance. The standard model may be written in differential form as[3,4]:

$$\frac{dq_F}{dt} = \frac{P}{\mu \, (C^* \alpha_W q_F + \alpha_M)} \tag{1}$$

in which q_F is the volume of filtrate per unit area, P = the applied hydraulic pressure in the suspension, μ = the viscosity of the filtrate, α_W = the specific filtration resistance (*SFR*), α_M = the medium resistance and C^* is a fictitious concentration = the mass of cake deposited per unit volume of filtrate. Eq. 1 is considered valid for compressible as well as for ideal cakes, provided that α_W is regarded as a function of P rather than a constant. Empirically, Lewis [13] advocated the equation:

$$\alpha_W = \alpha P^s \tag{2}$$

where α and s are the cake constant and the coefficient of compressibility of the material respectively.

The fluid pressure P, the driving force of the filtration process, will vary around the periphery of the screen cylinder of the screw press according to:

$$P = P_0 - \rho g r_P \sin\psi \tag{3}$$

where r_P is the radius of the periphery, ψ is the angle of rotation, P_0 is the hydraulic pressure in the horizontal center plane of the press (at $\psi=0$ and $\psi=\pi$).

The modelling of the screw press separation process is based on partitioning the process into a succession of batch processes that repeat themselves once every revolution (stationary conditions). The available filtration time t during one revolution is proportional to the angle θ, starting from the rear side of the screw flight (Fig. 4):

$$dt = \frac{1}{2\pi n} d\theta \tag{4}$$

where t = the actual time of filtration, and n = the rotational speed of the screw in reciprocal seconds.

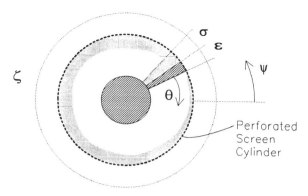

Figure 4 *Cross-sectional view of the screw press during operation. Here, the screw rotates counter-clockwise. The accumulated web is assumed to occupy a sector σ, gradually increasing as the web builds up.*

The cake will gradually build up in front of the flight, as it is being continuously doctored off by the flight. The portion of the screen available for filtration will then extend from $\theta = 0$ to $\theta = \zeta$. The remaining part of the perforated cylinder, from $\theta = \zeta$ to $\theta = 2\pi$, is considered to be unavailable for filtration: Covered by either cake or the screw flight. To obtain the volume of filtrate drained during one revolution of the screw flight, Eq.s 1-4 are combined and integrated over that part of the screen cylinder periphery where filtration occurs, obtaining:

$$\frac{dQ_F}{dz} = \sqrt{\frac{P_R r_P^2 \zeta(z)}{\pi n \alpha C^* \mu}} \int\limits_{\psi=0}^{2\pi} \sqrt{\left(\frac{P_0}{P_R} - \frac{\rho g r_P}{P_R} \sin\psi\right)^{1-s}} \; d\psi \tag{5}$$

Here, P_R is a reference pressure. ζ is a function of z, being reduced along the press as the cake builds up. At the moment, ζ is unknown except for its initial value, thus an iterating scheme must be used to determine it. The point along the axis where the channel is filled with cake coincides with $\zeta = 0$.

From Eq. 5 it is readily seen that ζ affects the drainage rate: The value of ζ depends on the degree of consolidation of the cake in front of the moving flight. If consolidation does not occur, ζ will be low and drainage will be reduced and vice versa.

The amount of cake formed is readily predicted as proportional to the amount of filtrate drained from the suspension:

$$\frac{dW_W}{dz} = C^* \frac{dQ_F}{dz} \tag{6}$$

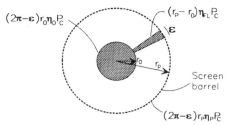

Figure 5 *Basis for the analysis of the static pressure balance in the threaded part of the press. The analysis is similar for the plug zone, except for the presence of the screw flight.*

2) Pressure buildup

Friction drag forces arising from the relative movement between the filter cake and the components of the press will create a mechanical pressure on the cake causing consolidation. Several attempts have been made to predict the pressure buildup in screw presses, however neglecting the variable mass flow rate along the press axis [10,11]. The analysis here is based on a balance of impulse over a differential element of the press;

$$\frac{d}{dt} \int_V \rho \, v_i \, dV + \int_A \rho \underline{v}^T \underline{u} v_i \, dA = \sum_k f_{k,i} \tag{7}$$

in which the term on the right-hand side is the sum of all external forces on the volume element V as well as inner forces (gravity etc.). The first term on the left-hand side is the time derivative of the total impulse in the volume element, and the second term is the flow of impulse in and out of the volume element. $\underline{v}$ is the velocity vector $[v_x, v_y, v_z]$, v_i is the velocity components (in the x,y,z directions), and $\underline{u}$ is a unit vector. In the present case, dynamic effects are ignored.

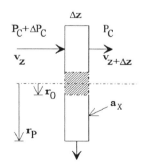

Figure 6 *Sketch of a differential element of the plug zone of a screw press.*

The total flow of impulse is:

$$\int_A \rho \underline{v}^T \underline{u} v_i \, dA = a_w \rho \left(v_z^2 |_z - v_z^2 |_{z+\Delta z} \right)$$

$$= \lim_{\Delta z \to 0} \rho a_w d(v_z^2)$$

(8)

-where $v_z \equiv v_z(z)$; the axial velocity of the cake in the screw press, and a_w is the cross-sectional area of the channel that is filled with filter cake. ρ is the density of the cake.

Analyzing the external forces exerted on the filter cake, the friction forces arising on the interfaces cake/cylinder, cake/flight and cake/shaft are considered, cf. Fig.s 5 and 6:

$$\sum_k f_{k,i} = \left((P_C + \Delta P_C) a_w - P_C a_w \right)$$
$$+ (P_C \eta_0 2\pi r_0 \Delta z)$$
$$+ (P_C \eta_P 2\pi r_P \Delta z)$$
$$= \Delta P_C \cdot a_w + 2\pi (r_0 \eta_0 + r_P \eta_P) P_C \Delta z$$

(9)

By choosing $\Sigma f_{k,i} = 0$ (constant mass flow rate in the channel), we end up with a static pressure balance similar to models for pressure buildup in screw extruders reported in the literature [1,2].

At the limits $\Delta P_C \to 0$ and $\Delta z \to 0$ we have:

$$-dP_C = \frac{2P_C}{r_P^2 - r_0^2} \left(r_0 \eta_0 + r_P \eta_P \right) dz - \rho d(v_z^2)$$

(10)

$d(v_z^2)$ can be found from the change in mass flow rate through the channel, caused by consolidation. From Eq. 10 one may note that the mechanical pressure in this part of the press decreases from the end of the threaded part toward the discharge point; here, where no flight is present, the cake slides along the annular channel at decreasing pressure, as the friction forces are being overcome. The analysis of the threaded part of the press is analogous to the one presented above, however, here there also will be the effect of the friction between the cake and the screw flight.

3) Cake Consolidation

The filter cake collected in front of the flight is subjected to pressure in several ways. It will respond by consolidation. Cake consolidation is a very complex process, however, it is often modeled by the following empirical relationship [20]:

$$c = c_0 + (B_1 + B_2 \log t) P_C^N$$

(11)

in which c is the mass concentration of the wet web, c_0 in its uncompressed state, B_1, B_2 and N are empirical constants. Eq. 11 is considered applicable to time intervals as short as 10^{-1} sec. [12], and is generally accepted at higher levels of pressure. In the present model, Eq. 11 is differentiated with respect to pressure and time, and a first order Taylor series expansions is applied to predict the change in mass concentration along the screw press axis.

4) Axial movement of the cake

The general equation for the flow of material in the channel is the product of the average material velocity and the cross sectional area of the screw channel, i.e.,

$$F_w = \overline{v}_z \cdot a_w$$

(12)

-where v_z = the average axial velocity of the solid material. One may start the analysis by considering the velocity components of a solid granular material moving in the helical screw channel, with negligible pressure buildup: In the ideal case, where the material slips perfectly on the screw flight (i.e., friction is ignored), $v_z = v \cos\phi$, in which v_z = the axial velocity of the material in the channel and ϕ is the pitch angle. In all practical situations, however, there will be friction and the material will not slip perfectly on the screw flight. This will be observed as an increase in the corotation. *Vierling and Ephremidis* [19] introduced a co-rotational angle (β) in their modelling of the transport phenomena in a screw conveyor (cf. Fig. 7).

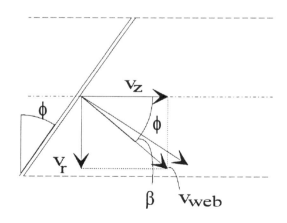

Figure 7 Velocity components on a granular solids material in the rotating screw channel, assuming no pressure buildup. From Vierling and Ephremidis [19].

The axial velocity of a solids particle can thus be found from a simple geometrical analysis:

$$v_z = v_r \frac{\sin\phi}{\cos\beta}\cos\omega \qquad (13)$$

where v_r is the rotational velocity of the screw at the periphery, and ω the materials angle: $\omega = \phi + \beta$. The velocity of the solid material in the axial direction is thus determined by the co-rotational angle (β) and the rotational speed for a press with a given geometry.

In their study, *Vierling* et al. [19], however, ignored that the pitch angle and thus the axial velocity is dependent on the radius (r). To take this into account, the average axial velocity in the channel can be estimated. Inserting for $v_r = 2\pi nr$ yields:

$$\bar{v}_z = \frac{1}{r_p - r_0(z)}\int_{r_0(z)}^{r_p} \frac{2\pi rn\sin\phi}{\cos\beta}\cos(\phi+\beta)dr \qquad (14)$$

The pitch angle (ϕ) is related to the pitch distance (H) and the radius (r) as; $\phi = tan^{-1}(H/2\pi r)$, the solution of Eq. 14 is best left to a numerical algorithm.

It seems obvious that β is interrelated with the friction coefficients, however we have not succeeded in modelling such an interrelation, thus β must be determined experimentally.

Model solving Procedure

The solving procedure is based on partitioning the press into a series of small cross sectional elements, each having equal length Δz (chosen to be 1 mm). All equations are solved in each element except those that are dependent of the processes occurring after the actual element, which is the forward flow of suspension through the element (flow rate and velocity). The equations for pressure buildup and cake consolidation are coupled, in that the degree of consolidation affects the drainage and thus the cake buildup, which in turn affects the degree of consolidation (cf. Fig. 4). Apparently, this is an effect that is physical as well as numerical. To solve this problem, an iterating scheme was applied, in that the equations are solved repeatedly until stability in the axial movement of the cake (dv_z^2). The numerical solving was performed using MatLab 386, cf. [6] for details.

The input data to the model is geometrical data and operating data of the press (feed pressure and consistency, rotational speed and discharge back-pressure), along with predetermined values for specific filtration resistance and consolidation data.

Experimental

The experimental results were obtained on a laboratory screw press, operating on a fibre suspension of unbeaten bleached kraft pulp of Norway Spruce (picea abies). Cf. [6] for experimental setup and data respectively. Measurements of volumetric flow rate from seven different sections of the press as well as measurements of throughput rate and discharge mass concentration were used as basis for mass balance calculations of the materials average moisture ratio (water to dry mass ratio) and the average velocity ratio in the screw channel (ϑ_z), the latter one being the ratio between the axial movement of the material and the apparent axial movement of the flight (nH). In the model verification experiments, the rotational speed was varied, while the remaining operating conditions were kept constant.

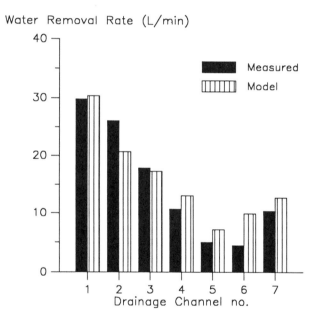

Figure 8 Water removal rate along the screw press axis; predicted and measured. $n=1\ s^{-1}$. no.1 is at the feed end.

Results and discussion

The experimental and modeled values for drainage rate along the press axis are depicted in Fig. 8. There one will see that the predictions of the model on the drainage rates are in fairly good harmony with the experimentally obtained rates, however, somewhat higher drainage rates are predicted than actually measured. A fairly good harmony is found between

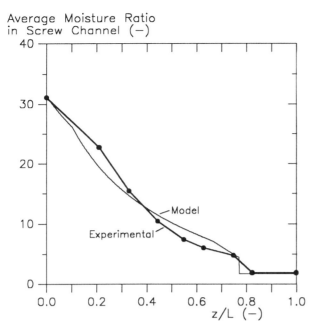

Figure 9 *Average moisture ratio of the material in the channel along the press axis (L is the total length of the press = 0.629m).*

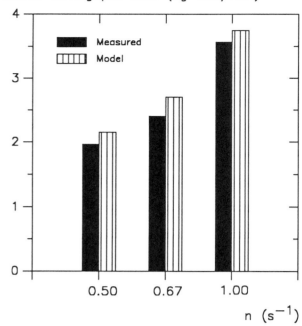

Figure 11 *Measured and a priori modelled solids throughput rates vs. rotational speed of the screw press.*

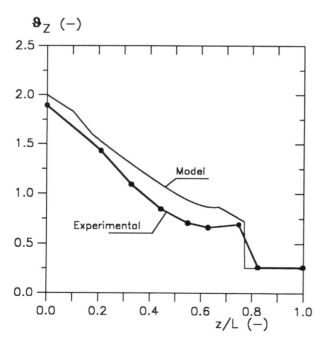

Figure 10 *Average material velocity ratio (ϑ_z) vs. position along the press axis.*

predicted and experimentally determined values for moisture ratio (Fig. 9), and average velocity ratio (Fig. 10) along the screw axis. From Fig. 11 one will note that the model predicts some 5-10% higher readings for solids throughput rate than actually determined. The probable reason for this is that one ignores the fluid pressure loss in the phase of free flowing suspension in the screw channel, from the feed end to the transition point [7]. An implication of the larger throughput rate predicted by the model than actual, are larger values predicted for average velocity ratio, simply because there is more material to convey forward in the channel (Fig. 10).

In Fig. 12, the measured and predicted discharge consistencies from the press are depicted. For obvious reasons, the model predicts higher values for discharge mass concentration than actually obtained, as steady state is not achieved in the consolidation- and plug zones of the press. Another effect, not accounted for in the model, is reabsorption of liquid by the expanding filter cake upon release of load: Neither experimental nor theoretical studies are available to predict the effect of reabsorption of liquid, although considered significant in all consolidation processes, at least when operating on fibrous materials.

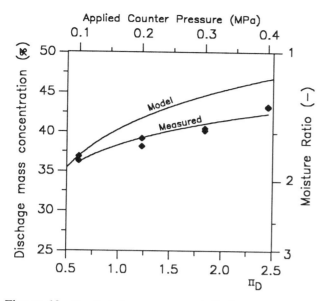

Figure 12 *Predicted vs. measured discharge mass concentrations for varying counter pressure.* $\Pi_D = P_D/P_R$, *where* $P_R = 10^5$ *Pa,* P_D *is the cake pressure at the discharge.*

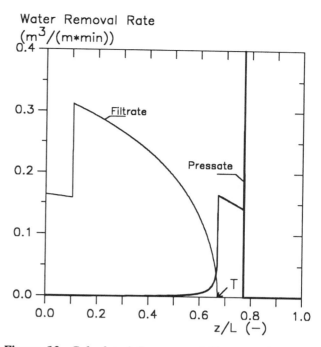

Figure 13 *Calculated flow rate of filtrate and pressate along the screw axis. T: Transition Point.*

Fig 13 depicts the modeled flow rates of pressate and filtrate along the press axis, the latter one gradually diminishing toward the transition point T (note that there is only a half screen cylinder at the beginning of the press, due to the hopper). The flow rate of pressate gradually increases along the press from the very beginning, becoming significant just ahead of the transition point, and peaking at the point where the cake reaches the end of the threaded distance, coinciding with the mechanical pressure maximum in the screw press (Fig. 15)

In Fig. 14 the modeled axial velocity ratio (ϑ_Z) of the material in the screw press is shown - the ratio between the axial forward movement of the material and the apparent forward movement of the screw flight. A value of unity means that the material moves forward at the same velocity as the flight, without rotation. It has previously been proven that $\vartheta_{Z,AVE}$ may exceed unity in the first part of the press, caused by rapid drainage and influx of suspension from the feed end [8]. The web ahead of the flight responds to the force excerted by the flight by moving forward whith pressure buildup and consolidation (Fig. 13). The sudden drop in ϑ_Z near the discharge end is caused by the plug zone.

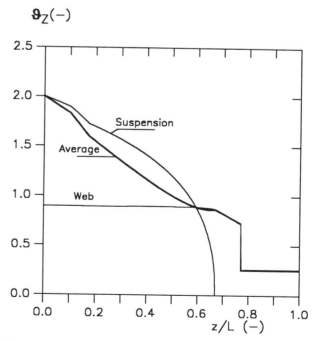

Figure 14 ϑ_Z *for suspension and filter cake along the press axis as calculated by the model.*

Summing up, it can be concluded that in the past, the screw press dewatering process has mainly been regarded as a process of volumetric displacement, at least in the latter part where the channel is filled with cake. Reminding that such a process requires the axial movement of the cake to be uniform and constant, the present work has shown that these requirements are not met. The reason is that the cake is consolidated due to friction pressure buildup as well as volumetric displacement. Some authors [e.g., 18] even assume a volumetric displacement in the filtration zone as well, although a significant fluid pressure cannot be created by the slowly rotating screw.

Despite the applied simplifications in the present modelling attempt, it may be concluded that the model predicts the water removal and transport processes occurring in screw presses fairly well.

Conclusions and Final Comments

Models for the drainage processes in a screw press have been developed along with models for pressure buildup and forward conveying of the formed web. The integrated model seems to reflect fairly well the processes that occur in a screw press when fed with suspensions of low apparent viscosity. As mentioned, few scientific studies on screw press modelling have been pressented. The most significant one is probably the referred work of Shirato and coworkers. It is thus relevant to comment upon their modelling approach: Despite that Shirato and coworkers applied a number of assumptions in their modelling that clearly do not harmonize with the findings of Egenes and Helle [5,9] they report a good fit between modeled and experimentally obtained data for solids throughput rate and discharge consistency. This conclusion is not surprising as the consolidation pressure along the press axis was measured rather than modeled. As Shirato et al. even used the feed flow rate as input variable in their model, the solids throughput rate is easily predicted from simple mass balance calculations. Unfortunately, Shirato et al. did not present results for the drainage profile along the press axis.

In the present work, some rheological properties of the suspension and the wet cake were not included in the model. Crucial to the operation of the screw press, as well as to the modelling of the process, is the response of the material to applied mechanical pressure; for a solid material, mechanical pressure will transmit unidirectional, whereas for a semi-solid material the mechanical pressure will partly transmit laterally. In the first case, pressure will build up and the cake is consolidated, while in the other case the cake may deform and slip out of the press with hardly any

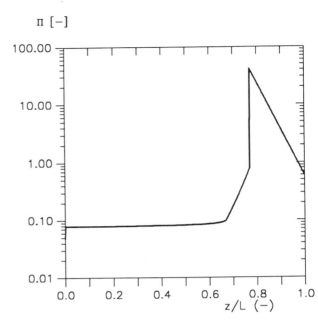

Figure 15 *Dimensionless pressure along the screw press axis as calculated by the model.*

consolidation. The properties of the wet filter cake will also affect the area of the screen cylinder available for filtration, the filtration rate and in turn the solids throughput rate. These problems have as yet scarcely been addressed.

Acknowledgements

The cooperation and financial support of Kværner Hymac, Norway, are greatfully acknowledged. Financial support from the *Royal Norwegian Council for Scientific and Industrial Research* is also gratefully acknowledged. The authors would also like to thank the technical staff at The Norwegian Institute of Technology, Laboratory of Chemical Engineering, for their collaboration.

Literature Cited

1   CARLEY, J.F., STRUB, R.A.
Ind. Eng. Chem. 45(5):970-973 (1953).

2   CARLEY, J.F., MALLOUK, R.S., MCKELVEY, J.M.
Ind. Eng. Chem. 45(5):974-978 (1953).

3   CHRISTENSEN, G.L., DICK, R.I.
J. of Environmental Eng. 111(3): 243-257 (1985).

4   CHRISTENSEN, G.L., DICK, R.I. ibid. 258-271 (1985).

5   EGENES, T.H., HELLE, T.
44th CSChE Conf., Calgary, 1994.

6   EGENES, T.H. Ph.D. Thesis, Norwegian Inst. of Technology, Trondheim, 1993

7   EGENES, T.H., HELLE, T. Pulp and Paper Canada. 95(2):65(1994)

8   EGENES, T.H., HELLE, T.
J. Pulp and Paper Sci. 18(3) J93(1992).

9   EGENES, T.H., HELLE, T. 23rd ABTCP Pulp and Paper Annual meeting, São-Paulo, Brazil, 113(1990).

10   FILIPPOV, V.I., LUNEV, V.D., EMEL'YANOV, YU. A., SHARIKOV, YU. V.
J. Appl. Chem. USSR 60(3):463-466 (1987).

11   FILIPPOV, V.I., EMEL'YANOV, YU. A., LUNEV, V.D., KUROCHKINA, M.I.
J. Appl. Chem. USSR 56(2):417-420 (1983).

12   GREN, U., HEDSTRÖM, B.
Sv. Papperstidning, 70(10):339-346 (1967).

13   LEWIS, W.K., ALMY, C.
J. Ind. Eng. Chem. 4:528(1912).

14   SHIRATO, M., MURASE, T., IWATA, M., HAYASHI, N., OGAWA, Y. Int. Chem. Eng. 25(1):88(1985).

15   SHIRATO, M., MURASE, T., HAYASHI, N., IWATA, M.
Proc. Pac. Chem. Eng. Congr. 4:377(1983).

16   SHIRATO, M., MURASE, T., HAYASHI, N., MIKI, K., FUKUSHIMA, N., TAZIMA, T.
Int. Chem. Eng. 18(4):680(1978).

17   SHIRATO, M., MURASE, T., TOKUNAGA, A., YAMADA, O. J. Chem Eng. Japan 7(3):229(1974).

18   TATENOBU, O. 6th World Filtration Congress, Nagoya, Japan 397-399(1993).

19   VIERLING, A., EPHREMIDIS, C.
Fördern und Heben 9, 433-440 (1957).

20   WILDER, H.D. Tappi J. 43(8)715(1960).

Index